Essential Mathematics

David Rayner

Book 9

Elmwood Press

David Rayner

First published 2002 by
Elmwood Press
80 Attimore Road
Welwyn Garden City
Herts. AL8 6LP

Reprinted 2002, 2003

British Library Cataloguing in Publication Data

Rayner, David

   1. Mathematics—1961–
   I. Title

   ISBN 1 902 214 145

Numerical answers are published in a separate book

Artwork and additional material by
Emma Djonokusumo
Sheena Shah
Paulina Spencer
Amy Jefferies

Acknowledgements
        Tony Gardiner for the use of past S.M.C. questions.
        Camelot plc for the use of their National Lottery Logo.

Typeset and illustrated by Tech-Set, Gateshead, Tyne and Wear
Printed and bound by WS Bookwell.

PREFACE

Essential Mathematics Books 7, 8 and 9 are written for more able pupils in years 7, 8 and 9. Most classrooms contain children with a range of abilities in mathematics. These books are written to cater for this situation.

The author is an enthusiastic supporter of the National Numeracy Strategy. The books have been prepared with the cooperation of teachers and pupils in NNS pilot schools. It is encouraging that most teachers are confident that this more structured approach will help to raise standards of understanding and attainment. There is a comprehensive NNS guide at the start of the book with references to all topics.

There is no set path through the books but topics appear in the order suggested in the NNS planning charts. Broadly speaking, parts 1 and 2 can be studied in the Autumn Term, parts 3 and 4 in the Spring Term and parts 5 and 6 in the Summer Term.

The author believes that children learn mathematics most effectively by *doing* mathematics. Many youngsters who find mathematics difficult derive much more pleasure and enjoyment from the subject when they are doing questions which help them build up their confidence. Pupils feel a greater sense of satisfaction when they work in a systematic way and when they can appreciate the purpose and the power of the mathematics they are studying.

No text book will have the 'right' amount of material for every class and the author believes that it is better to have too much material rather than too little. Consequently teachers should judge for themselves which sections or exercises can be studied later. On a practical note, the author recommends the use of exercise books consisting of 7 mm squares.

Opportunities for work towards the 'Using and Applying Mathematics' strand appears throughout the book. Many activities, investigations, games and puzzles are included to provide a healthy variety of learning experiences. The author is aware of the difficulties of teaching on 'Friday afternoons' or on the last few days of term, when both pupils and teachers are tired, and suitable activities are included.

The author is indebted to his co-authors David Allman, Laurence Campbell and Christine Godfrey whose work from the first edition of Essential Mathematics has been included where appropriate.

David Rayner

CONTENTS

Using and applying mathematics to solve problems

Applying mathematics and solving problems

5.4 • Solve increasingly demanding problems and evaluate solutions; explore connections in mathematics across a range of contexts: number, algebra, shape, space and measures, and handling data; *generate fuller solutions. Represent problems and sythesise information in algebraic, geometric or graphical form; move from one form to another to gain a different perspective on the problem.*

2.2 • **Solve substantial problems by breaking them**
2.4 **into simpler tasks, using a range of efficient techniques, methods and resources, including ICT;** *use trial and improvement where a more efficient method is not obvious.*

3.2 • **Present a concise, reasoned argument, using**
3.4 **symbols, diagrams, graphs and related**
3.5 **explanatory text; give solutions to problems to an appropriate degree of accuracy,** *recognising limitations on the accuracy of data and measurements; give reasons for choice of presentation, explaining selected features and showing insight into the problem's structure.*

5.6 • Suggest extensions to problems, conjecture and generalise; identify exceptional cases or counter-examples, explaining why; *justify generalisations, arguments or solutions; pose extra constraints and investigate whether particular cases can be generalised further.*

Numbers and the number system

Place value, ordering and rounding

2.1 • Extend knowledge of integer powers of 10; multiply and divide by any integer power of 10; *begin to write numbers in standard form.*

3.2 • Use rounding to make estimates; round numbers to the nearest whole number or to one, two or *three* decimal places, *and to a given number of significant figures; understand upper and lower bounds.*

Integers, powers and roots

2.1 • Use the prime factor decomposition of a number.

2.4 • Use ICT to estimate square roots and cube roots.

1.1 • Use index notation for integer powers and simple instances of the index laws; *know and use the index laws for multiplication and division of positive integer powers; begin to extend understanding of index notation to negative and fractional powers, recognising that the index laws can be applied to these as well.*

Fractions, decimals, percentages, ratio and proportion

1.5 • Understand the equivalence of simple algebraic fractions; know that a recurring decimal is an exact fraction; *use algebraic methods to convert a recurring decimal to a fraction in simple cases.*

1.5 • Use efficient methods to **add, subtract, multiply and divide** fractions, interpreting division as a multiplicative inverse; cancel common factors before multiplying or dividing.

4.4 • Recognise when fractions or percentages are needed to compare proportions; solve problems involving percentage changes.

4.4 **Use proportional reasoning to solve a**
2.1 **problem, choosing the correct numbers to**
5.4 **take as 100%, or as a whole;** *understanding and use proportionally and calculate the result of any proportional change using multiplicative methods; understand the implications of enlargement for area and volume;* compare two ratios; interpret and use ratio in a range of contexts, including solving word problems.

Calculations

Number operations and the relationships between them

2.1 • Understand the effects of multiplying and
3.2 dividing by numbers between 0 and 1; use the laws of arithmetic and inverse operations; *recognise and use reciprocals.*

Mental methods and rapid recall of number facts

2.5 • Use known facts to derive unknown facts; extend mental methods of calculation, working with decimals, fractions, percentages, factors, powers and roots, solve word problems mentally.

3.2 • **Make and justify estimates and approximations of calculations;** *estimate calculations by rounding numbers to one significant figure and multiplying or dividing mentally.*

Written methods

2.1 • Use standard column procedures to add and subtract integers and decimals of any size, including a mixture of large and small numbers with differing numbers of decimal places; multiply and divide by decimals, dividing by transforming to division by an integer. *For calculations with fractions and percentages, see above.*

Calculator methods

2.1 • Use a calculator efficiently and appropriately to perform complex calculations with numbers of any size, knowing not to round during intermediate steps of a calculation; use the constant, π and sign change keys, function keys for powers, roots and fractions, brackets and the memory; *use the reciprocal key.*

1.2 • Enter numbers and interpret the display in
5.4 context (negative numbers, fractions, decimals, percentages, money, metric measures, time, *numbers in standard form*).

Checking results

3.2 • Check results using appropriate methods.

Algebra

Equations, formulae and identities

1.3 • Distinguish the different roles played by letter symbols in equations, identities, formulae and functions.

1.1 • Use index notation for integer powers and simple instances of the index laws; *know and use the index laws in generalised form for multiplication and division of integer powers.*

1.3 • Simplify or transform algebraic expressions by
1.4 taking out single-term common factors; and simple algebraic fractions; *square a linear expression, expand the product of two linear expressions of the form $x + n$ and simplify the corresponding quadratic expression; establish identities such as $a^2 - b^2 = (a + b)(a - b)$*

1.3 • **Construct and solve linear equations with integer coefficients** (with and without brackets, negative signs anywhere in the equation, positive or negative solution), **using an appropriate method.**

4.5 • *Solve a pair of simultaneous linear equations by eliminating one variable; link a graphical representation of an equation or a pair of equations to the algebraic solution; consider cases that have no solution or an infinite number of solutions.*

6.4 • *Solve linear inequalities in one variable, and represent the solution set on a number line; begin to solve inequalities in two variables.*

2.4 • Use systematic trial and improvement methods and ICT tools to find approximate solutions to equations such as $x^3 + x = 20$.

• Solve problems involving direct proportion using algebraic methods, relating algebraic solutions to graphical representations of the equations; use ICT as appropriate.

4.3 • Use a formulae from mathematics and other
5.5 subjects; substitute numbers into expressions and formulae; derive a formula and, in simple cases, change its subject; *derive and use more complex formulae, and change the subject of a formula.*

Sequences, functions and graphs

4.4 • **Generate terms of a sequence using term-to-term and position-to-term definitions of the sequence, on paper and using ICT;**

find the next term and the nth term of quadratic sequences and functions and explore their properties.

4.3 • Generate sequences from practical contexts and **write an expression to describe the *n*th term of an arithmetic sequence;** *deduce properties of the sequences of triangular and square numbers from spatial patterns.*

5.2 • Find the inverse of a linear function *and plot its graph; know simple properties of quadratic functions.*

5.2 • Generate points and plot graphs of linear
6.3 functions (*y* given implicitly in terms of *x*), e.g. $ay + bx = 0$, $y + bx + c = 0$, on paper and using ICT; **given values for *m* and *c*, find the** gradient of lines given by equations of the form $y = mx + c$; *investigate the gradients of parallel lines and lines perpendicular to these lines; plot graphs of simple quadratic and cubic functions, e.g. $y = x^2$, $y = 3x^2 + 4$, $y = x^3$.*

3.4 • **Construct functions arising from real-life problems and plot their corresponding graphs; interpret graphs arising from real situations**, including distance–time graphs.

Shape, space and measures

Geometrical reasoning: lines, angles and shapes

5.6 • Distinguish between conventions, definitions and derived properties; *distinguish between practical demonstration and proof; know underlying assumptions, recognising their importance and limitations, and the effect of varying them.*

1.6 • Explain how to find, calculate and use:
– the sums of the interior and exterior angles of quadrilaterals, pentagons and hexagons;
– the interior and exterior angles of regular polygons

3.1 • **Solve problems using properties of angles, of parallel and intersecting lines, and of triangles and other polygons**, justifying inferences and explaining reasoning with diagrams and text; *understand and apply Pythagoras' theorem.*

2.2 • Understand congruence; *apply the conditions SSS, SAS, ASA or RHS to establish the congruence of triangles.*

5.1 • *Know that if two 2-D shapes are similar, corresponding angles are equal and corresponding sides are in the same ratio.*

1.6 • Know the definition of a circle and the names of its parts; explain why inscribed regular polygons can be constructed by equal divisions of a circle; *know that the tangent at any point on a circle is perpendicular to the radius at that point; explain why the perpendicular from the centre to the chord bisects the chord.*

4.2 • Visualise and use 2-D representations of 3-D objects; analyse 3-D shapes through 2-D projections, including plans and elevations.

Transformations

4.1 • Transform 2-D shapes by combinations of
4.2 translations, rotations and reflections, on paper and using ICT; **know that translations, rotations and reflections preserve length and angle and map objects on to congruent images;** identify reflection symmetry in 3-D shapes.

3.1 • Enlarge 2-D shapes, given a centre of
4.1 enlargement and a whole-number scale factor, on paper and using ICT; *extend to enlarging 2-D shapes, given a fractional scale factor; recognise the similarity of the resulting shapes;* identify the scale factor of an enlargement as the ratio of the lengths of any two corresponding line segments; recognise that enlargements preserve angle but not length, and understand the implications of enlargement for perimeter, *area and volume.*

3.1 • Use and interpret maps and scale drawings.

Coordinates

5.1 • *Find points that divide a line in a given ratio, using the properties of similar triangles; given the coordinates of points A and B, calculate the length of AB.*

Construction

2.2 • Use straight edge and compasses to construct a triangle, given right angle, hypotenuse and side (RHS); use ICT to explore constructions of triangles and other 2-D shapes; *know from experience of constructing them that triangles given SSS, SAS, ASA or RHS are unique, but that triangles given SSA or AAA are not.*

6.1 • Find the locus of a point that moves according to a simple rule, both by reasoning and by using ICT; *extend to more complex rules involving loci and simple constructions.*

Measures and mensuration

3.3 • Use units of measurement to calculate,
3.2 estimate, measure and solve problems in a variety of contexts; convert between area measures (mm^2 to cm^2, cm^2 to m^2 and vice versa) and between volume measures (mm^3 to cm^3, cm^3 to m^3, and vice versa); *recognise that measurements given to the nearest whole unit may be inaccurate by up to one half of the unit in either direction.*

5.3 • *Understand and use measures of speed (and other compound measures such as density or pressure) to solve problems; solve problems involving constant or average rates of change.*

3.1 • **Know and use the formulae for the circumference and area of a circle,** *and arcs and sectors of circles.*

3.3 • Calculate the surface area and volume of right prisms; *calculate lengths, areas and volumes in right prisms, including cylinders.*

6.5 • *Begin to use sine, cosine and tangent in right-angled triangles to solve problems in two dimensions.*

Handling data

Specifying a problem, planning and collecting data

3.5 • Suggest a problem to explore using statistical methods, frame questions and raise conjectures.

3.5 • Discuss how data relate to a problem; identify possible sources, including primary and secondary sources; *identify possible sources of bias and plan how to minimise it.*

3.5 • **Design a survey or experiment to capture the necessary data from one or more sources; determine the sample size and degree of accuracy needed; design, trial and if necessary refine data collection sheets;** construct tables for large discrete and continuous sets of raw data, choosing suitable class intervals; design and use two-way tables.

3.5 • Gather data from specified secondary sources, including printed tables and lists from ICT-based sources; *identify what extra information may be required to pursue a further line of enquiry.*

Processing and representing data, using ICT as appropriate

2.6 • Find summary values that represent the raw data, and select the statistics most appropriate to the problem; *find the median and quartiles for large data sets; estimate the mean, median and interquartile range of a large set of grouped data.*

2.3 • Select, construct and modify, on paper and
2.6 using ICT, suitable graphical representation to
3.4 progress an enquiry, including:
  – *frequency polygons;*
  – *line graphs for time series;*
  – scatter graphs to develop further understanding of correlation;
  – *lines of best fit by eye, understanding what they represent;*
  identify key features present in the data.

Interpreting and discussing results

3.4 • Interpret graphs and diagrams and draw inferences to support or cast doubt on initial conjectures; have a basic understanding of correlation; *analyse data to find patterns and exceptions, look for cause and effect and try to explain anomalies.*

2.6 • Compare two or more distributions and make inferences, using the shape of the distributions, the range of data and appropriate statistics.

3.5 • **Communicate interpretations and results of a statistical enquiry using selected tables, graphs and diagrams in support,** using ICT as appropriate; *examine critically the results of a* *statistical enquiry, and justify choice of statistical representation in written presentation, recognising the limitations of any assumptions and their effect on conclusions drawn.*

Probability

6.2 • Use the vocabulary of probability in interpreting results involving uncertainty and prediction.

6.2 • Identify all the mutually exclusive outcomes of an experiment; **know that the sum of**

probabilities of all mutually exclusive outcomes is 1 and use this when solving problems.

6.2 • *Estimate probabilities from experimental data; understand relative frequency as an estimate of probability and use this to compare outcomes of experiments.*

6.2 • Compare experimental and theoretical probabilities in a range of contexts; appreciate the difference between mathematical explanation and experimental evidence.

Part 1

1.1 Index laws

Indices are used as a convenient way of writing products.
For example $4^3 = 4 \times 4 \times 4$ and $7^5 = 7 \times 7 \times 7 \times 7 \times 7$.
For 7^5 we say '7 to the power 5' or just '7 to the 5'.

Multiplying   Consider the product $(3^2) \times (3^4)$.
We have $(3 \times 3) \times (3 \times 3 \times 3 \times 3) = 3^6$.
Similarly $8^4 \times 8^3 = 8^7$.

We observe that   To multiply : Add the indices.

Dividing   Consider the division $\dfrac{6^5}{6^2} = \dfrac{\not{6} \times \not{6} \times 6 \times 6 \times 6}{\not{6} \times \not{6}} = 6^3$

Similarly $\dfrac{7^9}{7^4} = 7^5$

We observe that   To divide : Subtract the indices.

Note that you cannot use either of the above rules if different numbers are raised to powers.
So $3^4 \times 5^2$ or $7^5 \div 8^3$ *cannot* be found using the rules.

Exercise 1

In Questions **1** to **24** write the answer in index form.

1. $2 \times 2 \times 2 \times 2$ **2.** $7 \times 7 \times 7 \times 7 \times 7 \times 7$ **3.** $3 \times 3 \times 2 \times 2 \times 2 \times 2$
4. $a \times a \times a \times a \times a$ **5.** $p \times p \times p$ **6.** $5 \times 5 \times 5 \times 5 \times 8 \times 8$
7. $3^4 \times 3^6$ **8.** $4^2 \times 4^3$ **9.** $8^6 \times 8^2$
10. $7^4 \times 7^{40}$ **11.** $9^2 \times 9^{22}$ **12.** $n^3 \times n^2$
13. $a^7 \times a^3$ **14.** $n^5 \times n^5$ **15.** $y^7 \times y$

16. $8^6 \div 8^2$ **17.** $7^5 \div 7^2$ **18.** $3^{10} \div 3^3$
19. $11^7 \div 11^2$ **20.** $6^9 \div 6$ **21.** $5^{11} \div 5^4$
22. $n^7 \div n^2$ **23.** $a^{10} \div a^3$ **24.** $x^{11} \div x$
25. $(3^5 \times 3^2) \div 3^4$ **26.** $(2^3 \times 2^4) \div 2^2$ **27.** $(4^7 \times 4^2) \div 4^3$
28. $2^3 \times (2 \times 2 \times 2)$ **29.** $4^5 \times 4 \times 4$ **30.** $n^5 \times n^2 \times n$

In Questions **31** to **39** copy and complete.

31. $5^3 \times 5^2 = \square$ **32.** $7^5 \div \square = 7^2$ **33.** $\square \times 3^{10} = 3^{12}$

34. $\square \div 7^{10} = 7^3$ **35.** $n^3 \times n^3 = \square$ **36.** $3^{100} \div \square = 3^{20}$

37. $3^6 \div 3 = \square$ **38.** $10^{10} \div \square = 10$ **39.** Half of $2^5 = \square$

In Questions **40** to **48** give the answer as an ordinary number.

40. $5^4 \div 5^2$ **41.** $2^5 \div 2^3$ **42.** $10^3 \div 10$

43. $3^5 \div 3^2$ **44.** $1^{11} \times 1^{10}$ **45.** $4^{12} \div 4^{10}$

46. 2×2^3 **47.** $10^6 \div 10^3$ **48.** $\left(\frac{1}{2}\right)^2 \times 4$

Negative indices Consider $\dfrac{5^2}{5^6} = \dfrac{\cancel{5} \times \cancel{5}}{\cancel{5} \times \cancel{5} \times 5 \times 5 \times 5 \times 5} = \dfrac{1}{5^4}$

Using the subtraction rule: $5^2 \div 5^6 = 5^{-4}$

We see that $5^{-4} = \dfrac{1}{5^4}$

Similarly we can show that $7^{-2} = \dfrac{1}{7^2}$ and $10^{-3} = \dfrac{1}{10^3}$

In general: $x^{-n} = \dfrac{1}{x^n}$

Exercise 2

Write the answer as an ordinary number.

1. 2^{-1} **2.** 3^{-1} **3.** 10^{-1}

4. 4^{-1} **5.** 8^{-1} **6.** n^{-1}

7. 2^{-2} **8.** 3^{-2} **9.** 10^{-2}

10. 10^{-3} **11.** 2^{-3} **12.** 5^{-2}

13. $10^3 \times 10^{-1}$ **14.** $4^3 \times 4^{-1}$ **15.** $5^4 \times 5^{-2}$

16. $3^{-3} \times 3^1$ **17.** $2^{-4} \times 2^2$ **18.** $10^3 \times 10^{-4}$

reminder

$4^{-2} = \dfrac{1}{4^2} = \dfrac{1}{16}$

In Questions **19** to **30**, answer 'True' or 'False'.

19. $3^2 \times 3^{-1} = 3^1$ **20.** $4^3 \times 4^{-1} = 4^2$ **21.** $6^5 \times 6^{-2} = 6^2$

22. $5^1 \times 5^{-2} = 5^{-1}$ **23.** $6^5 \times 6^5 = 6^{25}$ **24.** $3^{-2} \times 3^{-2} = 3^4$

25. $7^{-1} \times 7^{-1} = 7^{-2}$ **26.** $10^{-1} \times 10^2 = 10$ **27.** $n^5 \times n = n^5$

28. $8^7 \div 8^2 = 8^{\frac{7}{2}}$ **29.** $7^5 \div 7^3 = 7^2$ **30.** $5^2 \div 5^3 = 5^{-1}$

Raising to a power Consider $(3^2)^3$, which means '3 squared all cubed'.

$$(3^2)^3 = (3 \times 3) \times (3 \times 3) \times (3 \times 3)$$
$$(3^2)^3 = 3^6$$

In general: $(x^n)^m = x^{nm}$

To the power zero By division $\dfrac{7^3}{7^3} = 7^0 = 1$ and $\dfrac{3^{11}}{3^{11}} = 3^0 = 1$

$x^0 = 1$ for any non-zero value of x

Calculator

To work out $3 \cdot 5^3$, press | 3·5 | x^y | 3 | = | $[= 10 \cdot 5]$

To work out 5^{-4}, press | 5 | x^y | 4 | +/− | = | $[= 0 \cdot 0016]$

Exercise 3

Write the answer in index form.

1. $(2^3)^2$
2. $(3^4)^2$
3. $(10^2)^3$
4. $(4^3)^5$
5. $(6^2)^2$
6. $(7^3)^6$
7. $(n^2)^3$
8. $(a^4)^5$
9. $(5^{-1})^2$
10. $(2^2)^3 \times 2^4$
11. $(3^2)^4 \times 3^3$
12. $(5^3)^2 \times 5$
13. $(5^3)^{10} \div 5^{20}$
14. $(7^2)^3 \div 7^5$
15. $(a^2)^4 \times a^3$
16. Write as an ordinary number.
    (a) 3^0
    (b) 7^0
    (c) 111^0
    (d) $(-6)^0$
    (e) $3^2 \times (5^0)$
    (f) $2^3 \div (17^0)$

In Questions **17** to **28** answer 'True' or 'False'.

17. $\frac{1}{3} = 3^{-1}$
18. $(3^2)^{10} = 3^{20}$
19. $1^{15} = 15$
20. $5^{-2} = 2^{-5}$
21. $3^2 > 2^3$
22. $10^{-1} = -10$
23. $2^2 \times 3^2 = 6^4$
24. $7^{-2} > 7^{-3}$
25. $(-\frac{1}{4})^0 = 1$
26. $(5^2)^5 = 5^7$
27. $(10^{-2})^3 = 10^{-6}$
28. $2^{-1} > 3^{-1}$

Solve the equations for n.

29. $n^2 = 9$
30. $n^3 = 8$
31. $n^3 = 1000$
32. $2^n = 16$
33. $3^n = 27$
34. $5^n = 25$
35. $10^n = 100$
36. $3^n = \frac{1}{3}$
37. $4^n = \frac{1}{4}$
38. $n^4 = 0$
39. $8^n = 1$
40. $17^n = 1$

Use the | x^y | button on a calculator to evaluate the following

41. 5^3
42. 6^3
43. 3^4
44. 7^3
45. 3^5
46. $144^{0 \cdot 5}$
47. $289^{0 \cdot 5}$
48. 1^{17}
49. $2 \cdot 35^0$
50. $10\,000^{0 \cdot 5}$
51. $16^{0 \cdot 25}$
52. $625^{0 \cdot 25}$

4

Exercise 4

In Questions **1** to **6** give your answer in index form.

1. The number of grains of sand in a bucket is 2^{20}. The contents of the bucket are divided into two equal piles. How many grains of sand are there in each pile?

2. There are 6^5 small cubes in a large model skyscraper and each cube has 6 faces. How many faces are there on all the cubes in the model?

3. The distance of the sun from the Earth is about 10^8 miles. A spacecraft is about 10^5 miles from the Earth. How many times further from the Earth is the Sun than the spacecraft?

4. An imaginary cube of side 10^7 metres is drawn around the Moon. Calculate the volume of the cube in cubic metres.

5. A scientist estimates that there are 10^{11} bacteria in a specimen dish. After an antibiotic is added, the number is reduced to one millionth of the original. How many bacteria are left?

6. A spacecraft is moving at a steady speed of 10^4 m/s towards a planet which is 100 million km away. How long will it take the spacecraft to reach the planet? Give your answer in seconds and state whether the time required is more or less than one year.

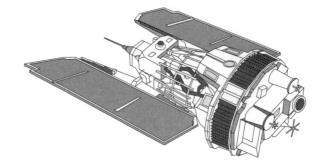

7. Fractional powers of numbers can be found using the $\boxed{x^y}$ button on a calculator. For example to work out $25^{\frac{1}{2}}$ press: $\boxed{25}\ \boxed{x^y}\ \boxed{0\cdot5}\ \boxed{=}$.

   (a) Use a calculator to work out the following.

   (i) $9^{\frac{1}{2}}$ (ii) $16^{\frac{1}{2}}$ (iii) $100^{\frac{1}{2}}$ (iv) $144^{\frac{1}{2}}$
   (v) $8^{\frac{1}{3}}$ (vi) $27^{\frac{1}{3}}$ (vii) $1000^{\frac{1}{3}}$ (viii) $16^{\frac{1}{4}}$

   (b) Copy and complete the sentences below.

   (i) $x^{\frac{1}{2}}$ means the same as _____
   (ii) $x^{\frac{1}{3}}$ means the same as _____

8. The graph shows the curve $y = 3^x$.

Use the graph to give an estimate for the value of x which satisfies the equation $3^x = 15$.

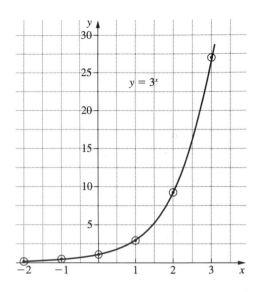

9. Draw the graph of $y = 2^x$ for values of x from -2 to $+4$. Use a scale of 2 cm to 1 unit for x and 1 cm to 2 units for y.

10.* Draw the graph of $y = \dfrac{x^2}{2^x}$ for values of x from 0 to 8.

Use a scale of 2 cm to 1 unit for x and 1 cm to 0·1 unit for y.

(a) For what value of x is the value of y maximum?

(b) Use your graph to give you two approximate solutions to the equation $\dfrac{x^2}{2^x} = 0\cdot 8$, correct to 2 decimal places.

11.* The cube root of 2 is written $\sqrt[3]{2}$. $\left[\text{In index form } \sqrt[3]{2} = 2^{\frac{1}{3}}.\right]$

The fourth root of 2 is written $\sqrt[4]{2}$. $\left[\text{In index form } \sqrt[4]{2} = 2^{\frac{1}{4}}.\right]$

The nth root of 2 is written $\sqrt[n]{2}$. $\left[\text{In index form } \sqrt[n]{2} = 2^{\frac{1}{n}}.\right]$

(a) Use a calculator to work out $\sqrt[n]{2}$ for $n = 4$, 5, 10, 100, 1000.
Copy and complete the following sentence:
'As n becomes larger and larger, $\sqrt[n]{2}$ gets closer and closer to _____.'

(b) Use a calculator to work out $\sqrt[n]{n}$ for $n = 4$, 5, 10, 100, 1000 and write a sentence similar to the one above.

1.2 Standard form

- (a) Using a calculator, work out 3 000 000 multiplied by 2 000 000. The answer is 6 000 000 000 000 but most calculators will give the answer as $\boxed{6.\ 12}$.

  The calculator cannot show the answer in full because there are too many zeros. The display $\boxed{6.\ 12}$ is short for 6×10^{12}, which is 'six times 10 to the power 12'.

  (b) Similarly for the division $0.006 \div 2\,000\,000$ the calculator will give the answer as $\boxed{3.\ -09}$. This is how the calculator shows 3×10^{-9}.

  (c) The numbers 6×10^{12} and 3×10^{-9} are written in *standard form*. Standard form is used to represent very large numbers or very small numbers.

- Here are some examples of changing numbers into standard form.

  (a) Numbers greater than 1.

  $$
  \begin{aligned}
  2000 &= 2 \times 1000 & = 2 \times 10 \times 10 \times 10 & = \mathbf{2 \times 10^3} \\
  800 &= 8 \times 100 & = 8 \times 10 \times 10 & = \mathbf{8 \times 10^2} \\
  140\,000 &= 1.4 \times 1000\,00 & = 1.4 \times 10 \times 10 \times 10 \times 10 \times 10 &= \mathbf{1.4 \times 10^5} \\
  25\,000\,000 &= 2.5 \times 10\,000\,000 & = \mathbf{2.5 \times 10^7}
  \end{aligned}
  $$

  (b) Numbers less than 1

  $$0.005 = \frac{5}{1000} = 5 \times \frac{1}{10^3} = \mathbf{5 \times 10^{-3}}$$

  $$0.000\,003 = \frac{3}{1\,000\,000} = 3 \times \frac{1}{10^6} = \mathbf{3 \times 10^{-6}}$$

  $$0.00087 = \frac{8.7}{10\,000} = 8.7 \times \frac{1}{10^4} = \mathbf{8.7 \times 10^{-4}}$$

- The numbers in bold type above are all in standard form. A number is in standard form when it has the form $a \times 10^n$, where a is a number between 1 and 10 [strictly $1 \leqslant a < 10$] and n is a positive or negative integer [whole number].

  So 5.2×10^7 *is* in standard form but 52×10^6 is *not*.

- Quick method

  (a) $8\,00\,000.0 = 8.0 \times 10^5$. The decimal point moves 5 places from A to B
  $$\uparrow \qquad \uparrow$$
  $$\text{B} \qquad \text{A}$$

  (b) $1\,600. \qquad = 1.6 \times 10^3$. The decimal point moves 3 places from A to B.
  $$\uparrow \quad \uparrow$$
  $$\text{B} \quad \text{A}$$

(c) $2\,000\,000 = 2 \times 10^6$. The decimal point moves 6 places from A to B.

   ↑   ↑
   B   A

(d) $0\cdot000\,032 = 3\cdot2 \times 10^{-5}$. The decimal point moves 5 places from A to B.

   ↑   ↑
   A   B

(e) $0\cdot00\,287 = 2\cdot87 \times 10^{-3}$. The decimal point moves 3 places from A to B.

  ↑ ↑
  A B

Notice: In large numbers the power of 10 is positive.
In small numbers the power of 10 is negative.

Exercise 1

Write the numbers in standard form.

1. 5000	**2.** 70 000	**3.** 3 million	**4.** 7500
5. 26 000	**6.** 14 million	**7.** 542 000	**8.** 5 billion
9. 61 million	**10.** 240	**11.** 1000	**12.** 165 million

Write the following small numbers in standard form.

13. 0·0002	**14.** 0·000 007	**15.** 0·005	**16.** 0·000 041
17. 0·000 000 82	**18.** 0·012	**19.** 0·000 072 3	**20.** 0·2

Write the following as decimal numbers.

21. 6×10^4	**22.** $5\cdot2 \times 10^3$	**23.** 6×10^{-3}	**24.** 5×10^{-1}
25. $3\cdot2 \times^6$	**26.** $1\cdot7 \times 10^{-4}$	**27.** $3\cdot25 \times 10^4$	**28.** $5\cdot8 \times 10^{-3}$

29. Every year the U.K. Government spends almost 200 thousand million pounds on defence, hospitals, schools etc. Write this number in standard form.

30. The thickness of very thin gold plate is 0·000 000 24 m. Write this in standard form.

31. The mass of the Earth is about 6 000 000 000 000 000 000 000 tonnes. Write this mass in standard form.

32. The population of Mexico City is about $1\cdot8 \times 10^7$. Write this in decimal form.

33. The hairs on the knee of the common flea are of length 0·000 007 m. Write this in standard form.

34. A swarm of locusts is estimated to contain 5×10^9 locust. Write this in decimal form.

35. The wavelength of a radio signal is $6\cdot2 \times 10^{-6}$ cm. Write this in decimal form (a) in cm (b) in m.

In 2002 the U.S. defence budget was 2 trillion dollars.

[1 trillion = 1000 billion, 1 billion = 1000 million].

(a) Write the 2002 budget in standard form.

(b) In 2003 the new President decides to reduce the budget to $\frac{1}{10}$ of its previous size. Write down the reduced budget in standard form.

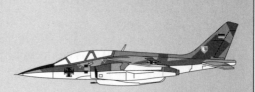

(a) \$2 trillion   = \$2 000 000 000 000

                     = \$2 \times 10^{12}

(b) Reduced budget = (\$2 \times 10^{12}) \div 10

                         = \$2 \times 10^{11}

[Remember: To divide, subtract the indices]

Exercise 2

1. A pile of 10 000 sheets of the paper used in this book is one metre high. Work out the thickness of one sheet of paper in metres, writing your answer in standard form.

2. If the number $3 \cdot 52 \times 10^{11}$ is written out in full, how many zeros follow the 2?

3. If the number $6 \cdot 2 \times 10^{-7}$ is written out in full, how many zeros would there be between the decimal point and the 6?

4. Write in order of size, smallest first: $p = 5 \times 10^5$
$$q = 6 \times 10^4$$
$$r = 8 \times 10^{-6}$$
$$s = 25\,000$$

5. Which of the following has the largest volume if $x = 2 \times 10^4$ and $y = 2 \times 10^{-2}$

   (a) xy (b) x^2 (c) $\dfrac{x}{y}$ (d) $\dfrac{1}{y^3}$?

6. The diagram shows a cube of side one metre. Complete the following statement:

'1 m^3 = ____ mm^3'

Write the missing number in standard form.

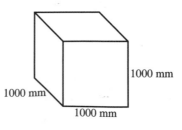

1000 mm

1000 mm

1000 mm

7. Very expensive salt can be bought in which every grain is a perfect cube. A packet contains $2 \cdot 5 \times 10^7$ grains of salt.

   (a) How many vertices are there altogether on the grains?
   (b) How many edges are there altogether on the grains?

8. At 1000, before treatment, Sasha's body contains 3×10^8 viruses which are making her feel rather ill. At 1001 she takes a drug which is designed to kill the viruses. At 1100 the number of viruses in her body is $\frac{1}{100}$ of the number at 1000. How many viruses were in her body at 1100?

9. A slug crawls a distance of 72 m in 100 hours. Find the average speed of the slug in cm/s. Give your answer in standard form.

10. The formula connecting s, a and t is $s = \frac{1}{2}at^2$.

Calculate the value of s, in standard form, when $a = 0.06$ and $t = 10^5$.

11. There is one Queen termite in every termite colony and on average she lays one egg every 2 seconds. She does this 24 hours a day for a whole year. In one part of Uganda there are 15 thousand termite colonies. How many eggs are laid in one year by the Queens in all of the colonies?

12. At the time of its 'migration' [i.e. jumping off a cliff into the sea] the average lemming has 15 million functioning brain cells. How many brain cells are there altogether in a herd of 200 thousand migrating lemmings?

13. Write down, in standard form, the next two numbers in each sequence.

(a) 5×10^2, 1.5×10^3, 4.5×10^3,

(b) 1.6×10^5, 8×10^4, 4×10^4,

(c) 4×10^{-3}, 1.6×10^{-3}, 6.4×10^{-2},

(d) 3×10^2, 6×10^3, 1.2×10^5,

10

Using a calculator

(a) Work out $(5 \times 10^7) \times (3 \times 10^{12})$

Use the $\boxed{\text{EXP}}$ button as follows:

$\boxed{5}$ $\boxed{\text{EXP}}$ $\boxed{7}$ $\boxed{\times}$ $\boxed{3}$ $\boxed{\text{EXP}}$ $\boxed{12}$ $\boxed{=}$ Answer $= 1 \cdot 5 \times 10^{20}$.

Notice that you do NOT press the $\boxed{\times}$ button after the $\boxed{\text{EXP}}$ button!

(b) Work out $(3 \cdot 2 \times 10^3) \div (8 \times 10^{-7})$

$\boxed{3 \cdot 2}$ $\boxed{\text{EXP}}$ $\boxed{3}$ $\boxed{\div}$ $\boxed{8}$ $\boxed{\text{EXP}}$ $\boxed{7}$ $\boxed{+/-}$ $\boxed{=}$ Answer $= 4 \times 10^9$

$\uparrow$

[Press this key for negative.]

(c) $(5 \times 10^{-8})^2$

$\boxed{5}$ $\boxed{\text{EXP}}$ $\boxed{8}$ $\boxed{+/-}$ $\boxed{x^2}$ Answer $= 2 \cdot 5 \times 10^{-15}$

Exercise 3

Use a calculator to work out the following and write the answer in standard form.

1. $2000 \times 30\,000$
2. $40\,000 \times 500$
3. $25\,000 \times 600\,000$
4. 3500×2 million
5. $600\,000 \times 1500$
6. $(40\,000)^2$
7. $18\,000 \div 400$
8. $(4 \times 10^5) \times (3 \times 10^8)$
9. $(6 \cdot 2 \times 10^4) \times (3 \times 10^6)$
10. $(5 \times 10^{-4}) \times (4 \times 10^{-7})$
11. $(3 \times 10^8) \times (2 \cdot 5 \times 10^{-20})$
12. $(5 \times 10^7) \div (2 \times 10^{-2})$
13. $(3 \times 10^5)^3$
14. $(7 \times 10^{-2}) \div (2 \times 10^4)$
15. $(9 \times 10^{-11})^2$
16. $(4 \cdot 2 \times 10^8) \times (1 \cdot 5 \times 10^5)$
17. $(3 \times 10^{-4}) \div (2 \times 10^{-20})$
18. $(4 \times 10^5) \times (2 \times 10^{-2})$
19. $(1 \cdot 4 \times 10^{-1}) \times (2 \times 10^{17})$
20. $(2 \times 10^5)^2 \times (4 \times 10^{-8})$
21. $(8 \times 10^{-5}) \div (2 \times 10^{-3})^2$
22. $(2 \times 10^{-4}) \div (1 \cdot 6 \times 10^8)$
23. $10^5 \div (2 \times 10^8)$
24. $(3 \times 10^{-7}) \times 10^{-4}$

Exercise 4

Give answers in standard form correct to 3 significant figures, where necessary.

1. The dimensions of a rectangular component in a computer are shown.

   (a) Calculate the area of one component.
   (b) How many of these components can be fitted into an area of 2×10^{-3} m^2?

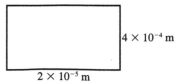
4×10^{-4} m

2×10^{-5} m

2. (a) A cuboid has dimensions 3000 cm by 2500 cm by 4000 cm. Calculate the volume of the cuboid in cm^3.
   (b) A cylinder has radius 500 mm and height 10 m. Calculate the volume of the cylinder in cm^3. [$V = \pi r^2 h$].

10

3. Water flows from a hose at the rate of 200 cm^3 per second. How long will it take to fill a tank of capacity $1{\cdot}2 \times 10^7$ cm^3? Give your answer in minutes.

4. A smallpox virus is approximately $2{\cdot}8 \times 10^{-7}$ m across. If these viruses were placed next to each other in a straight line across this page (0·186 m), how many viruses would there be?

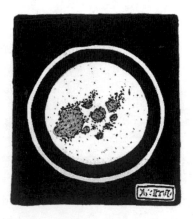

5. The mass of the Earth is $5{\cdot}97 \times 10^{21}$ tonnes and the mass of the Moon is $7{\cdot}35 \times 10^{19}$ tonnes.
   (a) Calculate the mass of the Sun, given that it is 333 000 times that of the Earth.
   (b) How many times heavier is the Sun than the Moon?

6. A light year is the distance travelled by light in one year (365·24 days). The speed of light is $2{\cdot}998 \times 10^5$ km/s. Calculate the length of a light year in km.

7. As the Earth moves in its elliptical orbit around the Sun, its average distance from the sun is $1{\cdot}5 \times 10^8$ km. How many minutes does it take light to travel from the Sun to Earth?

8. The light reaching Earth from the star 'Betelgeux', a *very* distant star of Orion, left Betelgeux in AD 1470. In the year 2000 how far away from Earth was Betelgeux in km?

9. The Sun uses up 4×10^9 kg of hydrogen every second.
   (a) Calculate how many tonnes of hydrogen are used up every year.
   (b) This might seem rather alarming since life on Earth depends entirely on heat and light from the Sun. Work out what percentage of the mass of the Sun is used up every year. Refer to question 6 for the mass of the Sun.

10. The most massive living thing on Earth is a tree (Sequoiadendron giganteum) in the U.S.A. It stands over 85 m tall and its weight is estimated at 2040 tonnes. The seed which produced this tree weighed approximately 4·5 mg. By what factor has the weight of the seed increased as the tree has grown to its present size?

1.3 Rules of algebra

Simplifying terms

Simplify the following expressions.

$3n \times 2 = 6n$ $\qquad$ $2m \times 10 = 20m$
$10a \div 2 = 5a$ $\qquad$ $8R \div 4 = 2R$
$m \times m = m^2$ $\qquad$ $2a \times a = 2a^2$
$3n \times 2n = 6n^2$ $\qquad$ $4t \times 5t = 20t^2$

Exercise 1

Do the following multiplications and divisions.

1. $3x \times 4$	**2.** $2x \times 5$	**3.** $7x \times 2$
4. $6y \times 2$	**5.** $3y \times 5$	**6.** $4a \times 6$
7. $6a \times 10$	**8.** $3c \times 9$	**9.** $4d \times 6$
10. $7 \times 2c$	**11.** $5 \times 4d$	**12.** $4 \times 3t$
13. $8 \times 2a$	**14.** $11 \times 3d$	**15.** $9 \times 2x$

16. $16b \div 4$	**17.** $32x \div 8$	**18.** $2T \div 2$
19. $44h \div 11$	**20.** $15R \div 5$	**21.** $9t \div 9$
22. $30n \div 6$	**23.** $6A \div 3$	**24.** $7M \div 7$
25. $24r \div 6$	**26.** $80t \div 8$	**27.** $36T \div 4$
28. $25a \div 5$	**29.** $90R \div 10$	**30.** $9b \div 3$

31. $n \times n$	**32.** $a \times a$	**33.** $T \times T$
34. $2c \times c$	**35.** $2n \times n$	**36.** $3b \times b$
37. $y \times 2y$	**38.** $A \times A$	**39.** $t \times 4t$
40. $n \times 5n$	**41.** $2x \times 3x$	**42.** $3c \times 4c$
43. $4a \times 2a$	**44.** $3t \times 3t$	**45.** $2n \times 3n$

Simplify the following expressions.

(a) $3(2n + 5) = 6n + 15$

(b) $2(5a - 3) = 10a - 6$

(c) $-3(2x - 7) = -6x + 21$

(d) $3(3n + 1) + 2n = 9n + 3 + 2n$
$\qquad\qquad\qquad = 11n + 3$

(e) $4(a + 2) + 3(2a + 1)$
$\qquad = 4a + 8 + 6a + 3$
$\qquad = 10a + 11$

Exercise 2

Remove the brackets from the following expressions.

1. $2(3x + 4)$	**2.** $5(5y - 2)$
3. $10(2x - 1)$	**4.** $3(2x + 5)$
5. $4(7y + 2)$	**6.** $6(2a + 3)$
7. $7(10 - 3x)$	**8.** $5(2y - 5)$
9. $3(4a - 5)$	**10.** $2(3y + a)$
11. $7(2a + 9)$	**12.** $8(3y - 5)$
13. $5(12c - 1)$	**14.** $9(3d - 4)$
15. $-2(x + 5)$	**16.** $-4(y - 3)$
17. $-3(a - 1)$	**18.** $3(t + 4)$
19. $-2(x + 3)$	**20.** $4(y - 2)$
21. $10(b - 3)$	**22.** $-5(c + 10)$
23. $-6(d + h)$	**24.** $2(x + y)$
25. $7(a + 2b)$	**26.** $-2(2x - y)$
27. $-3(5a - 3)$	**28.** $4(2a - 1)$

Exercise 3

Simplify the following expressions.

1. $3(x + 2) + 4x$

2. $5(2y - 1) - 3y$

3. $2(4x + 1) - 7$

4. $4(2n + 1) + 2(n - 1)$

5. $5(a + 2) + 2(2a + 1)$

6. $3(t - 1) + 2(2t + 1)$

7. $2(4x + 3) + 4(3x - 4)$

8. $3(4d + 1) - 2(6d - 5)$

9. $5a + 2(3a + 4) - 2a$

10. $9y - 5(y + 2) - 3$

11. $11b + 3 - 3(2b - 5)$

12. $4(a - 2) + 2(3a - 1) - 3a$

13. $5(3x - 2) - 4 - 2(4 + x)$

14. $2c + 5(c - 2) - 3(2c + 3)$

15. $6y + 2(3y + 1) - 7 + 2y$

16. $5 - 3(2x + 3) + 4(5x + 3)$

17. $20 - 3(a + 3) - 4(2a - 1)$

18. $9(x + 2) - 4 + 3(2 - 3x)$

19. $15(n + m) - 6(2n - m)$

20. $8(a - b) + 10(a - 3b)$

Exercise 4

In Questions **1** to **15** answer 'true' or 'false'.

1. $3 \times n = n \times 3$ **2.** $5 \times a = 5 + a$ **3.** $n \times n = n^2$

4. $c \times d = cd$ **5.** $m \times 3 = 3m$ **6.** $a - b = b - a$

7. $2(n + 1) = 2n + 1$ **8.** $t + t = t^2$ **9.** $2h \times h = 2h^2$

10. $m \times 3m = 3m^2$ **11.** $3(a - b) = 3a - 3b$ **12.** $n^2 + n^2 = n^4$

13. $n \div 3 = \dfrac{n}{3}$ **14.** $t \div 2 = \dfrac{t}{2}$ **15.** $(x + y) \div 2 = \dfrac{(x + y)}{2}$

16. In the expression $2(3n - 5)$, three operations are performed in the following order:

Draw similar diagrams to show the correct order of operations for the following expressions.

(a) $6n + 1$ (b) $3(5n - 2)$ (c) $\dfrac{4n + 5}{3}$

(d) $n^2 + 7$ (e) $(n - 7)^2$ (f) $\dfrac{(3n + 1)^2 + 5}{7}$

Remove the brackets and simplify

(a) $n(n + 2)$
   $= n^2 + 2n$

(b) $x(2x + 1)$
   $= 2x^2 + x$

(c) $a(3a - 2)$
   $= 3a^2 - 2a$

(d) $2m(m + 1)$
   $= 2m^2 + 2m$

(e) $5n(2n + 3)$
   $= 10n^2 + 15n$

(f) $2n(3n + 1)$
   $= 6n^2 + 2n$

Exercise 5

Remove the brackets and simplify.

1. $n(n + 3)$ **2.** $n(n + 7)$ **3.** $a(a - 3)$
4. $t(t - 5)$ **5.** $a(a - 10)$ **6.** $m(m + 11)$
7. $2a(a + 1)$ **8.** $3n(n + 2)$ **9.** $5t(t + 1)$

10. $x(2x + 1)$ **11.** $y(y - 7)$ **12.** $3y(y + 3)$
13. $h(h - 100)$ **14.** $5a(a + 5)$ **15.** $p(p + 3)$
16. $2e(3e + 1)$ **17.** $3x(3x + 2)$ **18.** $2a(5a - 1)$

14

Exercise 6

1. Four rods P, Q, R and S have lengths, in cm, as shown.

In each diagram find the length l, in terms of x. Give your answers in their simplest form. [The diagrams are not drawn to scale.]

(a)

(b)

(c)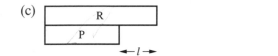

(d)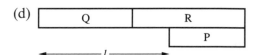

(e)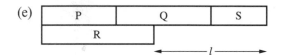

(f)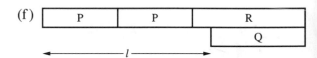

(g)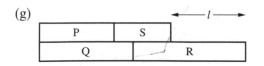

(h)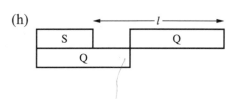

(i)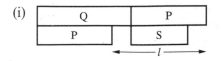

(j)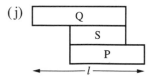

(k)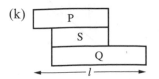

(l)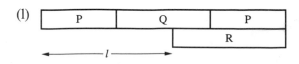

2. (a) A solid rectangular block measures x cm by x cm by $(x + 3)$ cm. Find a simplified expression for its surface area in cm^2.

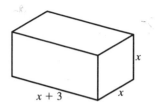

(b) The block above is divided into two rectangular blocks by cutting as shown in the diagram. Find a simplified expression for the total surface area of the two blocks formed, in cm^2.

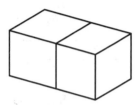

Solving equations

Solve the equations

(a) $4n - 3 = 13$

     ⊕+3 ⊕+3

     $4n = 16$

     ⊕÷4 ⊕÷4

     $n = 4$

(b) $4n - 3 = 2n + 11$

     ⊖−2n ⊖−2n

     $2n - 3 = 11$

     ⊕+3 ⊕+3

     $2n = 14$

     $n = 7$

Exercise 7

Solve the equations.

  1. $3x - 2 = 13$ **2.** $4x + 1 = 25$ **3.** $7x - 2 = -1$
  4. $5 + 2x = 6$ **5.** $7 + 3x = 22$ **6.** $3 = 4x + 1$
  7. $5 = 3x - 1$ **8.** $7 = 15 + 2x$ **9.** $10 = 12 + 3x$
10. $4 = 6x + 5$ **11.** $7x - 1 = -8$ **12.** $13 + x = 10$

In Questions **13** to **24**, begin by putting the x terms on one side of the equation.

13. $4x + 3 = 2x - 5$ **14.** $7x - 5 = 2x + 8$ **15.** $3x + 7 = 8x + 2$
16. $6x + 1 = 2 - 3x$ **17.** $7x - 2 = 1 - 3x$ **18.** $5 - x = 2x - 7$
19. $2x - 8 = 11x + 12$ **20.** $3x - 9 = 4x + 4$ **21.** $2 + 8x = 5 - x$
22. $16x + 9 = 12x - 3$ **23.** $1 - 10x = 6 - 5x$ **24.** $4 - 5x = 4 + 7x$

25. $4(x + 1) = 2(x - 1)$ **26.** $5(2x + 1) = 3(x - 2)$ **27.** $4(3 - x) = 2(2x + 1)$
28. $5(x + 2) - (x - 2) = 0$ **29.** $6(1 - 2x) - 3(x + 1) = 0$ **30.** $5(x - 7) = 2(x + 1)$
31. $(x - 1) - (2x - 3) = 0$ **32.** $5(1 - x) = 4(10 + x)$ **33.** $3(2x - 3) = 4(5 - x)$
34. $3(3 - 2x) - 2(1 - x) = 10$ **35.** $6 - 3(x + 1) = 7$ **36.** $9 - 5(2x - 1) = 6$

Equations with fractions

(a) $\dfrac{2x}{3} = 5$

$2x = 15$ [Multiply by 3]

$x = \frac{15}{2}$ [Divide by 2]

$x = 7\frac{1}{2}$

(b) $\dfrac{4}{x} = -2$

$4 = -2x$ [Multiply by x]

$\dfrac{4}{-2} = x$ [Divide by -2]

$-2 = x$

(c) $\dfrac{x}{2} + 3 = 7$

$\dfrac{x}{2} = 4$ [Subtract 3 from both sides.]

$\cancel{2} \times \dfrac{x}{\cancel{2}} = 4 \times 2$ [Multiply both sides by 2.]

$x = 8$

(d) $\dfrac{4}{x} - 1 = 14$

$\dfrac{4}{x} = 15$ [Add 1 to both sides.]

$\cancel{x}\,\dfrac{4}{\cancel{x}} = 15x$ [Multiply both sides by x.]

$4 = 15x$

$\frac{4}{15} = x$

Exercise 8

Solve the equations.

1. $\dfrac{x}{3} = 4$ **2.** $\dfrac{x}{5} = 2$ **3.** $5 = \dfrac{x}{4}$ **4.** $\dfrac{x}{7} = -2$

5. $\dfrac{x}{5} = -5$ **6.** $\dfrac{2x}{3} = 1$ **7.** $\dfrac{3x}{4} = 2$ **8.** $\dfrac{5x}{2} = 2$

9. $\dfrac{6}{x} = 7$ **10.** $\dfrac{4}{x} = 9$ **11.** $\dfrac{2}{x} = 1$ **12.** $\dfrac{3}{x} = \dfrac{1}{4}$

13. $3 = \dfrac{8}{x}$ **14.** $\dfrac{2}{3} = \dfrac{10}{x}$ **15.** $\dfrac{8}{x} = -11$ **16.** $-2 = \dfrac{100}{x}$

For Questions **17** to **24** see the examples above.

17. $\dfrac{x}{3} + 1 = 5$ **18.** $\dfrac{x}{2} - 1 = 8$ **19.** $\dfrac{x}{5} + 9 = 8$ **20.** $6 + \dfrac{x}{3} = 10$

21. $\dfrac{1}{2}x + 9 = 20$ **22.** $\dfrac{1}{3}x - 6 = 11$ **23.** $\dfrac{2}{3}x + 8 = 10$ **24.** $\dfrac{4}{5}x - 1 = 0$

Questions **25** to **33** are more difficult.

25. $\dfrac{3}{2x+1} = 2$ **26.** $\dfrac{3}{x} = \dfrac{2}{x-1}$ **27.** $\dfrac{9}{x+2} = \dfrac{7}{2x+1}$

28. $\dfrac{x-3}{5} = \dfrac{2x+1}{3}$ **29.** $\dfrac{1-x}{2} = \dfrac{1}{4}$ **30.** $\dfrac{3x}{5} = 2(x+1)$

31. $\dfrac{3}{x+1} + 3 = 0$ **32.** $\dfrac{8}{1-x} = 16$ **33.** $\dfrac{5(x-3)}{2} = \dfrac{2(x-1)}{5}$

Solving problems with equations

Exercise 9

In Questions **1** to **8** write an equation and solve it to find the number I am thinking of.

1. If I double the number and then add 5 the answer is 8.

2. If I subtract 5 from the number and then multiply the result by 4, the answer is 16.

3. If I double the number, add 7 and then treble the result, the answer is 22.

4. If I multiply the number by 6 and subtract 4, I get the same answer as when I add 6 to the number and then double the result.

5. If I multiply the number by 5, add 11 and then double the result, I get the same answer as when I treble the number and then add 36.

6. If I subtract 7 from the number and then multiply the result by 9, I get the same answer as when I take the number away *from* 7 and then double the result.

7. If I subtract the number *from* 11 and then multiply the result by 4, I get the same answer as when I add $1\frac{1}{2}$ to the number and then multiply the result by 4.

8. If I double the number, add 7 and then divide the result by 3, I get the same answer as when I subtract the number from 12 and then divide the result by 5.

9. Find three consecutive numbers such that three times the middle number is 12 more than the sum of the other two numbers. [Hint. Let the three numbers be x, $x + 1$, etc.]

10. Find four consecutive *odd* numbers whose sum is 224.

11. The area of this rectangle is 20 square units. Find x and hence find the length and width of the rectangle. [Hint: Do not use the area to start with.]

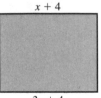

$x + 4$

$3x + 4$

12. The length of a rectangle is three times its width. If the perimeter is 48 cm, find its width. [Let the width be x.]

13. An equilateral triangle has sides of length $2x + 4$, $3x + 1$ and $3x + 1$. Find x.

14. Find the value of x so that the areas of the shaded rectangles are equal.

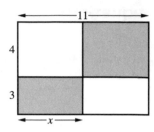

15. Two angles of an isosceles triangle are $a°$ and $(a + 10)°$. Find two possible values of a.

16. When Steve was asked how old he was, he replied: 'In 30 years I'll be twice as old as I was 8 years ago'. How old is he?

17. Neha has x 10p coins and $(x + 3)$ 20p coins. Find x if she has £2·70 altogether.

18. The mean height of Alan, Ben and Chris is 150 cm. Alan is $(2x - 1)$ cm tall, Ben is $3(x + 2)$ cm tall and Chris is $2(2x - 7)$ cm tall.
Find the value of x and hence find the height of Chris.

19. The diagram shows the semi-circular end of a running track.
Dave runs straight across the field from A to B at a speed of x m/s. His brother Jim runs around the track at a speed of $(x + 2)$ m/s.

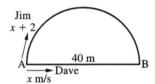

Find the value of x, correct to 2 s.f., if they both take the same time to get from A to B.

Factors

- The expression $8x + 6$ has two terms, $8x$ and 6.
  The number 2 is a factor of both terms.
  We can write $8x + 6 = 2(4x + 3)$.
  This process is called factorising.

- Here are some examples:
  $6a + 15 = 3(2a + 5)$ $18m + 24n = 6(3m + 4n)$
  $4x^2 + 6x = 2x(2x + 3)$ $7n^2 + 5n = n(7n + 5)$

Exercise 10

Copy and complete.

1. $8a + 10 = 2(4a + \square)$
2. $6x + 3 = 3(2x + \square)$
3. $6a + 9 = 3(2a + \square)$
4. $10a + 15 = 5(\square + \square)$
5. $18x - 12 = 6(\square - \square)$
6. $18c + 24 = \square(\square + \square)$
7. $3x + 15 = \square(\square + \square)$
8. $7n - 35 = 7(\square - \square)$
9. $16m + 40 = \square(2m + \square)$
10. $45a + 36 = \square(5a + \square)$

In Questions **11** to **25** factorise the expressions.

11. $4a + 10$
12. $6c + 21$
13. $10c - 5$
14. $18m + 9$
15. $9m + 12$
16. $15a + 25$
17. $14x - 21t$
18. $18x + 24t$
19. $24p - 20q$
20. $6a + 9b + 3c$
21. $10a + 15b + 25c$
22. $9x + 9y + 21t$
23. $7c + 14d - 7e$
24. $24m + 12n + 16t$
25. $18a - 27b + 36c$

Factorise the following.

26. $x^2 + 6x$
27. $3x^2 + 4x$
28. $6x^2 + x$
29. $2a^2 + a$
30. $5n^2 + n$
31. $2a^2 + 6a$
32. $3n^2 - n$
33. $5m^2 - 15m$
34. $x^3 + x^2 + x$
35. $12a^2 - 8a$
36. $6a^2 - a$
37. $mn + m^2$
38. $x^2 - xy$
39. $2x^2 + 4xy$
40. $x^3 + xy^2$

1.4 Multiplying brackets

- The rectangle shown has length $(x + 5)$ and width $(x + 2)$. The area of the rectangle is, therefore, $(x + 5)(x + 2)$.

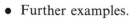

  The large rectangle can be split into four smaller rectangles.
  Total area of 4 smaller rectangles
    $= x^2 + 2x + 5x + 10$

  We see that $(x + 5)(x + 2) = x^2 + 2x + 5x + 10$.

- Further examples.
  (a) $(x + 7)(x + 3) = x(x + 3) + 7(x + 3)$
      $ = x^2 + 3x + 7x + 21$
      $ = x^2 + 10x + 21$

  (b) $(2x + 1)(x - 3) = 2x(x - 3) + 1(x - 3)$
      $ = 2x^2 - 6x + x - 3$
      $ = 2x^2 - 5x - 3$

20

(c) $(x-3)^2 = (x-3)(x-3)$
$= x(x-3) - 3(x-3)$
$= x^2 - 3x - 3x + 9$
$= x^2 - 6x + 9$

(d) $(3x+1)^2 = (3x+1)(3x+1)$
$= 3x(3x+1) + 1(3x+1)$
$= 9x^2 + 3x + 3x + 1$
$= 9x^2 + 6x + 1$

● The ability to multiply pairs of brackets enables us to solve a wide range of problems in mathematics. Here is a proof of Pythagoras' theorem in which we require the product $(x-y)^2$.

The square ABCD is drawn on the hypotenuse of the right-angled triangle ABE. The square ABCD is then split into four equal triangles and a square in the middle, as shown.

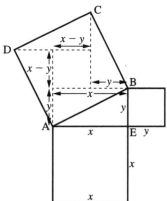

Area of square ABCD

$= 4 \times (\tfrac{1}{2}xy) + (x-y)^2$

$= 2xy + x^2 - 2xy + y^2$

$= x^2 + y^2$

So the square on the hypotenuse is equal to the sum of the squares on the other two sides.

Exercise 1

Remove the brackets and simplify.

1. $(x+3)(x+5)$
2. $(x+7)(x+2)$
3. $(x+9)(x+1)$
4. $(x+3)(x-3)$
5. $(x+3)(x-5)$
6. $(x+11)(x+4)$
7. $(x+4)(x+2)$
8. $(x+3)(x-1)$
9. $(x+3)^2$
10. $(x+1)^2$
11. $(x+5)^2$
12. $(x-2)(x+7)$
13. $(x+5)(x+7)$
14. $(x+3)(x-2)$
15. $(x-4)(x+1)$
16. $(x-4)(x-2)$
17. $(x-3)(x-1)$
18. $(x-1)^2$

Remove both sets of brackets and simplify.

19. $(x-3)(x+1) + (x+2)(x+5)$
20. $(x-7)(x-1) + (x+3)(x+2)$
21. $(x+1)^2 + (x-3)(x-5)$
22. $(2x+1)(x+1) + (x-4)(x+3)$
23. $(2x+1)(x-3) + x(x+5)$
24. $(x-3)(3x+1) + 3x(x+1)$
25. $(2x+1)^2 + (x+4)^2$
26. $(x+2)^2 - x(x+3)$
27. $(3x+1)(2x+3) + 3x(x-2)$
28. $(3x+1)(x-5) - 3x(x-5)$

(a) Solve the equation

$$(x - 1)(x + 2) = (x + 3)^2$$
$$x(x + 2) - 1(x + 2) = (x + 3)(x + 3)$$
$$x^2 + 2x - x - 2 = x^2 + 3x + 3x + 9$$

[Subtract x^2 from both sides.]

$$-2 - 9 = 3x + 3x - 2x + x$$
$$-11 = 5x$$
$$-2\tfrac{1}{5} = x$$

(b) Find the lengths of the sides of the right angled triangle.

By Pythagoras' theorem:

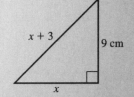

$$(x + 3)^2 = x^2 + 9^2$$
$$x^2 + 3x + 3x + 9 = x^2 + 81$$
$$6x = 72$$
$$x = 12$$

The sides of the triangle are of length 9 cm, 12 cm, 15 cm

Exercise 2

Solve the equations.

1. $(x + 3)(x - 1) = (x + 4)(x - 3)$
2. $x(x + 7) = (x - 3)(x - 1)$
3. $(x + 5)^2 = (x + 6)(x + 3)$
4. $(3x + 1)(x - 1) = 3x(x - 2)$
5. $(2x + 1)(x + 3) = x(2x - 5)$
6. $(x + 3)^2 = (x - 2)^2$
7. $(2x + 1)^2 = (4x - 1)(x + 1)$
8. $(x - 3)(x + 3) = x^2 - 18x$
9. $(x + 1)^2 + (x + 2)^2 = (2x + 1)(x + 1)$
10. $(x + 2)^2 + (2x - 1)^2 = 5x(x + 1)$

In Questions 1 to 17 form an equation involving x and then solve it.

11. Use Pythagoras' theorem to form an equation.
    Solve the equation to find x.

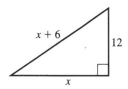

12. Find x, and hence the three sides of the triangles shown.

(a)

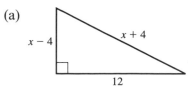

(b)

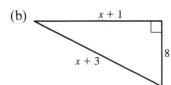

13. A rectangle measures x by 10. The length of a diagonal of the rectangle is 2 cm greater than the longer side x. Find x

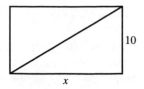

14. The rectangle and the square have the same area. Find x.

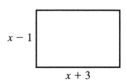

15. The sum of the areas of the two rectangles is equal to the area of the square. Find x.

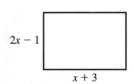
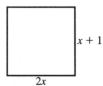
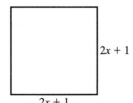

16. The rectangle and the triangle have the same area. Find x.

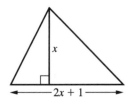
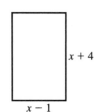

17.* If the radius of a circle is increased by 3 cm the area is increased by $99\,\pi$ cm^2. Find the radius of the original circle.

18.* An approximate formula for the stopping distances when travelling in a car is given by

$$d = \frac{v(v+20)}{60} \qquad d = \text{distance in metres}, \quad v = \text{speed in m.p.h.}$$

If a driver increases his speed by 10 m.p.h. it takes him 15 metres extra to stop. What is his initial speed?

1.5 Fractions

As you progress further in mathematics, the ability to handle fractions with confidence becomes more and more important. Mistakes are frequently made when algebraic expressions contain fractions.
Fractions involving algebraic symbols can be manipulated in the same way as ordinary numerical fractions. This section begins with a discussion of arithmetic with fractions.

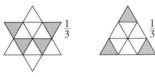

Multiplying

(a) $\frac{3}{4}$ of $12 = \frac{3}{4} \times \frac{12}{1}$ (b) $\frac{2}{3} \times \frac{5}{7} = \frac{10}{21}$ (c) $2\frac{1}{2} \times \frac{1}{4} = \frac{5}{2} \times \frac{1}{4}$

$\qquad\qquad\quad = \frac{36}{4} \qquad\qquad\qquad\qquad\qquad\qquad = \frac{5}{8}$

$\qquad\qquad\quad = 9$

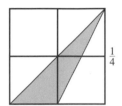

Method: (i) Write any mixed fractions as top heavy fractions.
(ii) Multiply the numbers on the top
(iii) Multiply the numbers on the bottom.
(iv) Cancel down if necessary. This can be done either before or after multiplying.

[Example (a) could be $\dfrac{3}{\overset{}{\underset{1}{\cancel{4}}}} \times \dfrac{\overset{3}{\cancel{12}}}{1} = \dfrac{9}{1} = 9$]

Dividing

(a) How many quarters are there in 3?

There are four quarters in one, so there are 12 quarters in 3.
That is $3 \div \frac{1}{4} = 12$.

(b) Similarly we find that $3 \div \frac{1}{5} = 15$

$\qquad\qquad$ and $8 \div \frac{1}{3} = 24$

Method: (i) Invert the fraction you are dividing by and then multiply the two fractions.
(ii) Write any mixed fractions as top heavy fractions.

Examples: $\quad \frac{3}{5} \div \frac{2}{3} \qquad\qquad\qquad 2\frac{1}{3} \div \frac{3}{4}$

$\qquad\qquad = \frac{3}{5} \times \frac{3}{2} \qquad\qquad = \frac{7}{3} \times \frac{4}{3}$

$\qquad\qquad = \frac{9}{10} \qquad\qquad\quad = \frac{28}{9}$

$\qquad\qquad\qquad\qquad\qquad\qquad = 3\frac{1}{9}$

Addition and subtraction

We know that $\frac{1}{3}+\frac{1}{3}=\frac{2}{3}$ and $\frac{2}{7}+\frac{3}{7}=\frac{5}{7}$

but $\frac{1}{5}+\frac{1}{3}$ is not so easy.

> Method: (i) The fractions to be added must be written as fractions with the same denominator.
> (ii) Mixed fractions should be written as top heavy fractions.

Examples: (a) $\frac{1}{5}+\frac{1}{3}$

$= \frac{3}{15}+\frac{5}{15}$

$= \frac{8}{15}$

(b) $\frac{3}{4}+\frac{1}{5}$

$= \frac{15}{20}+\frac{4}{20}$

$= \frac{19}{20}$

(c) $\frac{5}{6}-\frac{2}{9}$

$= \frac{15}{18}-\frac{4}{18}$

$= \frac{11}{18}$

(d) $3\frac{1}{5}-2\frac{1}{2}$

$= \frac{16}{5}-\frac{5}{2}$

$= \frac{32}{10}-\frac{25}{10}$

$= \frac{7}{10}$

Exercise 1

Work out and give the answer in its simplest form.

1. $\frac{1}{4}+\frac{3}{8}$
2. $\frac{3}{5}+\frac{1}{10}$
3. $\frac{2}{3}+\frac{1}{6}$
4. $\frac{5}{12}+\frac{1}{4}$

5. $\frac{7}{8}-\frac{1}{2}$
6. $\frac{1}{3}+\frac{1}{2}$
7. $\frac{3}{5}-\frac{1}{4}$
8. $\frac{4}{7}-\frac{1}{2}$

9. $\frac{2}{3}+\frac{1}{4}$
10. $\frac{2}{5}+\frac{1}{3}$
11. $\frac{1}{7}+\frac{1}{2}$
12. $\frac{1}{5}-\frac{1}{6}$

13. $\frac{2}{3}-\frac{5}{12}$
14. $\frac{7}{9}-\frac{1}{6}$
15. $\frac{4}{5}-\frac{2}{7}$
16. $\frac{7}{10}-\frac{1}{3}$

17. $1\frac{1}{4}-\frac{2}{5}$
18. $1\frac{3}{4}-\frac{2}{3}$
19. $3\frac{1}{4}+1\frac{3}{5}$
20. $2\frac{5}{6}+1\frac{1}{4}$

Questions **21** to **40** involve either multiplying or dividing.

21. $\frac{2}{3}\times\frac{1}{5}$
22. $\frac{3}{5}\times\frac{3}{4}$
23. $\frac{5}{9}\times\frac{3}{4}$
24. $1\frac{3}{4}\times\frac{1}{5}$

25. $\frac{3}{8}\times\frac{4}{5}$
26. $\frac{2}{9}\times\frac{6}{7}$
27. $\frac{5}{12}\times\frac{3}{10}$
28. $\frac{5}{8}\times\frac{6}{15}$

29. $\frac{5}{6}\div\frac{1}{2}$
30. $\frac{7}{8}\div\frac{2}{3}$
31. $\frac{5}{9}\div\frac{3}{4}$
32. $2\frac{1}{2}\div\frac{1}{5}$

33. $3\frac{1}{4}\times2\frac{1}{2}$
34. $\frac{5}{8}\div1\frac{1}{2}$
35. $\frac{5}{9}\div\frac{1}{3}$
36. $\frac{3}{5}\div\frac{9}{100}$

37. $\frac{3}{5}\div2$
38. $\frac{4}{7}\div3$
39. $1\frac{1}{4}\div4$
40. $5\frac{1}{2}\div3$

Exercise 2

Copy each square and fill in the missing numbers or symbols (+, −, ×, ÷). The arrows act as equals signs.

1.

	÷	2	→	$1\frac{1}{2}$
÷		÷		
	×		→	2
↓		↓		
	×	8	→	

2.

$\frac{1}{4}$	−	$\frac{1}{16}$	→	
		+		
$\frac{1}{8}$	÷		→	1
↓		↓		
$\frac{1}{8}$			→	$\frac{5}{16}$

3.

	−	$\frac{1}{5}$	→	$\frac{7}{15}$
−		×		
	÷		→	$1\frac{1}{2}$
↓		↓		
	÷	$\frac{1}{20}$	→	

4.

	−	$\frac{1}{5}$	→	$\frac{1}{20}$
×		÷		
2	÷		→	
↓		↓		
	×	$\frac{4}{5}$	→	

5.

$\frac{2}{3}$	×	4	→	
		÷		
$\frac{1}{2}$	÷		→	$\frac{1}{16}$
↓		↓		
$\frac{1}{3}$			→	$\frac{5}{6}$

6.

	×	$\frac{1}{3}$	→	$\frac{1}{8}$
		÷		
$\frac{1}{4}$			→	$\frac{11}{12}$
↓		↓		
$\frac{5}{8}$	−		→	$\frac{1}{8}$

Problems

After 45 ml is poured from a full bottle of wine, the bottle is $\frac{5}{8}$ full.
How many ml are there in a full bottle?

The difference between a full bottle and $\frac{5}{8}$ of a bottle is $\frac{3}{8}$ of a bottle.

So $\frac{3}{8}$ of a bottle = 45 ml

$\therefore$ $\frac{1}{8}$ of a bottle = $\frac{45}{3}$ = 15 ml

$\therefore$ $\frac{8}{8}$ of a bottle = 15×8

$\qquad\qquad\qquad = 120$ ml

A full bottle contains 120 ml of wine.

Exercise 3

1. Of the 495 pupils at Cantonna College, $\frac{1}{3}$ travel by bus, $\frac{1}{5}$ travel by car and the rest cycle.
   How many pupils cycle to the college?

2. Of his weekly income, Gary spends $\frac{1}{4}$ on food and $\frac{1}{3}$ on rent.
   What fraction of his income is left for other things?

3. (a) Mrs Picasso has $3\frac{1}{4}$ pounds of flour. The recipe for a cake calls for $\frac{1}{4}$ of a pound of flour. How many cakes can be made?
   (b) Suppose she has $4\frac{2}{3}$ pounds and the recipe calls for $\frac{2}{5}$ pound per cake. How many complete cakes can be made now?

4. The number of magazines sold by a newsagent is $2\frac{1}{4}$ times the number of books sold. If 549 magazines are sold, how many books are sold?

5. The reciprocal of 3 is $\frac{1}{3}$. The reciprocal of 8 is $\frac{1}{8}$. The reciprocal of x is $\frac{1}{x}$.
   (a) Find the reciprocal of [the reciprocal of 3 + the reciprocal of 4].
   (b) Find the reciprocal of the reciprocal of the reciprocal of $\frac{3}{4}$.

6. A bottle is $\frac{9}{10}$ full of coke. After 800 ml is drunk, the bottle is $\frac{1}{2}$ full. How many ml are there in a full bottle?

7. At midday Wembley Stadium is $\frac{1}{5}$ full. By 2.00 p.m. a further 39 200 people have arrived and the stadium is $\frac{2}{3}$ full. What is the capacity of the stadium?

8. A glass contains some water, a peach and some air. The peach occupies $\frac{7}{8}$ of the volume of the glass. There is $24\,\text{cm}^3$ of water and $5\,\text{cm}^3$ of air.
   Find the volume of the peach.

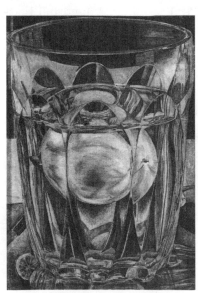

9. Work out

   (a) $\left[\frac{1}{2} \text{ of } \left(\frac{1}{3} + \frac{1}{4}\right)\right] \div \frac{1}{5}$
   (b) $\dfrac{\frac{1}{2} + \frac{1}{3} + \frac{1}{4}}{\frac{1}{2} \times \frac{1}{3} \times \frac{1}{4}}$

10. Two whole numbers a and b are chosen such that $a < b$ and $b < 7$. How many *different* fractions are there of the form $\dfrac{a}{b}$?

11. If three fifths of a number is 45, what is two thirds of it?

12.* Find two whole numbers, x and y, such that $\dfrac{x}{y}$ is equal to π, correct to 3 decimal places. You are not allowed $\frac{22}{7}$ or multiples of these numbers.

Recurring decimals

We have seen that fractions can be converted into decimals by dividing the numerator by the denominator. [E.g. $\frac{3}{4} = 3 \div 4 = 0\cdot75$]

Sometimes the division gives a decimal which recurs, for example $\frac{1}{3} = 1 \div 3 = 0\cdot33333\ldots$

It is important to realise that all recurring decimals can be written as exact fractions. Here is a method for converting recurring decimals to fractions.

(a) Change $0\cdot7777\ldots$ to a fraction.

$$\text{Let} \quad r = 0\cdot7777\ldots$$
$$10r = 7\cdot7777\ldots \quad \text{(multiply by 10)}$$
$$9r = 7 \quad \text{(subtract)}$$
$$r = \frac{7}{9}$$
$$\text{So } 0\cdot7777\ldots = \frac{7}{9}$$

(b) Change $0\cdot373737\ldots$ to a fraction.

$$\text{Let} \quad r = 0\cdot373737\ldots$$
$$100r = 37\cdot373737\ldots$$
$$99r = 37$$
$$r = \frac{37}{99}$$
$$\text{So } 0\cdot3\dot{7} = \frac{37}{99}$$

Exercise 4

1. Copy and complete to change $0\cdot4444\ldots$ to a fraction.

$$\text{Let} \quad r = 0\cdot4444\ldots$$
$$10r = \square \quad \text{(multiply both sides by 10)}$$
$$9r = \square \quad \text{(subtract)}$$
$$r = \square$$

2. Copy and complete to change $0\cdot28282828\ldots$ to a fraction.

$$\text{Let} \quad r = 0\cdot28282828\ldots$$
$$100r = \square$$
$$99r = \square$$
$$r = \square$$

In Questions **3** to **10** change the recurring decimals to fractions.

3. $0.2222\ldots$ **4.** $0.737373\ldots$ **5.** $0.5\dot{1}$ $(=0.515151\ldots)$

6. $0.\dot{2}\dot{9}$ **7.** $0.245245245\ldots$ **8.** $0.3\dot{2}\dot{6}$

9. $0.4\dot{1}\dot{7}$ **10.** $0.\dot{8}\dot{2}$

11. Change these fractions to recurring decimals.

(a) $\dfrac{1}{6}$ (b) $\dfrac{8}{9}$ (c) $\dfrac{2}{7}$ (d) $\dfrac{5}{13}$

Algebraic fractions

Rewrite the following as single fractions:

(a) $\dfrac{x}{3}+\dfrac{x}{3}=\dfrac{2x}{3}$

(b) $\dfrac{1}{2}y-\dfrac{1}{9}y=\dfrac{y}{2}-\dfrac{y}{9}$

$$=\dfrac{9y}{18}-\dfrac{2y}{18}$$

$$=\dfrac{7y}{18}$$

(c) $\dfrac{3}{5}\times\dfrac{t}{4}=\dfrac{3t}{20}$

(d) $\dfrac{x}{5}\div\dfrac{x}{4}=\dfrac{x}{5}\times\dfrac{4}{x}$

$$=\dfrac{4x}{5x}=\dfrac{4}{5}.$$

Notice:
(i) In part (b) $\dfrac{1}{2}y$ is written as $\dfrac{y}{2}$ and $\dfrac{1}{9}y$ is written as $\dfrac{y}{9}$.

The fractions $\dfrac{y}{2}$ and $\dfrac{y}{9}$ are easier to work with.

(ii) The methods for adding, subtracting, multiplying and dividing are the same as for numerical fractions.

Exercise 5

Rewrite the following as single fractions.

1. $\dfrac{x}{5}+\dfrac{x}{5}$ **2.** $\dfrac{2}{7}x+\dfrac{1}{7}x$ **3.** $\dfrac{1}{2}z+\dfrac{1}{4}z$ **4.** $\dfrac{x}{5}+\dfrac{x}{10}$

5. $\dfrac{3}{4}x-\dfrac{1}{8}x$ **6.** $\dfrac{2}{3}x-\dfrac{1}{4}x$ **7.** $\dfrac{x}{5}+\dfrac{x}{4}$ **8.** $\dfrac{2}{5}x-\dfrac{1}{4}x$

9. $\dfrac{x}{4}\times\dfrac{x}{3}$ **10.** $\dfrac{2}{5}t\times\dfrac{1}{2}$ **11.** $\dfrac{1}{4}a\times\dfrac{1}{2}b$ **12.** $\left(\dfrac{3}{4}x\right)^2$

13. $\left(\dfrac{y}{3}\right)^2$ **14.** $\dfrac{4t}{5} \div \dfrac{1}{2}$ **15.** $\dfrac{5y}{3} \div \dfrac{y}{2}$ **16.** $2\frac{1}{2}x \times 1\frac{1}{2}x$

17. $\dfrac{3}{x} + \dfrac{5}{x}$ **18.** $\dfrac{9}{t} - \dfrac{3}{t}$ **19.** $\dfrac{11}{P} + \dfrac{10}{P}$ **20.** $\dfrac{4}{x} \times \dfrac{3}{x}$

21. (a) $\dfrac{3}{5} + \dfrac{1}{2}$ (b) $\dfrac{3}{5}x + \dfrac{1}{2}x$ (c) $\dfrac{3}{5} \times \dfrac{1}{2}$ (d) $\dfrac{3}{5} \div \dfrac{1}{2}$

22. (a) $\dfrac{1}{3} - \dfrac{1}{4}$ (b) $\dfrac{m}{3} - \dfrac{m}{4}$ (c) $\dfrac{m}{3} \times \dfrac{m}{4}$ (d) $\dfrac{m}{3} \div \dfrac{m}{4}$

23. (a) $\dfrac{3}{8} + \dfrac{1}{3}$ (b) $\dfrac{3s}{8} + \dfrac{s}{3}$ (c) $\dfrac{3s}{8} \times \dfrac{1}{3}$ (d) $\dfrac{3s}{8} \div \dfrac{s}{8}$

24. (a) $\dfrac{5}{7} - \dfrac{1}{2}$ (b) $\dfrac{5t}{7} - \dfrac{t}{2}$ (c) $\dfrac{5t}{7} \times \dfrac{t}{2}$ (d) $\dfrac{5t}{7} \div \dfrac{t}{2}$

25. Here are some cards

$\boxed{\dfrac{n}{2}}$ $\boxed{\dfrac{2}{n}}$ $\boxed{\left(\dfrac{n}{2}\right)^2}$ $\boxed{\dfrac{n}{2} + \dfrac{2}{n}}$ $\boxed{\dfrac{n}{2} - \dfrac{n}{4}}$ $\boxed{2 \div n}$

$\boxed{n^2 \div 2}$ $\boxed{\dfrac{1}{2}n}$ $\boxed{\dfrac{n+2}{2n}}$ $\boxed{\dfrac{4}{n} - \dfrac{2}{n}}$ $\boxed{\dfrac{n}{2} \times \dfrac{n}{2}}$

(a) Which cards will always be the same as $\boxed{n \div 2}$?

(b) Which cards will always be the same as $\boxed{\dfrac{n^2}{4}}$?

(c) Which card will always be the same as $\boxed{\dfrac{n}{4}}$?

(d) Draw a new card which will always be the same as $\boxed{\dfrac{n^2}{2} \div \dfrac{n}{4}}$.

The last twelve questions are more difficult. Rewrite as a single fraction and simplify the final answer as far as possible.

26. $\dfrac{3}{x} + \dfrac{2}{y}$ **27.** $\dfrac{x}{t} \times \dfrac{3}{x}$ **28.** $\dfrac{4}{p} - \dfrac{5}{q}$ **29.** $\dfrac{\pi r^2}{h} \div \dfrac{\pi}{h}$

30. $\dfrac{p}{x} + \dfrac{q}{x}$ **31.** $\dfrac{5}{x} + \dfrac{1}{2x}$ **32.** $\dfrac{m}{n} \times \dfrac{n^2}{m^2}$ **33.** $\dfrac{3pq}{x} \div \dfrac{p^2}{x}$

34. $\dfrac{x}{a^2} \div \dfrac{ax}{y}$ **35.** $\dfrac{x}{2\frac{1}{2}} + \dfrac{x}{1\frac{1}{2}}$ **36.** $\frac{1}{2}$ of $a - \frac{1}{5}$ of b **37.** $\frac{3}{4}$ of $t + \frac{1}{3}$ of z

1.6 Geometrical reasoning

Properties of quadrilaterals

Square   Four equal sides;
All angles 90°;
Four lines of symmetry.

Rectangle (not square):   Two pairs of equal
and parallel sides;
All angles 90°;
Two lines of symmetry.

Rhombus: Four equal sides;
Opposite sides parallel;
Diagonals bisect at right angles;
Diagonals bisect angles of rhombus;
Two lines of symmetry.

Parallelogram: Two pairs of equal and parallel
sides;
Opposite angles equal;
No lines of symmetry (in general).

Trapezium: One pair of parallel sides.

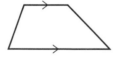

Kite: AB = AD, CB = CD;
Diagonals meet at 90°;
One line of symmetry.

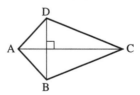

Arrowhead or **Delta**
Two pairs of adjacent edges of equal length.
One interior angle larger than 180°.
One line of symmetry.
Diagonals cross at right angles outside the shape.

For all quadrilaterals the sum of the interior angles is 360°.

Exercise 1

1. Name each of the following shapes:
   (a) ABEH
   (b) EFGH
   (c) CDFE

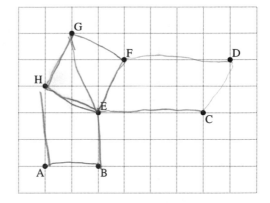

2. (a) Write down the coordinates of point D
      if ABCD is a kite
   (b) Write down the coordinates of point
      E if ABCE is a parallelogram
   (c) Write down the coordinates of point G
      if BCGF is an arrowhead.
      [There is more than one answer.]

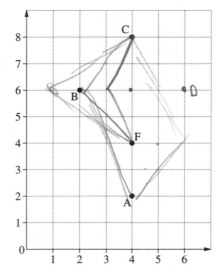

3. Copy the table and fill all the boxes with either 'Yes', 'No' or a number.

	How many lines of symmetry?	How many pairs of opposite sides are parallel?	Diagonals always equal?	Diagonals are perpendicular?
Square				
Rectangle				
Kite				
Rhombus				
Parallelogram				
Arrowhead				

4. Find the angle x.

(a)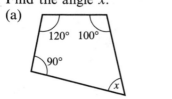

(b)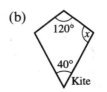

(c)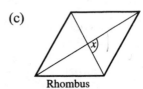

(d)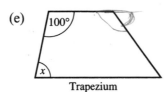

Parallelogram

(e)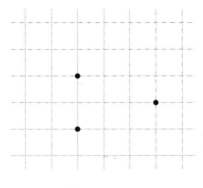

Trapezium

(f)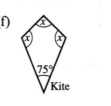

5. The diagram shows three vertices (corners) of a parallelogram. Copy the diagram and mark with crosses the *three* possible positions of the fourth vertex.

6. Line AC is one *diagonal* of a rhombus ABCD. Draw *two* possible rhombuses ABCD.

7. Suppose you cut along the diagonal of a rectangle to make two congruent triangles. Join the diagonals together in a different way. What shape is formed?

8. Suppose you had two identical isosceles triangles. Put the equal sides together to make as many different shapes as possible. Name the shapes formed.

9. An equilateral triangle has vertices P, Q, R.
   (a) Suppose the vertex P moves perpendicular to QR. What different types of triangle can be made?
   Can you make: a right-angled triangle;
   an obtuse-angled triangle;
   a scalene triangle?
   (b) If the vertex P moves *parallel* to QR, what different types of triangle can be made?

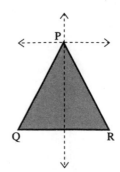

Angles in polygons

- We already know that angles in a triangle add up to 180° and angles in a quadrilateral add up to 360°.

  What happens in polygons with a greater
  number of sides?

- First draw any pentagon (5 sided shape).
  Choose one of the corners, A say, and join this
  to all the other corners. (B and E will already
  be joined by the sides of the pentagon).

  This divides the pentagon into 3 triangles.
  As we already know that the angles in each of these triangles adds
  up to 180° the angles in our pentagon must add up to:

  $3 \times 180° = 540°$

  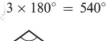

> The angles in a pentagon add up to 540°

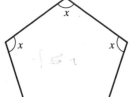

If we had started with a *regular* pentagon all the sides would
have been the same length and all the angles would be the
same. As there are 5 equal angles, each angle $= 540 \div 5$
$= 108°$

Exercise 2

1. Copy and complete the following table. Split up polygons with
6, 8 and 10 sides into triangles as in the example above.

Look for a pattern in the numbers and try to complete the rest
of the table without drawing the polygon first.

Number of sides	Number of triangles	Total of interior angles	Interior angle of regular polygon
3	1	$1 \times 180° = 180°$	$180° \div 3 = 60°$
4	2	$2 \times 180° = 360°$	$360° \div 4 = 90°$
5	3	$3 \times 180° = 540°$	$540° \div 5 = 108°$
6			
8			
10			
20			
n			

> **Teachers note:**
> The result for the sum
> of the angles in a
> polygon with n sides
> obtained from the
> bottom row is needed
> in subsequent questions.

2. Find the angles marked with letters.

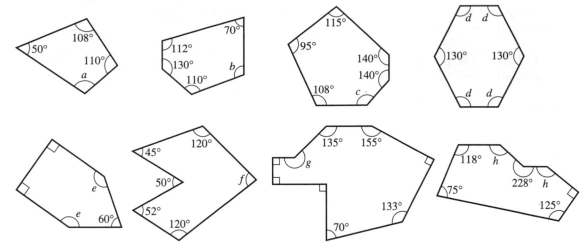

3. ABCDEF is a regular hexagon. AE and DF intersect at point X. Find the size of angle DXE.

4. ABCD is a square. Equilateral triangles ABE and ADF are drawn with points E and F either inside or outside the square. Find angle AEF if,
  (a) E and F are both outside the square,
  (b) E is outside and F is inside the square,
  (c) E and F are both inside the square.

Exterior angles of a polygon

The exterior angle of a polygon is the angle between a produced side and the adjacent side of the polygon. The word 'produced' in this context means 'extended'.

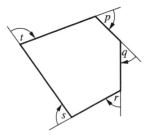

If we put all the exterior angles together we can see that the sum of the angles is 360°. This is true for any polygon.

> The sum of the exterior angles of a polygon= 360°

Note:
(a) In a regular polygon all exterior angles are equal.

(b) For a regular polygon with n sides, each exterior angle $= \dfrac{360°}{n}$.

Exercise 3

1. Find the angles marked with letters.

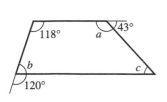 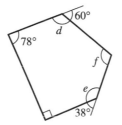 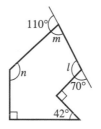 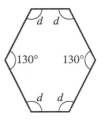

2. Find   (a) the exterior   (b) the interior angles of regular polygons with
(i) 9 sides   (ii) 18 sides   (iii) 45 sides   (iv) 60 sides

3. Below are two sets of tiling patterns used for flooring. Each set consists of two regular polygons. Describe the polygons that are used.

(a) 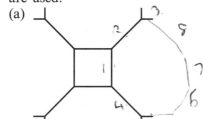   (b)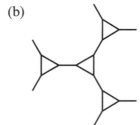

4. Find the labelled angles in this regular 9-sided polygon. Point O is the centre of the polygon.

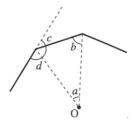

Questions **5** to **14** are more difficult.

5. Each interior angle of a regular polygon is 140°. How many sides has the polygon?

6. Each exterior angle of a regular polygon is 18°. How many sides has the polygon?

7. The sum of the interior angles in a polygon is 3780°. How many sides has the polygon?

8. The sides of a regular polygon subtend angles of 18° at the centre of the polygon. How many sides has the polygon?

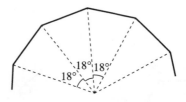

9. In a regular polygon each interior angle is 135° greater than each exterior angle. How many sides has the polygon?

10. A polygon with 7 sides (a heptagon) has 6 equal angles x and one angle $2x$. Find the value of x and draw a sketch of the polygon.

11. Which of the following could be the interior angle of a regular polygon: 144°, 160°, 163°, 172°?

12. The diagram shown is formed by joining regular pentagons. Find the angles x and y.

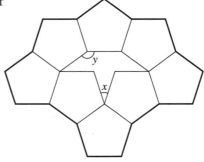

13. PQ is one side of a regular polygon with centre O.
   If $y = 4\frac{1}{2}x$ find the number of sides in the polygon.

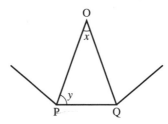

14. Half of the exterior angles of a polygon are 8° and the other exterior angles are each 12°. How many sides has the polygon?

Part 2

2.1 Number review

Factors, multiples, prime numbers

Exercise 1

1. Write down all the factors of:
   (a) 12   (b) 15   (c) 24

2. Write down the first four multiples of:
   (a) 7   (b) 20   (c) 15

3. Work out the lowest common multiple (L.C.M.) of:
   (a) 4 and 6   (b) 6 and 8   (c) 5 and 8

4. Find the highest common factor (H.C.F.) of:
   (a) 12 and 20   (b) 36 and 45   (c) 30 and 42

5. Write down a list of all the prime numbers below 20.

6. Which of these numbers are prime? $\boxed{39}$ $\boxed{71}$ $\boxed{41}$ $\boxed{47}$ $\boxed{91}$ $\boxed{93}$ $\boxed{81}$

> The factors of 10 are 1, 2, 5, 10
>
> The multiples of 10 are 10, 20, 30, 40, ...

7. Copy and complete these prime factor trees.

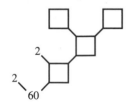

8. As a product of primes, a number is given by $2^3 \times 5 \times 7$. What is the number?

9. Write 42 as a product of primes.

10. Answer 'true' or 'false':
    (a) 'Any multiple of 6 must be a multiple of 12.'
    (b) 'Any factor of 60 must be a factor of 30.'

11. Write as ordinary numbers
    (a) 5^2 (b) 10^3 (c) $6^2 - 1^2$ (d) $\sqrt{144}$

    (e) $\sqrt{17^2}$ (f) $\sqrt[3]{27}$ (g) $1^3 + 2^3 + 3^3$ (h) $\sqrt[3]{1000}$

Ratio and proportion

Exercise 2

1. Write each ratio in its simplest form
   (a) 4 : 20   (b) 12 : 16   (c) 18 : 12   (d) 20 to 30

2. Write the following ratios in their simplest form
   (a) 5 cm to 55 cm   (b) £39 to £13   (c) 1p to £1
   (d) 50p to £5   (e) 10 cm to 1 m   (f) 200g to 1 kg

   > Think about the units!

3. Divide £30 between 2 people in the ratio 1 : 2.

4. Divide the amounts in the ratios stated
   (a) £40 in the ratio 2 : 3
   (b) £2000 in the ratio 3 : 7
   (c) 36 kg in the ratio 1 : 2 : 3

5. What proportion of this diagram is shaded?
   Give your answer as a fraction.

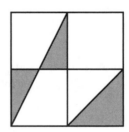

6. In a mixed class of 25 children, there are 16 girls.
   What proportion of the class are boys?

7. A recipe for marmalade uses 60 g of oranges for every 100 g of
   marmalade. I am making 2·5 kg of marmalade.
   How many grams of oranges do I need?

8. A 450 g packet of sugar costs 99p. How much is that per 100 g
   of sugar?

9. The sides of a rectangle are in the ratio 6 : 1. Its perimeter is
   98 cm. Calculate the area of the rectangle.

10. A recipe for 5 people calls for 1·5 kg of beef. How much beef is
    required if the recipe is adapted to feed 8 people?

11. If $\frac{3}{7}$ of the children in a school are girls, what is the ratio of girls
    to boys?

12. A lake is 2·5 cm long on a map of scale 1 : 10000. What is the
    actual length of the lake?

Order of operations

Exercise 3

Work out

1. $7 + 5 \times 2$

2. $10 - 3 \times 3$

3. $4^2 - 3 \times 2$

4. $20 \div 5 + 7$

5. $8 + 12 \div 4$

6. $20 - (4 + 11)$

7. $36 + 2^2$

8. $(8 - 5)^2 + 1$

9. $16 - 2^4$

10. $2 + 3 \times 4 + 1$

11. $(14 - 2) \div (3^2 + 3)$

12. $(7 - 6)^5 + 11$

13. $\dfrac{150}{7 + 3}$

14. $\dfrac{10}{2} + \left(\dfrac{1}{2} \times 30\right)$

15. $\dfrac{(4^2 - 6) \times 10}{12 - 7}$

Copy each question and write brackets so that each calculation gives the correct answer.

16. $6 \times 8 - 2 = 36$

17. $9 + 12 \times 5 = 105$

18. $4 + 5 \times 5 = 45$

19. $11 + 7 \times 3 = 32$

20. $22 - 10 \times 6 = 72$

21. $8 \times 6 - 4 = 16$

22. $5 \times 6 - 4 \div 2 = 13$

23. $81 \div 9 \times 12 - 4 = 104$

24. $9 + 8 \div 4 \times 0 = 0$

25. $3 + 5 \times 9 - 7 = 16$

Inverse operations

The word inverse means 'opposite'.

- The inverse of adding is subtracting
- The inverse of subtracting is adding
- The inverse of multiplying is dividing
- The inverse of dividing is multiplying

Exercise 4

Copy and complete.

1. (a)
```
   3 7 5
+ □ 4 2
───────
  6 □□
```

(b)
```
  6 2 □
+ □ 5 4
───────
  7 □ 3
```

(c)
```
  □ 7 6
+ 3 4 □
───────
  9 □ 9
```

2. (a)
```
  6 7 9
+ 2 □ 5
───────
□ 3 □
```

(b)
```
  3 □ 4
+ 4 8 9
───────
□ 7 3
```

(c)
```
  6 8 7
+ □ 9 □
───────
  9 □ 3
```

3. (a)
```
    4 □
×     6
───────
  2 6 4
```

(b)
```
    8 □
×     7
───────
□ 8 1
```

(c)
```
  □ □ 5
×     8
───────
2 6 0 0
```

4. (a) ▢▢▢ $\div 7 = 35$ (b) ▢▢ $\times 13 = 182$

    (c) $15 \times$ ▢ $= 120$ (d) ▢▢▢ $\div 9 = 108$

5. There is more than one correct answer for each of these questions. Ask a friend to check your solution.

    (a) $\boxed{3}\boxed{8}$ − ▢▢ + ▢▢ $= 37$

    (b) $\boxed{4}\boxed{2}$ × ▢ ÷ ▢ $= 21$

    (c) $\boxed{1}\boxed{5}$ × ▢▢ ÷ ▢ $= 45$

6. Each of these calculations has the same number missing from all three boxes. Find the missing number in each calculation.

    (a) ▢ × ▢ − ▢ $= 42$

    (b) ▢ ÷ ▢ + ▢ $= 7$

    (c) ▢ × ▢ + ▢ $= 90$

7. In the circle write $+$, $-$, $\times$ or $\div$ to make the calculation correct.

    (a) $8 \times 7 \bigcirc 2 = 54$ (b) $6 \times 8 \bigcirc 3 = 16$

    (c) $5 \bigcirc 6 + 3 = 2$ (d) $60 \div 5 \bigcirc 8 = 20$

8. (a)   7 ▢ 6   (b)   6 ▢ 4   (c)   ▢ 6 ▢

      − 3 8 ▢   − ▢ 4 ▢   − 4 ▢ 5

      ⎯⎯⎯⎯   ⎯⎯⎯⎯   ⎯⎯⎯⎯

      ▢ 6 3   2 0 5   3 8 8

Using a calculator

Exercise 5

Use the memory and/or bracket keys to work out the following. Give answers correct to 1 d.p.

1. $\dfrac{1{\cdot}23 + 4{\cdot}7}{1{\cdot}4}$ **2.** $15{\cdot}7 - (1{\cdot}2 \times 11)$ **3.** $7{\cdot}2 + (8{\cdot}2 \div 13)$

4. $\dfrac{2{\cdot}9}{5{\cdot}2 - 4{\cdot}38}$ **5.** $\dfrac{18{\cdot}2 - 5{\cdot}27}{1{\cdot}72 + 1{\cdot}35}$ **6.** $1{\cdot}7^2 - 0{\cdot}95$

7. $6{\cdot}91 - 2{\cdot}3^2$ **8.** $(8{\cdot}1 - 6{\cdot}27)^2$ **9.** $1{\cdot}12^2 + 1{\cdot}4^2$

10. $1{\cdot}7 + \dfrac{2{\cdot}7}{3{\cdot}5}$ **11.** $\dfrac{1{\cdot}7^2}{8{\cdot}2 - 6{\cdot}38}$ **12.** $\dfrac{2{\cdot}5}{1{\cdot}4} - \dfrac{3{\cdot}6}{2{\cdot}81}$

Calculator words

On a calculator the number ⌈ЧЅ□Ь⌉ spells the word 'Gosh'
when held upside down. You have to use your imagination with
some letters. For example a zero can either be an 'O' or a 'D'. The
number ⌈□.⅂□⌉ reads 'Old' when held upside down. (You ignore
the decimal point.)

Use a calculator to find the missing words in the story below.

When the $\left[750^2 + 150\,000 + \sqrt{145\,202\,5}\right]$ came up,

$\left[50^2 \times 3 + 15^2 - 7\right]$ took his $\left[(3\cdot3 \times 10^2 + 2\cdot7 \times 10^2)^2 + \dfrac{150}{0\cdot4}\right]$ to

the $\left[2777^2 + 2889 \quad \text{(two words)}\right]$ to collect some snow for his
$\left[0\cdot2^2 \times 1\cdot9025\right]$.

While there, he met a $\left[904^2 + 89\,621\,818\right]$ called $\left[0\cdot4^2 - 0\cdot1^2\right]$.

Now [1·5% of 10] was a rather $\left[\dfrac{323\cdot6 - 289\cdot5}{154\cdot6 + 45\cdot4}\right]$ animal who had just

offended $\left[6\cdot2 \times 0\cdot987 \times 1\,000\,000 - 860^2 + 118\right]$ the

$\left[(5 \times 10^3 + 3 \times 10^4) + 6\right]$ because, without thinking, he had

$\left[\sqrt{0\cdot1369} + (1\cdot2 \times 0\cdot03^2)\right]$ his $\left[5 \times 58^4 + 48\,226 \text{ (two words)}\right]$

So $\left[2318 \times 2319 + 2^3 \times 3 \times 7^2\right]$ started to $\left[(6\cdot1 \times 25) \times \sqrt[3]{64}\right]$ a

$\left[60^2 + 10^2 + 2^2\right]$ to $\left[(50 \times 60) + (2 \times 7)\right]$ in where he could

$\left[(5^2 \times 6 \times 2) + (2 \times 5) + 6 + 1\right]$ in wait for $\left[\frac{1}{8} + \frac{1}{40}\right]$. This meant

that he could take his revenge on the $\left[448 \times 449 \times 450 - 17^4 + 4155\right]$
by spraying him with a $\left[(0\cdot6^2 + 0\cdot8^2) \times 4 + (5^3 \times 2^2 \times 7)\right]$. But

meanwhile, $\left[(\frac{1}{2})^2 - (\frac{1}{2} \text{ of } \frac{1}{5})\right]$ had heard of the plan, and so he asked

$\left[2 \times (2^4 + 1^7) \times 227\right]$ to pretend to be a $\left[34 \times 35 \times 36 \times 37 \times 38 + 451^2 - 407\right]$.

When $\left[(11 \times 12)^2 + 174 \times 175 \times 176 - \left(\dfrac{3}{0\cdot5}\right)\right]$ heard $\left[7 \times 11 \times 10^2 + (3^2 \times 2)\right]$

coming, he jumped up onto a $\left[\dfrac{(2^2 \times 4 \times 5^2 \times 6)}{4} + 7\right]$ so quickly that

$\left[(22\frac{3}{5} + \frac{1}{10}) \times 340\right]$ did not have time to $\left[\frac{73}{100} + 1\cdot45 \times 10^{-3}\right]$ himself

from the $\left[\sqrt{(700\cdot8 \div 0\cdot2)^2 \times 0\cdot5 \times 2}\right]$.

Remember:

□ can be '0' or 'D'

However, $\left[0\cdot4^2 - 0\cdot3^2 + 2(0\cdot2^2)\right]$, was already hiding on the

$\left[2 \times \sqrt{\sqrt{\left(\dfrac{7^4}{4^2}\right)}} + (63 - \sqrt{9}) \times 5 \times 2\right]$, and he stabbed the

$\left[3\cdot5 \times 10^4 + \dfrac{6 \times 5 \times 4 \times 3 \times 2}{5 \times 4 \times 3 \times 2}\right]$ with his prickles to protect his

friend. Unfortunately, $\left[15\,483 \times 300 - 1 + 89^3 + \dfrac{642}{0\cdot2 \times 0\cdot3 \times 0\cdot4}\right]$

could not carry out his plans for revenge, because he had all the

Never-Say- $\left[\left(\dfrac{1}{\left(\dfrac{1}{2}\right)^5} - 1\right) \div \left(\dfrac{0\cdot021}{0\cdot21}\right)\right]$ qualities of a kamikaze pilot,

so at the first $\left[\dfrac{10^3}{2^3} \times \left(\dfrac{\sqrt{2^6}}{0\cdot331 - 0\cdot206}\right) + 2\cdot5\% \text{ of } 3120\right]$ of

$\left[13 \times 6 \div 100^2\right]$, he gave up and $\left[3\cdot4 \times 10^{-4} + \left(\dfrac{191}{382}\right)^2 + \dfrac{1\frac{1}{2}}{5^2}\right]$.

Negative numbers

Exercise 6

Work out

1. $-2 + 6$
2. $6 - 9$
3. $-4 - 3$
4. $10 - 15$
5. $-7 - 3$
6. $-10 + 13$
7. $18 - 14$
8. $-7 + 7$
9. $3 + (-4)$
10. $8 - (-2)$
11. $6 + (-6)$
12. $10 - (-3)$
13. $-4 - (-6)$
14. $7 + (-8)$
15. $8 - (-18)$
16. $-4 + (-4)$
17. $(-3) \times 4$
18. $(-5) \times (-2)$
19. $12 \times (-1)$
20. $(-8) \times (-3)$
21. $(-2) \times (-3)$
22. $4 \times (-5)$
23. -7×7
24. -6×0
25. $6 \div (-2)$
26. $-8 \div 4$
27. $10 \div (-2)$
28. $(-8) \div (-4)$
29. $-8 + 15$
30. $-7 - 30$
31. $8 - (-4)$
32. $(-7) \times (-5)$

Copy and complete these magic squares.

33.

		3
	0	
−3	2	

34.

		−2
	1	
4		−1

35.

	1	
2	−3	−2

Find the letters

Perform each calculation and write down the corresponding letter
from the list below, to make a sentence.

A. $5-8$; $-3-2$; $(-2)^2$; 3^2-20; $6\div(-6)$; $(-2)^2+3$; $-5+(-3)$; $(-49)\div(-7)$;
$-3-(-5)$; $(-5)\times(-1)$; $-7+11$; 4^2-4; $-1+13$; $(-1)^2\times4$; $30\div(-10)$;
$-2+9$; $(-3\frac{1}{2})\times2$; $(-8)\div(-2)$; $(-1)\div\frac{1}{10}$; $8-11$; $(-7)^2+(-1)^2$; $-6-5$;
$(-10)\times\frac{1}{2}$; $-3+10$; $(-2)^3-2$; $3-(-5)$; $(-3)\times(-4)$; $(-16)\div(-2)$; $2\div(-4)$?
$(-6-2)\times(-1)$; $2\times(-5)^2$; $(-6)^2\div3$; $(-2)\times(-2)\times2$; $-5+13$; $-12-(-2)$.

B. $-11+8$; $-3+(-2)$; $(-2)^2$; $1-12$; $3\times(-1)$; $1-(-6)$; $-2+4$; $(-3)\times(-4)$;
$6\div(-6)$; $(-16)\div2$; $(-3\frac{1}{2})\times(-2)$; 2^2-2; $1\div(\frac{1}{2})$; $-7-(-7)$; $(-3)^2-1$;
$-3-8$; $(-14)\div(-2)$; $-3+8$; $-8+15$; $(-1)^2+(-1)^2$; $(-5)\times2$; $-1-10$;
$(-2)\div(-\frac{1}{2})$; $-2-2-1$; 2^3; $4+(-6)$; $(-1)^5$; $-3+10$; $(-6)\div(-1)$; $2-(-3)$;
$(-3-4)\times(-1)$; $19-22$; $(-5)\times0$?
$(-2)^3\div(-2)$; $-2+7$; $1-(-6)$; $3\times(-1)$; $(-50)\div(-10)$; 0.1×20; $3^2+2^2-1^2$;
$(-1)\div(-\frac{1}{4})$; $(-2)^3-3$; $\frac{1}{7}\times49$; 4^3-66.

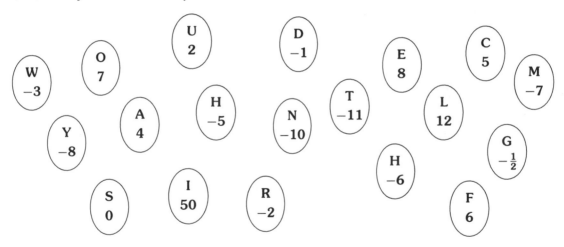

Long multiplication and division

```
        54                          16 remainder 15
      × 23                       17)287
      ───                          −17↓
      162    (3 × 54)              ───
     1080    (20 × 54)             117
     ────                         −102  ←(6 × 17)
     1242                          ───
                                    15
```

44

Exercise 7 (No calculators!)

Work out

1. 28×24
2. 53×27
3. 45×35
4. 127×23
5. 208×33
6. 248×43
7. $555 \div 15$
8. $774 \div 43$
9. $1104 \div 24$
10. $4452 \div 53$
11. $784 \div 26$
12. $516 \div 37$

13. Every day 213 slaves each had to carry 58 huge stones to build pyramids. How many stones were carried altogether in 10 days?

14. A storage tank contains 5375 litres of oil. Each day 42 litres are used. After how many days will the tank be empty?

15. It cost £26520 to lay 17 km of electric cable. Calculate the cost per km for this cable.

16. A shop keeper bought 232 melons at 58p each. How much did he spend altogether?

17. How many 42-seater coaches will be needed for a school trip for a party of 516?

Fractions, decimals, percentages

Exercise 8

1. Change to fractions.
   (a) 80% (b) 0·15 (c) 0·05 (d) 9%

2. Change to decimals.
   (a) 63% (b) $\frac{3}{4}$ (c) $\frac{5}{8}$ (d) 4%

3. Change to percentages.
   (a) 0·21 (b) $\frac{2}{5}$ (c) $\frac{1}{4}$ (d) 0·99

4. Write in order, smallest first.
   (a) $\frac{1}{5}$, 0·19, 22%   (b) 0·035, 4%, $\frac{1}{20}$

5. What percentage of the diagram is shaded?

6. Work out.
   (a) 7% of 2·5 kg   (answer in grams)
   (b) 16% of £3·50   (answer in pence)
   (c) 30% of 11 cm   (answer in mm)
   (d) 4% of 10 hours (answer in minutes)

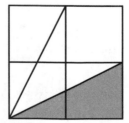

7. What percentage of the numbers from 1 to 100 inclusive are square numbers?

2.2 Construction and congruence

There are several ways in which different triangles can be described.
By convention we use:
S   when a side is given,
A   when an angle is given,
R   when a right angle is given,
H   when the hypotenuse of a right angled triangle is given.

Here are five examples.

1.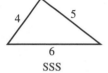

SSS

[All 3 sides]

2.

SAS

[2 sides and the included angle]

3.

ASA

[2 angles and one side]

4.

RHS

[right angle, hypotenuse and side]

5.

SSA

[2 sides and an angle (not included)]

Exercise 1

1. Using a ruler, protractor and a pair of compasses construct each of the triangles **1**, **2**, **3** and **4** above.
Label the triangles SSS, SAS, ASA, RHS.

2. Construct triangle **5** above and, using a pair of compasses, show that it is possible to construct two different triangles with the sides and angle given.

3. Construct the triangle shown. You are given SSA.
Show that you can construct two different triangles with the sides and angle given.

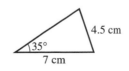

4. Copy and complete these two sentences:

'When we are given SSS, SAS, ☐ or ☐ the constructed triangle is unique.
When we are given ☐ the triangle is not unique and it is sometimes possible to construct two different triangles.'

These are the conditions for triangles to be congruent

5. State whether each pair of triangles are congruent. Give the conditions for congruency if they are congruent.

(a)
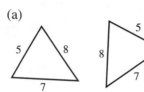

(b)
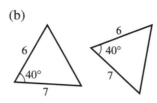

(c)
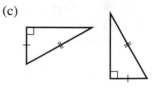

(d)
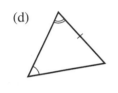

(e)
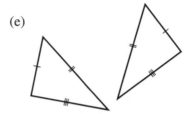

(f)
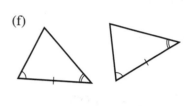

6. Suppose you are given two triangles and they each have the same three angles (say 60°, 40°, 80°). This is condition 'AAA'. Are the two triangles always congruent?

7. This is the construction of a perpendicular from a point P on a line, using ruler and compasses.
(a) With centre P, draw arcs to cut the line at A and B.
(b) Now construct the perpendicular bisector of AB.

8. This is the construction of a triangle given RHS.
(a) Draw a line and construct a perpendicular at point P as in Question **7**.
(b) Complete the triangle, given PQ = 5 cm and RQ = 8 cm.
(c) Measure the side PR.

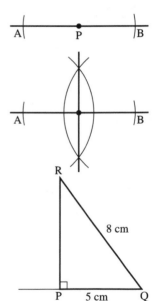

9. 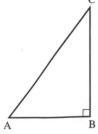 Construct the triangle shown, using ruler and compasses. BC = 7 cm and AC = 9 cm.

Measure the side AB

[*Teacher's note:* There are more questions involving congruent triangles and proof in section 5.6.]

2.3 Scatter graphs

Scatter graphs can be drawn to investigate
if there is a connection, or *correlation*,
between sets of data.

When the height and armspan of a group of
people are recorded, we would expect a scatter
graph like the one shown.
This scatter graph shows *strong positive* correlation.
You would expect a tall person to have a
long armspan.

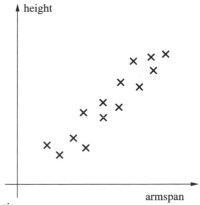

The correlation between two sets of data can be positive or negative
and it can be strong or weak as indicated by the scatter graphs
below. Sometimes there is *no* correlation.

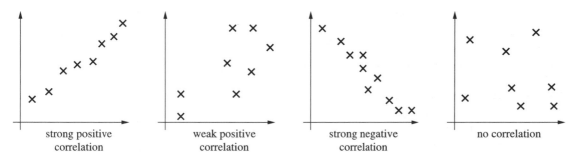

| strong positive correlation | weak positive correlation | strong negative correlation | no correlation |

Exercise 1

Plot the points given on a scatter graph, with x across the page and
y up the page. Draw axes with values from 0 to 20.
Describe the correlation, if any, between the values of x and y.
[i.e. 'strong negative', 'weak positive' etc.]

1.

x	8	14	4	12	19	6	20	4	10	12
y	7	13	6	12	18	9	18	7	10	13

2.

x	2	9	12	15	17	5	6	17	8
y	3	3	10	17	6	10	17	11	15

3.

x	12	2	16	7	3	19	8	4	13	19
y	6	13	7	14	17	1	11	8	11	4

Line of best fit

When a scatter graph shows either positive or negative correlation, a *line of best fit* can be drawn. The sums of the distances to points on either side of the line are equal and there should be an equal number of points on each side of the line. The line is easier to draw when a transparent ruler is used.

Here are the marks obtained in two tests by 9 students.

Student	A	B	C	D	E	F	G	H	I
Maths mark	28	22	9	40	37	35	30	23	?
Physics mark	48	45	34	57	50	55	53	45	52

A line of best fit can be drawn as there is strong positive correlation between the two sets of marks.

The line of best fit can be used to estimate the maths result of student I, who missed the maths test but scored 52 in the physics test.

We can *estimate* that student I would have scored *about* 33 in the maths test. It is not possible to be *very* accurate using scatter graphs. It is reasonable to state that student I 'might have scored between 30 and 36' in the maths test.

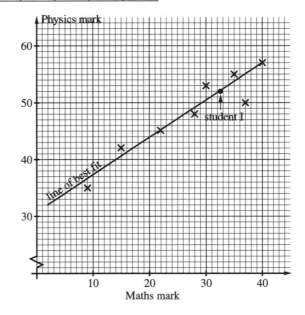

Here is a scatter graph in which the heights of boys of different ages is recorded. A line of best fit is drawn.

(a) We can estimate that the height of an 8 year old boy might be about 123 cm [say between 120 and 126 cm].
(b) We can only predict a height within the range of values plotted. We could not extend the line of best fit and use it to predict the height of a 30 year old! Why not?

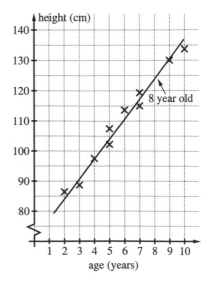

Exercise 2

In Questions 1, 2 and 3 plot the points given on a scatter graph, with s across the page and p up the page.
Draw axes with values from 0 to 20.
If possible draw a line of best fit on the graph.
Where possible estimate the value of p on the line of best fit where $s = 10$.

1.

s	2	14	14	4	12	18	12	6
p	5	15	16	6	12	18	13	7

2.

s	2	15	17	3	20	3	6
p	13	7	5	12	4	13	11

3.

s	4	10	15	18	19	4	19	5
p	19	16	11	19	15	3	1	9

4. The following data gives the marks of 11 students in a French test and in a German test.

French	15	36	36	22	23	27	43	22	43	40	26
German	6	28	35	18	28	28	37	9	41	45	17

(a) Plot this data on a scatter graph, with the French marks on the horizontal axis.
(b) Draw the line of best fit.
(c) Estimate the German mark of a student who got 30 in French.
(d) Estimate the French mark of a student who got 45 in German.

5. The data below gives the petrol consumption figures of cars, with the same size engine, when driven at different speeds.

Speed (m.p.h.)	30	62	40	80	70	55	75
Petrol consumption (m.p.g)	38	25	35	20	26	34	22

(a) Plot a scatter graph and draw a line of best fit.
(b) Estimate the petrol consumption of a car travelling at 45 m.p.h.
(c) Estimate the speed of a car whose petrol consumption is 27 m.p.g.

2.4 Trial and improvement

Exercise 1

Find the answers to these questions by trying different numbers until you find the dimensions that give the required area.

1. In the 3 rectangles below, the length is *twice* the width. Find the dimensions of each rectangle.

(a)

area = 98 cm^2

(b)

area = 12.5 cm^2

(c)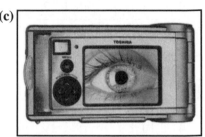

area = 9.68 cm^2

2. In these rectangles, the length is *three* times the width. Find the dimensions of each rectangle.

(a)

area = 48 cm^2

(b)

area = 36.75 cm^2

(c)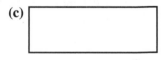

area = 3.63 cm^2

3. In the rectangle below, the length is *1 cm greater* than the width. Find the dimensions of each rectangle.

(a)

area = 72 cm^2

(b)

area = 210 cm^2

(c)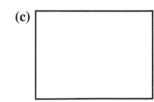

area = 60.59 cm^2

4. The volume of the box is given by the formula $n(n-1)(n+1)$. The box has a volume of $10\,626\,\text{cm}^3$. Find the dimensions of the box.

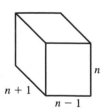

In the questions in the last exercise, we could always find dimensions which gave the *exact* answer required. In many problems this is not the case and we have to give the answer as an approximate value. This is not a major drawback because the solution can generally be found correct to as many decimal places as are required, especially when a computer is used.

The rectangle shown has width h cm, length $(h + 5)$ and area 525 cm². Find the value of h, giving your answer in the form:

'h is between _____ and _____'.

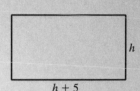

The two numbers to be found differ by 0.01 [e.g. 3·61 and 3·62]

The equation to be solved is $h(h + 5) = 525$.

Try $h = 15$:	$15 \times 20 = 300,$	$h = 15$ is too small.
Try $h = 25$:	$25 \times 30 = 750,$	$h = 25$ is too large.
Try $h = 20$:	$20 \times 25 = 500,$	$h = 20$ is too small.
Try $h = 21$:	$21 \times 26 = 546,$	$h = 21$ is too large.
Try $h = 20{\cdot}5$:	$20{\cdot}5 \times 25{\cdot}0 = 522{\cdot}75,$	$h = 20{\cdot}5$ is too small.
Try $h = 20{\cdot}6$:	$20{\cdot}6 \times 25{\cdot}6 = 527{\cdot}36,$	$h = 20{\cdot}6$ is too large.
Try $h = 20{\cdot}55$:	$20{\cdot}55 \times 25{\cdot}55 = 525{\cdot}0525,$	$h = 20{\cdot}55$ is too large.
Try $h = 20{\cdot}54$:	$20{\cdot}54 \times 25{\cdot}54 = 524{\cdot}5916,$	$h = 20{\cdot}54$ is too small.

When $h = 20{\cdot}55$, the area of the rectangle is greater than 525 cm² and when $h = 20{\cdot}54$, the area of the rectangle is less than 525 cm².

Answer: The value of h is between 20·54 and 20·55.

Exercise 2

1. The picture shown has width h cm, length $(h + 1)$ cm and area 200 cm².

You need to find h so that $h(h + 1) = 200$.

Between which *one decimal place* numbers does h lie?

Write your answer as 'h is between _____ and _____'.

Here is the start of the solution:

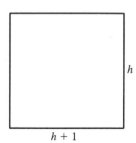

Try $h = 10$:	$10 \times 11 = 110$	too small
Try $h = 20$:	$20 \times 21 = 420$	too large
Try $h = 15$:	$15 \times 16 = 240$	too large
Try $h = 14$:	etc	

2. Find the value of h for each rectangle. Give your answer in the form: 'h is between _____ and _____', where the two numbers to be found differ by 0·1.

(a)

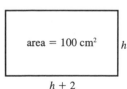

area = 100 cm² h

$h + 2$

(b)

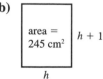

area = 245 cm² $h + 1$

h

3. Solve the equations below. Give your answers in the form 'x is between _____ and _____', where the two numbers to be found differ by 0·1.

(a) $x(x+10) = 210$ (b) $x^2 + x = 300$ (c) $x(x-1) = 100$

Accuracy

In the last exercise the answers were given in the form 'h is between 20·54 and 20·55'.

Sometimes it is more convenient to give a solution which is correct to a specific degree of accuracy, like 2 decimal places or 3 significant figures.

In the example below, the answer is found correct to 2 decimal places.

Solve the equation $z(z-2) = 50$, giving the answer correct to 2 decimal places.

(a) Try different values for z.

$z = 10$	:	$10(10-2) = 80$	Too large
$z = 8$	:	$8(8-2) = 48$	Too small
$z = 8·1$	:	$8·1(8·1-2) = 49·41$	Too small
$z = 8·2$	:	$8·2 \times 6·2 = 50·84$	Too large
$z = 8·13$	:	$8·13 \times 6·13 = 49·83$	Too small
$z = 8·14$	:	$8·14 \times 6·14 = 49·996$	Too small
$z = 8·15$	:	$8·15 \times 6·15 = 50·1225$	Too large

(b) At this stage we know that the answer is between 8·14 and 8·15. We also note that the value of $z = 8·14$ gave the value closest to 50. [i.e. 49·996]

(c) We can take the solution to be $x = 8·14$, correct to 2 decimal places.

(d) Notes: (i) We have tried values of x just above and just below 8·14 [namely 8·15 and 8·13].

(ii) Strictly speaking, to ensure that our answer *is* correct to 2 decimal places, we should try $x = 8·145$. This degree of complexity is unnecessary at this stage.

Solve the equation $x^3 + 10x = 100$, giving the answer correct to one decimal place.

Try $x = 3$: $3^3 + (10 \times 3) = 57$ $x = 3$ is too small.

Try $x = 4$: $4^3 + (10 \times 4) = 104$ $x = 4$ is too large.

Try $x = 3·9$: $3·9^3 + (10 \times 3·9) = 98·318$ $x = 3·9$ is too small.

Now 98·318 is closer to 100 than 104.

∴   The solution is $x = 3·9$, correct to 1 decimal place.

53

Exercise 3

1. Find the value of h, correct to 1 decimal place.

(a)

area = 738 cm² h

$h + 10$

(b)

area = 200 cm² h

$h + 5$

2. Solve the equations, correct to 1 decimal place.

(a) $x^2 + x = 13$ (b) $x^2 - x = 80$ (c) $x^3 - x = 70$

3. Use trial and improvement to find the cube root of 60, correct to 2 decimal places.
The cube root of 60 is written $\sqrt[3]{60}$.
Here is the start of the method:

Try 3: $3 \times 3 \times 3 = 27$ too small
Try 4: $4 \times 4 \times 4 = 64$ too big
Try 3·5:   etc

4. Use trial and improvement to find these roots, correct to 2 d.p.

(a) $\sqrt[3]{150}$ (b) $\sqrt[3]{58}$ (c) $\sqrt[3]{84}$ (d) $\sqrt{90}$ $\begin{bmatrix} \text{square root} \\ \text{not cube root} \end{bmatrix}$

5. A cuboid has a square base of side x cm, height $(x + 1)$ cm and volume 2000 cm³.
Find the value of x, correct to 2 d.p.

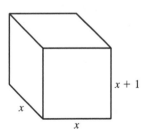

$x + 1$

x

x

6. Find a solution to the equation $4x + 1 = x^2$. Try values of x between $x = 1$ and $x = 6$.
Give your answer correct to 2 d.p.

Hint: Rewrite the equation as $x^2 - 4x = 1$

7. In this question we require much greater accuracy. The area of the picture is 40 cm².
Find the value of h correct to *five* decimal places.

h

$h + 1$

8. The 'L' shaped card shown has an area of $45\,\text{cm}^2$. Find the value of x, correct to 2 decimal places.

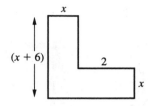

9. So far, you have solved equations involving powers of x like x^2 or x^3. Solve the equations below where numbers are raised to the power x. Give your answers correct to 1 decimal place.

   (a) $3^x = 10$　　　(b) $12^x = 100$　　　(c) $7^x = 0.1$

   (d) This time a number x is raised to the power x.
   Solve the equation $x^x = 150$.

10. A rectangle has length $(x+2)\,\text{cm}$, perimeter $(4x+6)\,\text{cm}$ and area $52\,\text{cm}^2$.
   (a) Using the perimeter, find an expression for the width of the rectangle.
   (b) Form an equation and solve it to find the value of x, correct to 3 significant figures.

11. The large triangle is an enlargement of the small triangle. Form an equation in x and solve it, giving your answer correct to 1 decimal place.

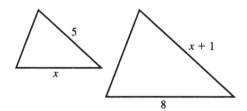

12. A window is in the shape of a semicircle joined to a rectangle. Find the radius of the semicircle, correct to 1 decimal place, if the total area of the window is $12\,\text{m}^2$.

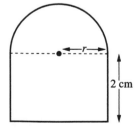

13. The length of a diagonal of the rectangle shown is $19\,\text{cm}$. Find the value of x, correct to 1 decimal place.

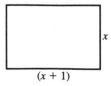

14. In the early stages of its growth, the height of an Elmer plant increases as shown.

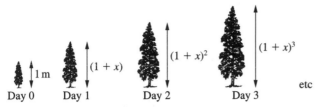

After 10 days the height of the plant is 2 m so we have the equation

$$(1 + x)^{10} = 2.$$

Find the value of x, correct to 2 decimal places.

15. In triangle ABC, angle BAC $= x°$, BC $= x$ cm and AC $= (x + 10)$ cm.

Find the value of x, correct to the nearest whole number.

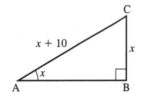

16. Find the number whose square is ten times as large as its square root. Give your answer correct to 2 decimal places.

$$\left((?)^2 \right) = \left(10\sqrt{?} \right)$$

17. (a) The area of circle D is equal to the sum of the areas of circles A, B and C. Find the radius of circle D correct to 2 decimal places.

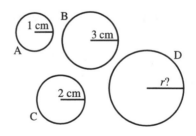

(b) The area of circle A plus the area of circle B is equal to the area of circle C. Find the value of x, correct to 1 decimal place.

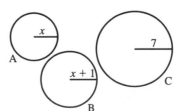

2.5   Mental arithmetic

Reminder of some basic methods.

A	'Easy to add' numbers	$\overbrace{18 + 57 + 32} = 50 + 57 = 107$
B	Splitting numbers	$46 + 37 = 40 + 30 + 6 + 7 = 70 + 13 = 83$
C	Add/subtract with adjustment	$57 + 19 = 57 + 20 - 1 = 76$
D	Doubling from the left	double $78 =$ double $70+$ double $8 = 156$
E	Multiply by 50, 25	$44 \times 25 = 44 \times 100 \div 4 = 100$
F	Multiply by 19, 29... 21, 31, ...	$15 \times 21 = 15 \times 20 + 15 = 315$

The questions in the tests below should be read out by a teacher and you should not be looking at them. Each question should be repeated once and then the answer, and only the answer, should be written down.

Test 1

1. Add together 15, 25 and 70.

2. How many millimetres are there in a kilometre?

3. Find the length of the perimeter of a regular hexagon of side 20 cm.

4. Find the change from £10 when you buy two magazines for 75p each.

5. Give a rough estimate for the square root of 150.

6. Find the cost of 60 eggs at £1 per dozen.

7. A car is travelling at a steady speed of 30 m.p.h. How far does it go in 30 minutes?

8. Find the difference between $8\frac{1}{2}$ and 20.

9. Work out $1 + 2^2 + 3^3$.

10. Through what angle does the minute hand of a clock move between 8·50 and 9·30?

11. Work out roughly the area of a circle of radius 10 cm.

12. A bridge was built in Paris in 1780. How many years ago was that?

13. What is 40% as a fraction?

14. How many items costing £25 each can you buy with £2000?

15. What five coins make 75p?

16. Calculate the length of the perimeter of a rectangular field measuring 110 m by 80 m.

17. Work out 0·03 multiplied by 100 000.

18. Increase a price of £700 by 1%.

19. Answer true or false: $\left(\frac{1}{3}\right)^2$ is greater than $\frac{1}{3}$.

20. A large brick weighs 1 kg. Roughly what does it weigh in pounds?

21. Work out 1% of £134.

22. A plant grows 5 cm every day. How many days will it take to grow 65 cm?

23. A charity collection is made into a pile of 1000 20p coins. How much was collected?

24. Add together 67 and 77.

25. True or false: At a steady speed of 30 m.p.h. you go 1 mile every 2 minutes.

26. Glen has one of each of the coins from 1 p to 1 pound. What is their total value?

27. Three angles of a quadrilateral are 80°, 120° and 60°. What is the fourth angle?

28. How many inches are there in a foot?

29. A pie chart has a pink sector representing $33\frac{1}{3}\%$ of the whole chart. What is the angle of the sector?

30. Write down the next prime number after 31.

Test 2

1. Which of these fractions is the larger: $\frac{2}{3}$ or $\frac{3}{4}$?

2. True or false: a weight of 5 stones is less than 50 kg.

3. Work out 1% of £45.

4. Write in words the answer to $10 \times 100 \times 1000$.

5. Add together 5, 6, 7 and 8.

6. A car travels 30 miles in 30 minutes. How far will it travel at this speed in $\frac{3}{4}$ hour?

7. Sam spends 40% of his money on tapes and 50% of his money on clothes. If he had £5 left, how much did he have at first?

8. Write as a decimal: $\frac{1}{5}$ plus $\frac{3}{100}$.

9. A bucket contains 2 litres of milk. How much is left, in ml, after 100 ml is removed?

10. How many hours and minutes is it from 8·15 a.m. until noon?

11. One bag weighs 250 g. How many bags weigh 5 kg?

12. If 20 drinks cost £28, find the cost of 5.

13. A magazine costing 47p was paid for with a £1 coin. Which three coins were given as change?

14. What is the number which is 200 less than 20 000?

15. Find the change from a £5 note after buying 3 pounds of apples at 22p per pound.

16. A girl faces West and turns clockwise through $1\frac{1}{2}$ right angles. In which direction is she now facing?

17. A film, lasting $1\frac{1}{2}$ hours, starts at 6·20. When does it finish?

18. Work out $100 - 4·9$.

19. Name the date which is 4 months before the 1st of February.

20. Write down the next prime number after 90.

21. Write $\frac{1}{20}$ as a percentage.

22. Of the people in a room, a fifth were French, ten per cent were German and the rest were Irish. What percentage were Irish?

23. In January, Steve weighs 70 kg. By July his weight is reduced by 10%. What does he weigh in July?

24. Find the total surface area of a cube of side 1 cm.

25. Work out $(5 \times 10^3) + 50$.

26. Write 1·6 recurring correct to one decimal place.

27. A 10p coin is 1·7 mm thick. What is the height, in cm, of a pile of coins worth £10?

28. Estimate the length of a side of a square of area 50 cm².

29. Work out $\frac{2}{3}$ of £120.

30. True or false: 15 cm is about 6 inches.

Test 3

1. If I have 35 pence change from a ten pound note, how much have I spent?

2. My train leaves at 1618. How many minutes do I have to wait if I arrive at the station at 1555?

3. The area of a triangle is $75\,cm^2$. Its base measures 25 cm. What is the height of the triangle?

4. One eighth of the children in a class walk to school. What percentage of the class is this?

5. A man was born in 1939. How old will he be in 2002?

6. A piece of string 54 cm long is cut into four equal parts. How long is each part?

7. True or false: Five miles is about the same as eight km.

8. The time in Miami is 5 hours earlier than the time in England. If I want to telephone Miami at 1330 their time, what time will it be here?

9. I think of a number, multiply it by 5 and subtract 8. The result is 12. What number am I thinking of?

10. A plank of wood measures 2 metres by 50 cm. What is the area of the plank in square metres?

11. Which is largest: $\frac{1}{9}$ or 10%?

12. A bar of chocolate costs 18p. I buy as many as I can for £1. How much change will I receive?

13. Add together 1, 2, 3, 4, 5, 6.

14. Write down ten million millimetres in kilometres.

15. By how much does a half of 130 exceed 49?

16. Work out two squared plus three squared plus four squared.

17. Work out 5% of £4·80.

18. Two angles in a quadrilateral are each 85° and a third angle is 100°. What is the fourth angle?

19. Give an *estimate* for 291·4 × 0·486.

20. What number is a quarter of 130?

21. What is a half of a half of a third?

22. Rosie is going on a 2 week holiday. She leaves on the 20th of July. On what date will she return?

23. What is 4% as a simplified fraction?

24. What is the fraction exactly half way between $\frac{1}{4}$ and $\frac{1}{2}$?

For the last six questions you may write down the numbers in the question.

25. Work out 15% of £1·80.

26. I think of a number, subtract 8 and then divide by 2. The result is 1. What number am I thinking of?

27. My newspaper costs 45p per day from Monday to Friday and 50p on Saturday. How much do I spend on papers from Monday to Saturday?

28. The coordinates of the 4 corners of a rectangle are (1, 1), (5, 1), (5, 4) and (1, 4). What is the area of the rectangle in square units?

29. How many seconds are there in 2 hours?

30. A train journey of 304 miles took 4 hours. What was the average speed of the train?

Test 4

1. How many 20 pence coins are needed to make £8?

2. What number is mid-way between 0·1 and 0·11?

3. Work out 5% of £320.

4. True or false: one yard is approximately one metre.

5. Work out 2·2 divided by ten thousand.

6. One sector of a pie chart represents 10% of the whole chart. What is the angle of the sector?

7. Find the approximate area of a circle of diameter 6 cm.

8. I pay for a pen costing £3.40 with a £20 note. What change do I receive?

9. Who is taller: Jan who is 5 feet tall or Sam who is 1 metre 10 tall?

10. A jar contains 1000 5p coins. Find the total value of the coins.

11. A rectangle measures 2·4 m by 10 cm. What is its area in square metres?

12. A rope of length 1 foot 4 inches is cut in half. How long is each piece?

13. A film started at 7·10 and finished at 10·55. How long was the film in hours and minutes?

14. Which has the longer perimeter: a square of side 10 cm or a circle of diameter 10 cm?

15. What fraction is equivalent to 40%?

16. Find the cost of 4 litres of wine at £3·15 per litre.

17. How many 24p stamps can be bought for £3?

18. Add together 34 and 164.

19. How long will it take to travel 60 miles at a speed of 30 m.p.h.?

20. Work out $3 \times 300 \times 3000$.

21. What is the angle between the hands of a clock at 4 o'clock?

22. Find the cost of buying a newspaper for 40 days if each paper costs 45p.

23. Work out two fifths of £105.

24. How many prime numbers are there between 10 and 20?

25. I am thinking of a number. If I double it, add one and then square the result the answer is 25. What number am I thinking of?

26. Work out $\frac{1}{4}$ plus $\frac{3}{5}$ and give the answer as a decimal.

27. Divide one million by 20.

28. A rectangle has area 12 cm². What is the area of a rectangle whose sides are twice as long as those of this rectangle?

29. In a quiz, David got 11 out of 20. What percentage is that?

30. Increase a price of £330 by 10%.

Test 5	**Test 6**	**Test 7**	**Test 8**
1. $39 + 22$	**1.** 65×2	**1.** $7 + 77$	**1.** 25% of 880
2. $160 - 21$	**2.** $184 - 7$	**2.** $330 - 295$	**2.** $400 \div 20$
3. 20% of 500	**3.** $0·7 + 0·25$	**3.** $(8 - 2)^2$	**3.** 8×700
4. $0·2 + 0·62$	**4.** 23×100	**4.** $37 + 63$	**4.** $3·5 + 0·35$
5. 20×60	**5.** $7^2 + 3^2$	**5.** 30×70	**5.** 1% of 20 000
6. $200 - 145$	**6.** £10 − 50p	**6.** 25×200	**6.** $301 - 102$
7. £5 − £1·20	**7.** 50% of 684	**7.** $12 \times 0·7$	**7.** $(3 + 8)^2 - 100$
8. 9×70	**8.** $1 - 0·22$	**8.** $5^2 - 5$	**8.** Half of 630
9. $14 + 1400$	**9.** 25×12	**9.** $76 + 14$	**9.** $1000 \times 0·5$
10. 50×22	**10.** $8 + 9 + 10$	**10.** 5% of 440	**10.** $3 \times 4 \times 5$
11. 5% of 300	**11.** $210 \div 7$	**11.** $500 - 85$	**11.** 25×16
12. Half of 330	**12.** 100×100	**12.** $(0·6 + 0·4)^2$	**12.** $54 \div 9$
13. $600 - 245$	**13.** $5·5 + 1·5$	**13.** $10^3 + 10^2$	**13.** 30×60
14. $2·4 + 7·7$	**14.** $(2 + 3 + 6)^2$	**14.** $425 - 198$	**14.** $22 + 23 + 24$
15. $200 \div 5$	**15.** $240 \div 3$	**15.** 200×8	**15.** $6^2 - 2^2$

KS3 tests

The next 2 tests are written in the form of the Key Stage 3 mental arithmetic tests.

Each question will be repeated once. You have 5 seconds to answer questions 1 to 6, 10 seconds to answer questions 7 to 20 and 15 seconds to answer the remaining questions. You will be told to put down your pen after the correct time interval for each question.

Work out the answer to each question in your head and write down only the answer. Sometimes other useful information, such as the numbers used in the question, has been written down to help you. Look at the sheets on page 63.

Test 1

● Time: 5 seconds

1. Look at the numbers on your answer sheet. What is half their total?
2. Change one hundred and ninety millimetres into centimetres.
3. What is seventy-two divided by eight?
4. Look at the equation. Write down the value for x.
5. Your answer sheet shows a fraction. Write the fraction in its simplest form.
6. Write two fifths as a decimal number.

● Time: 10 seconds

7. What is half of two hundred and thirty-six?
8. A TV film starts at five minutes to ten. It lasts forty-five minutes. At what time does the film finish?
9. Write all the prime numbers between ten and twenty.
10. On a coach there are 45 pupils. 20 of the pupils are boys.
    A pupil is chosen at random. What is the probability that a boy is chosen?
11. Look at your answer sheet. Work out the answer.
12. One per cent of a number is six. What is the number?
13. A path is six feet wide. About how many metres is that?
14. Write the number ten and a half million in figures.
15. Look at the equation. Use it to work out the value of x plus two.
16. On your sheet is a scale. Estimate the number shown by the arrow.
17. Estimate the value of forty-eight per cent of eighteen pounds twenty pence.
18. A book costs two pounds ninety-five pence. How much change is there from ten pounds?
19. What is two thousand minus one hundred and fifty?
20. n stands for a number. Write an expression for the following: 'add four to n, then multiply the result by five'.

- Time: 15 seconds

21. Sixty pounds is shared in the ratio of one to three. How much money is the smaller share?

22. What is one eighth of four hundred thousand?

23. Look at the equation on your answer sheet. If *n* equals six, what is *h*?

24. Use the calculation on your answer sheet to help you to work out how many fifteens there are in one thousand eight hundred.

25. Divide thirty-three pounds between six people. How much money does each person get?

26. Write an approximate answer to the calculation on your answer sheet.

27. A square has a perimeter of twenty-eight metres. What is the area of the square?

28. Your answer sheet shows the marks by five pupils in a test. What is the mean mark?

29. Look at the equation. *m* and *n* are consecutive integers. Write down the values of *m* and *n*.

30. A price goes up from four pounds to five pounds. What is the percentage increase?

Test 2

- Time: 5 seconds

1. Change four and a half metres into centimetres.

2. What is three point seven multiplied by one thousand?

3. Work out twenty-five per cent of two hundred.

4. Simplify the expression on your answer sheet as fully as possible.

5. What is the sum of the numbers on your answer sheet?

6. What is one tenth of half a million?

- Time: 10 seconds

7. Look at the expression. What is its value when *x* equals five?

8. A roll of wall paper is nine metres long. How many one point five metre lengths can be cut?

9. Five per cent of a number is eight. What is the number?

10. Two angles in a triangle are each thirty-five degrees. What is the size of the third angle?

11. In a group of seventy-five children, twenty-six are girls. How many are boys?

12. What is the area of this triangle?

13. The value of three *x* plus *y* is fifteen.
Write down the value of six *x* plus two *y*.

14. Look at your answer sheet. What is the greatest integer n can be?

15. Michelle got thirty-five out of fifty on a test. What percentage did she get?

16. Multiply nought point two by thirty.

17. Look at the inequalities on your answer sheet. Write down one possible value for x.

18 Work out two plus four plus six all squared.

19. Multiply five point nought seven by one thousand.

20. On the answer sheet find the missing number.

● Time: 15 seconds:

21. What is the cost of five items at one pound ninety-nine pence each?

22. Look at these numbers. Put a ring around the smallest number.

23. Write an approximate answer to the calculation on your answer sheet.

24. Each side of a square is forty-two centimetres. What is the perimeter of the square?

25. Look at the calculation on your answer sheet.
    What is four hundred and eighty divided by one point five?

26. How long will it take to travel 40 miles at a speed of twenty miles per hour?

27. A map has a scale of one to ten thousand.
    What is the actual length of a path which is five cm long on the map?

28. Look at the expression on your answer sheet. Write down the value of the expression when x equals one.

29. Work out a quarter plus a fifth and give the answer as a decimal.

30. Find the approximate area of a circle of radius 10 cm.

Test 1 Answer sheet

Time: 5 seconds

Question	Answer	
1		37 53
2	cm	
3		
4		$x^2 = 49$
5		$\frac{18}{24}$
6		

Time: 10 seconds

7		
8		
9		10 20
10		45 pupils, 20 boys
11		$25 - (7\cdot2 + 0\cdot8)$
12		
13	m	
14		
15		$x - 11 = 20$
16		
17		48% £18.20
18		£2·95
19		
20		

Time: 15 seconds

21	£	1:3 £60
22		
23	$h =$	$h = 12n - 10$
24		$15 \times 240 = 3600, 1800$
25		
26		$\dfrac{81\cdot6 \times 4\cdot17}{2\cdot09}$
27	m^2	
28		1, 4, 5, 5, 15
29		$2m + n = 22$
30	%	

Test 2 Answer sheet

Time: 5 seconds

Question	Answer	
1	cm	
2		3·7
3		
4		$3a + b - a + 3b$
5		2·2 4·8 1·5 2·5
6		

Time: 10 seconds

7		$2(x + 1)$
8		1·5 m 9 m
9		
10		
11		
12	cm^2	
13		$3x + y$ $6x + 2y$
14		$n^2 < 49$
15	%	
16		
17		$-3 < x < 2$
18		$(2 + 4 + 6)^2$
19		5·07
20		$5 \times \square - 2 = 28$

Time: 15 seconds

21	£	
22	0·0101 $\frac{1}{100}$ 0·011 0·099	
23		$405\cdot7 \div 19\cdot3$
24	cm	
25		$32 \times 15 = 480$
26		20 m.p.h.
27		1 : 10 000 5 cm
28		$2x(x + 2)$
29		$\frac{1}{4}$ $\frac{1}{5}$
30	cm^2	radius 10 cm

2.6 Representing data

Averages and range

Exercise 1

1. (a) Find the mean of the numbers   3, 2, 7, 8, 11
   (b) Find the median of the numbers   8, 5, 3, 1, 4, 3, 9
   (c) Find the mode of the numbers   4, 3, 4, 4, 3, 2, 4, 3

2. Write a sentence which describes how you would find the median of a set of nine numbers.

3. Find the range of each set of numbers
   (a) 5, 2, 11, 25, 7, 10
   (b) 2, 2, 2, 2, 2, 2, 2
   (c) 8, 0, −3, 6, 15, 7

4. For the set of numbers below, find the mean and the median.

   | 0, | 0, | 1, | 1, | 1, | 2, | 51 |

   Which average best describes this set of numbers? Explain why.

5. In a medieval jousting competition, marks were awarded for gallantry, courage, skill and so on using the 'Agincourt Scale'.
   Prince Gibson scored marks of 0, 0, 0, −2, 1, −5.
   What was his mean score?

6. Duncan has three test results with a mean of 25 and a range of 20. His first result was 21.
   What did he get on the other two tests?

7. Prini has 5 cards. The 5 cards have a mean of 11 and a range of 8.
   What are the numbers on the last two cards?

   | 11 | 11 | 11 | ? | ? |

8. Philip has three dart scores with a median score of 36 and a mean score of 32. The range of the three scores is 20.
   What are the three scores?

9. The mean height of 10 people is 150 cm. One person of height 141 cm leaves the group. Find the mean height of the remaining nine people.

10. The masses of 20 stones are given in the table.

mass	5 g	8 g	9 g	10 g
number of stones	7	4	7	2

Find the mean mass of the stones.

11. The marks achieved by 30 grandmothers in a football quiz were as follows:

mark	1	2	3	4	5
frequency	4	7	7	9	3

Find (a) the mean mark
      (b) the median mark
      (c) the modal mark

12. Here is the stem and leaf diagram showing the weights, in pounds, of animals in a pet shop.

(a) Write down the range of the masses.
(b) How many animals were in the shop?
(c) What is the median weight?

Stem (tens)	Leaf (units)
1	2 5 8
2	1 3
3	2 7 8 8
4	5 6

1|2 means 12

13. Here are two stem and leaf diagrams showing the marks of children in two tests, Maths and Science.

Maths:

Stem	Leaf
2	8
3	3 4 5 8
4	2 4 7 7 9
5	1

2|8 means 28

Science:

Stem	Leaf
2	1 2 5
3	6 7
4	5 6
5	5 7
6	3 8

(a) What was the median mark for each test?
(b) What was the range for each test?
(c) In which test were the marks spread out more widely?

14. Here are five cards, written in terms of n, which is a whole number.

$\boxed{n+2}$ $\boxed{n-2}$ $\boxed{2n+4}$ $\boxed{5n+7}$ $\boxed{n+4}$

(a) Find, in terms of n,
   (i)   the range of the five cards
   (ii) the median of the five cards
   (iii) the mean of the five cards

(b) The mean is 3 greater than the median. Find the value of n.

Frequency distributions

Parcelforce weighed the parcels carried by one of their delivery vans in a day.

The parcels weighed up to 25 kg. The range from 0 to 25 is divided into equal intervals. The interval 5–10 kg includes weights from 5 kg up to just less than 10 kg.

A parcel weighing 10 kg goes in the 10–15 kg interval. Similarly a parcel weighing 20 kg goes in the 20–25 kg interval.

The diagram is called a frequency chart.

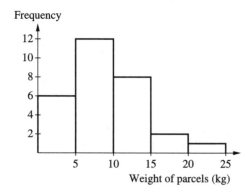

The information displayed on the chart can be written in a table, as shown on the right. this table is a *frequency distribution*.

Notice that the table does not tell us the actual weight of each parcel. For example, all we know is that there is one parcel in the interval 20–25 kg.

Weight of parcel (kg)	Number of parcels [Frequency]
0–5	6
5–10	12
10–15	8
15–20	2
20–25	1

Calculating the mean

We can obtain an *estimate* for the mean weight of the parcels by *assuming* that all the parcels in each interval have the weight at the mid-point of the interval.
So we are assuming that we have 6 parcels weighing 2·5 kg, 12 parcels weighing 7·5 kg, 8 parcels weighing 12·5 kg and so on.

Weight (kg)	Mid-point	Frequency
0–5	2·5	6
5–10	7·5	12
10–15	12·5	8
15–20	17·5	2
20–25	22·5	1

$$\text{The mean weight} = \frac{\text{Total weight of parcels}}{\text{Number of parcels}}$$

$$= \frac{(2\cdot5 \times 6) + (7\cdot5 \times 12) + (12\cdot5 \times 8) + (17\cdot5 \times 2) + (22\cdot5 \times 1)}{29}$$

$$= 9\cdot05 \text{ kg (to 3 s.f.)}$$

Realistically, we can *estimate* the mean weight of the parcels to be about 9 kg.

Notice that the mid-point of the 0–5 interval is $\dfrac{0+5}{2} = 2\cdot5,$

and that the mid-point of the 5–10 interval is $\dfrac{5+10}{2} = 7\cdot5$ etc.

Exercise 2

1. The heights of 30 children were measured and are shown in the table.
   (a) Calculate an estimate of the mean height of the children.
   (b) Why is your answer only an *estimate* of the mean height?

Height (cm)	Mid-point	Frequency
110–120	115	6
120–130		10
130–140		8
140–150		4
150–160		2

2. In an archeological dig, several Greek coins were found. The weights of the coins are shown in the table.
   Calculate an estimate for the mean weight of the coins.

Weight (g)	Mid-point	Frequency
4–7		5
7–10		10
10–13		15
13–16		7
16–19		4
19–22		2
22–25		2

3. Calculate an estimate for the mean for each frequency distribution.

(a)

Length (cm)	Frequency
0–10	5
10–20	11
20–40	7
40–50	7

(b)

Mass (kg)	Frequency
20–25	1
25–30	5
30–35	9
35–40	3
40–80	2

(c)

Times (s)	Frequency
20–40	5
40–60	21
60–70	15
70–90	9

4. Students were timed as they attempted to perform a simple test of dexterity. The incomplete table of results is shown. Find x, if the mean time taken was 16 seconds.

Time taken (s)	Frequency
0–10	20
10–20	50
20–30	x

5. A biologist measured the lengths of 20 worms as they slid across a special 'worm-meter' board.
Find the value of x if the mean length of the worms was 15·5 cm.

Length of worm (cm)	Frequency
0–x	5
x–20	10
20–40	5

Frequency polygons

A frequency polygon can be drawn by joining the mid-points of the tops of the bars on a frequency chart.
Frequency polygons are used mainly to compare data.

- Here is a frequency chart showing the heights (or lengths!) of the babies treated at a hospital one day.

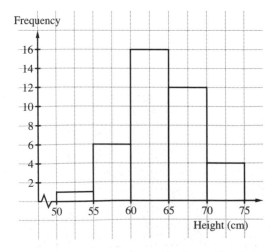

- Here is the corresponding frequency polygon, drawn by joining the mid-points of the tops of the bars.

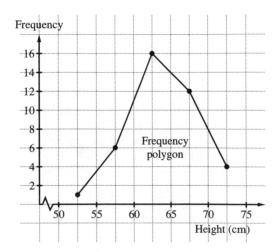

It is not necessary to draw the bars if you require only the frequency polygon.

The diagram on the right shows the frequency polygons for the exam results of 34 pupils in two subjects, Maths and French.

Two main differences are apparent:
(a) The marks obtained in the Maths exam were significantly lower for most pupils.
(b) The marks obtained in the French exam were more spread out than the Maths marks. The French marks were distributed fairly evenly over the range from 0 to 100% whereas the Maths marks were mostly between 0 and 40%.

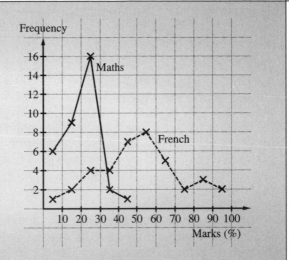

Exercise 3

1. Draw a frequency polygon for the distribution of weights of children drawn in the diagram.

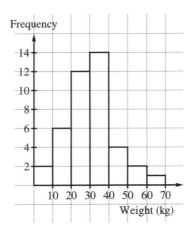

2. Here is a frequency polygon showing the weights of the people on a coach trip.
   (a) How many people weighed between 50 kg and 70 kg?
   (b) How many people were weighed altogether?
   (c) What percentage of the people weighed less than 50 kg?

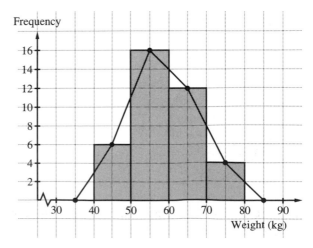

3. Using the same axes, with heights from 80 cm to 200 cm, draw frequency polygons for the heights of five year olds and sixteen year olds.

   Describe briefly the main differences between the two frequency polygons.

Five year olds	
height (cm)	frequency
80–90	0
90–100	6
100–110	15
110–120	3
120–130	1
130–140	0

Sixteen year olds	
height (cm)	frequency
120–130	0
130–140	2
140–150	3
150–160	4
160–170	7
170–180	6
180–190	3
190–200	0

4. Fourteen year-old Lindsey and her Dad kept a record of the length of their telephone calls for a week. Draw frequency polygons for both Lindsey and Dad on the same set of axes.

	−2	−4	−6	−8	−10	−12	−14	−16	−18	−20	−22	−24	−26	−28	−30
Dad	10	12	14	8	0	4	0	1	0	0	0	0	0	0	0
Lindsey	0	0	0	0	0	0	0	2	6	0	2	4	8	10	6

Note: The interval '−2' mean 0 up to and including 2 min, similarly '−4' means more than 2 and up to 4 min and so on.
(a) Comment on the differences between the two polygons.
(b) Who made the most calls?
(c) Who spent longest on the phone altogether?

5. As part of a program designed to increase understanding between different generations, teachers in two schools were given a comprehension test in which they had to interpret expressions commonly used by 14/15 year olds.
   For example, the teachers were asked to describe briefly what is meant by words like 'wicked', 'sorted', 'tragic', 'mega' and 'chill' and to give an approximate translation of the sentence
   'Get a life, you sad apology for a well out of order dog!'
   The marks attained by the teachers from schools A and B are shown on the frequency polygons.
   School A is situated in a remote part of Scotland and school B is an inner-city school.
   Decide which frequency polygon corresponds to each school. Give reasons for your choice.

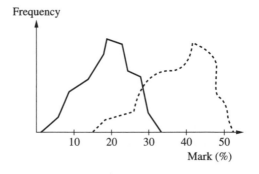

6. In a supermarket survey, shoppers were asked two questions as they left:
(a) How much have you just spent?
(b) How far away do you live?

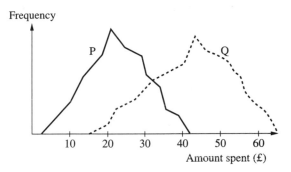

The results were separated into two groups: shoppers who lived less than 2 miles from the supermarket and shoppers who lived further away. The frequency polygons show how much shoppers in each group had spent.
Decide which polygon, P or Q, is most likely to represent shoppers who lived less than 2 miles from the supermarket. Give your reasons.

7. Scientists doing research in genetic engineering altered the genes of a certain kind of rabbit. Over a period of several years, measurements were made of the adult weight of the rabbits and their lifespans. The frequency polygons below show the results.

What can you deduce from the two frequency polygons? Write one sentence about weight and one sentence about lifespan.

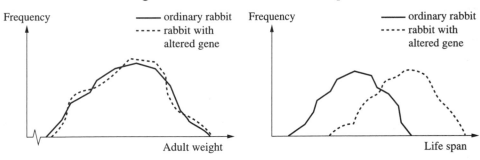

8. A large number of children were asked to state the approximate price of two items:
(a) a Mars bar; (b) a large cauliflower.

Which frequency polygon, X or Y, do you think shows the approximate prices they gave for a Mars bar?
Give your reasons.

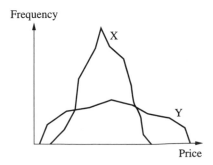

72

Cumulative frequency diagrams

A large set of grouped data can be displayed effectively on a *cumulative frequency* diagram

Here is a cumulative frequency diagram which shows the marks obtained by 100 people in a test.

Point A shows that 80 people got a mark of 40 or less.

Point B shows that 30 people got a mark of 20 or less

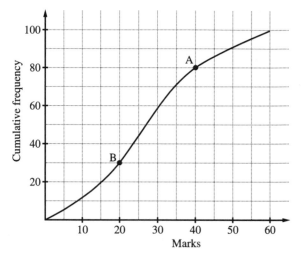

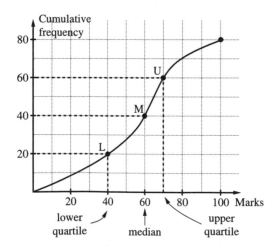

Here is another cumulative frequency diagram showing marks obtained by 80 people in a different test.

Point M is at the *median* value (half-way up the C.F. scale). We see that the median value is 60 marks.

The lower *quartile*, L, is one quarter up the C.F. axis. Here the lower quartile mark is 40.

The upper *quartile*, U, is three quarters up the C.F. axis. The upper quartile mark is 70.

The *interquartile range* is the difference between the upper and lower quartiles, in this case it is equal to $70 - 40 = 30$.

The interquartile range is an important measure of spread. It shows how widely or closely the data is spread.

Exercise 4

1. The two graphs below show the marks obtained in two tests.

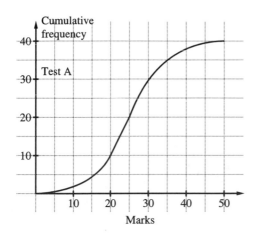 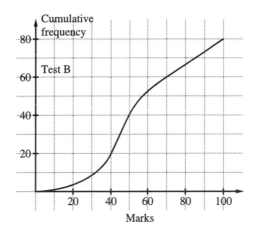

(a) How many people took test A and how many took test B?
(b) Find the median mark for each test.
(c) Find the upper and lower quartiles for each test.
(d) Find the interquartile range for each test.

2. The diagram shows the times taken by 60 pupils to solve a problem.

(a) What was the median time taken?
(b) Find the upper and lower quartiles.
(c) Find the interquartile range.

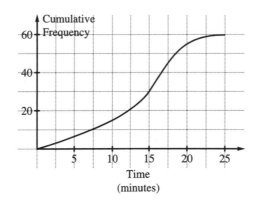

2.7 Puzzles

The questions below are taken from past School Mathematics Challenge papers. They are reproduced here with the kind permission of Dr Tony Gardiner of the U.K. Mathematics Foundation, Birmingham.

1. Weighing the baby at the clinic was a problem. The baby would not keep still and caused the scales to wobble. So I held the baby and stood on the scales while the nurse read off 78 kg. Then the nurse held the baby while I read off 69 kg. Finally I held the nurse while the baby read off 137 kg. What would the combined weight of nurse, baby and me be (in kilograms)?

    A 142   **B** 147   **C** 206   **D** 215   **E** 284

2. Baby's nearly 1 now. We've worked out how to weigh her, but nurse and I still have trouble measuring her height. She just *will* not stand up straight against our measuring chart. In fact she can't stand up at all yet! So we measure her upside down. Last year nurse held Baby's feet, keeping them level with the 140 cm mark, while I read off the mark level with the top of Baby's head: 97 cm. This year it was my turn to hold the feet. Being taller than nurse I held them against the 150 cm mark while nurse crawled on the floor to read the mark level with the top of Baby's head: 84 cm. How many centimetres has Baby grown in her first year?

    A 13   **B** 237   **C** 53   **D** 23   **E** 66

3. Baby's 2 now and drinks milk by the quarter pint, so we have decided to call her GILL. Getting her to recognise her name proved difficult, so we put the four letters G, I, L, L on separate building blocks. She loves arranging them, but rarely gets them in the right order. One day she managed to produce every possible four-letter 'word' (L I L G is one such). How many different four-letter words did she produce that day?

    A 3   **B** 4   **C** 12   **D** 16   **E** 24

4. Gill's back! This year, was her fourth birthday. The highlight of her party was a game of musical chairs. The game got down to herself, nurse, and me. Only two chairs were left – the hard chair and the comfy chair, with a big gap between them. The music stopped and we all piled onto the nearest chair, some on top of one another. If Gill's bottom was firmly in contact with one of the two chairs, in how many different ways could this have happened?

    A 4   **B** 6   **C** 8   **D** 10   **E** 12

5. Gill has now started primary skool and is learning to spell. We got her to help by writing out this queschun for us. We gave her a score of 100 to start with, and deducted 10% of her running total each time we found a word spelt rong. What was her final score?

A 70   **B** 72.9   **C** 80   **D** 81   **E** 90

6. Gill is just six and boasts that she can count up to 100. However, she often mixes up nineteen and ninety, and so jumps straight from nineteen to ninety one. How many numbers does she miss out when she does this?

A 70   **B** 71   **C** 72   **D** 78   **E** 89

7. Gill arranges the fingers of her right hand so that her thumb points upwards, her first finger points north and her second finger points west: we write this for short as "TU, 1N, 2W". She then keeps her fingers fixed like this, but can twist her arm and her wrist if she likes. Which of the following arrangements can she *not* achieve? (D = down, S = south, E = east.)

A TD, 1N, 2E   **B** TN, 1D, 2W   **C** TS, 1E, 2U
D TE, 1U, 2S   **E** TW, 1S, 2D

8. Last year's carnival procession was $1\frac{1}{2}$ km long. The last float set off, and finished, three quarters of an hour after the first float. Just as the first float reached us, young Gill escaped. She trotted off to the other end of the procession and back in the time it took for half the procession to pass us. Assuming Gill trotted at a constant speed, how fast did she go?

A 3 km/h   **B** 4 km/h   **C** 5 km/h   **D** 6 km/h   **E** 7 km/h

Hidden words

(a) Start in the top left box.
(b) Work out the answer to the calculation in the box.
(c) Find this answer in the top corner of another box.
(d) Write down the letter in that box.
(e) Repeat steps (b), (c) and (d) until you arrive back at the top left box. What is the message?
(f) Where necessary, numbers are rounded off to 2 decimal places.

1.

92·2	$\frac{7}{8}$	−8	193·5	36
	A	E	E	H
Solve $\dfrac{3}{x} = \dfrac{1}{2}$	$25\cdot1 \div 0\cdot1$	$\frac{1}{2}+\frac{1}{3}+\frac{1}{4}$	$0\cdot\dot{3}+0\cdot\dot{1}$	$\dfrac{7\cdot32}{8\cdot1-1\cdot94}$
5·5	$1\cdot5 \times 10^{-10}$	−1	$-\frac{4}{7}$	2×10^{7}
S	O	F	S	E
$(-3)^2 + (-2)^2$	$3\cdot2\%$ of 2500	$1^3 + 2^3 + 3^3$	Solve $\dfrac{x}{3}+4=7$	$18 - 12 \div 3$
13	6	9	14	$1\frac{1}{12}$
O	N	H	S	T
Solve $3x-1=-4$	$-7-(-2)+(-3)$	$\frac{3}{4}+\frac{1}{8}$	$5\cdot2 + 87$	Solve $\dfrac{3}{x+1}=7$
$\frac{4}{9}$	$-\frac{3}{4}$	80	1·19	251
L	L	T	O	V
(5×10^{-3}) $\times (3\times10^{-8})$	(8×10^5) $\div(4\times10^{-2})$	$12\frac{1}{2}\%$ of 44	$-\frac{1}{2}+(-\frac{1}{4})$	$\frac{3}{4}$ of 258

2.

6·575	3·6	$1\cdot6 \times 10^{-9}$	3·55	$\frac{3}{5}$
	O	H	I	T
$(5\cdot3 \times 10^4) \times$ (2×10^9)	$(-12) \div (-\frac{1}{2})$	$\dfrac{2\cdot3^2 - 1\cdot9^2}{8\cdot2 - 7\cdot71}$	Solve $6-3x=2$	Half of $13\cdot15$
24	−49	0·81	106·26	36·96
F	A	S	U	P
$\frac{1}{6}+\frac{1}{7}+0\cdot2314$	$\dfrac{8\cdot2+1\cdot99}{1\cdot7\times4\cdot7}$	Solve $3(x+1)$ $=2(3-x)$	$\dfrac{2\cdot75}{1\cdot09} - \sqrt{\dfrac{1\cdot21}{0\cdot41}}$	Solve $\dfrac{18}{x}-1\cdot5$ $=3\cdot5$
2·34	−8	$1\cdot06 \times 10^{14}$	$\frac{13}{30}$	$\frac{4}{5}$
S	A	H	A	I
$\frac{5}{6}-\frac{2}{5}$	12% of $\frac{2}{5}$ of 770	$\dfrac{3}{2\cdot51}+\dfrac{4}{1\cdot7}$	$(2\cdot4\times10^{-6})$ $\div(1\cdot5\times10^3)$	$\sqrt{\dfrac{10}{\pi}}+\sqrt{\dfrac{\pi}{10}}$
$1\frac{1}{3}$	1·28	0·54	262·5	3·43
S	R	R	C	E
Increase 250 by 5%	$\frac{3}{5} \div \frac{3}{4}$	$\dfrac{5^5 - 4^4}{3^3}$	$(-7)^2 \times (-1)^3$	$-7+(-6)-(-5)$

3.

$\frac{11}{20}$	$\frac{1}{2}$	16	7.5×10^{10}	54.4
	U	L	H	O
$0.3 \times \frac{1}{3}$	$-8 - (-3)$	Find x	Solve $\dfrac{9}{x} + 7 = 10$	$\frac{1}{2} \times \frac{2}{3} \times \frac{3}{4}$
4.17	6.71	12	2	$-\frac{1}{4}$
T	P	E	I	N
$(3 \times 10^4) \times$ (2.5×10^6)	Decrease 64 by 15%	$\frac{3}{5} + \frac{1}{2}$	Increase 56.5 by 8%	$(-2)^2 \times (-3)^3$
61.02	$\frac{1}{4}$	0.1	4.08	210
S	I	P	O	E
$3.984 - \left(\dfrac{2.61}{1.4}\right)$	Solve $5(x+1)$ $= 3(1-x)$	Solve $\frac{1}{3}x = 9.9$	$\frac{5}{12} - \frac{1}{4}$	$\frac{1}{4} + \left(\frac{1}{2} \text{ of } \frac{3}{5}\right)$
-108	2.25×10^{-10}	$\frac{1}{6}$	2×10^{-4}	5.83
T	O	N	H	Y
6% of $\frac{2}{3}$ of 102	Solve $\dfrac{3}{x+1} = 2$	$4.2 \div 0.02$	$x^2 - 6x,$ when $x = -2$	$\dfrac{2.9}{1.2 - 0.71^2}$
29.7	3	-5	1.1	2.12
I	R	G	E	R
$\left(-\frac{1}{2}\right) \div \left(-\frac{1}{4}\right)$	$3x^2,$ when $x = 2$	1% of 2%	Find x	$(1.5 \times 10^{-5})^2$

Part 3

3.1 Shape, space, measures review

Angles and bearings

Exercise 1

Find the angles marked with letters

1.

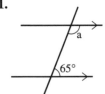

2.

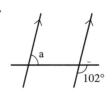

3.

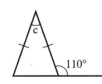

4.

5.

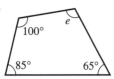

6.

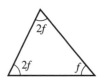

7.

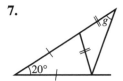

8.

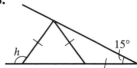

In Question **9** to **14** use the fact that the tangent at any point on a circle is perpendicular to the radius at that point.

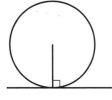

9.

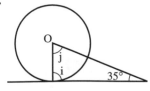

10.

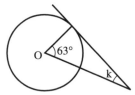

11.

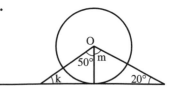

12.

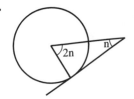

13.

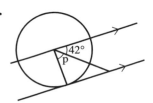

14.

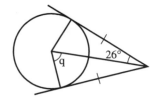

15. Measure the bearings on which ships A, B, C, D, E are sailing

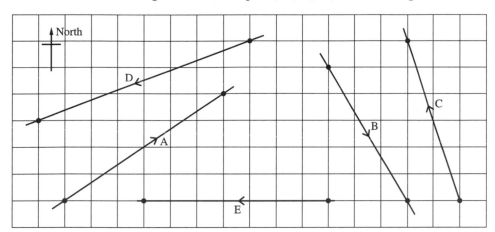

Remember: Bearings are measured clockwise from North.

16.

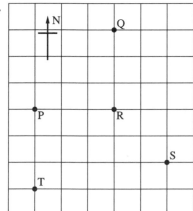

State the bearings of (a) Q from P
(b) R from P
(c) S from R
(d) R from Q
(e) T from R
(f) P from R

17. A ship sails 8 km on a bearing 041° and then a further 6 km on a bearing 090°. Make a scale drawing (1 km = 1 cm) and find how far the ship is from its starting point.

18. A ship sails 9 km on a bearing of 072° and then a further 7 km on a bearing of 130°. How far is the ship from its starting point?

19. Copy the diagram on squared paper. Mark a point P such that
(a) the bearing of P from A is 038°
(b) the bearing of P from B is 300°.

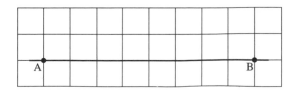

80

20. Write down the coordinates of the point which is:
    (a) on a bearing 090° from A and 180° from B
    (b) on a bearing 045° from A and 180° from C
    (c) on a bearing 135° from A and 270° from D
    (d) on a bearing 315° from B and 045° from A
    (e) on a bearing 045° from A and 315° from D
    (f) on a bearing 180° from C and 270° from B

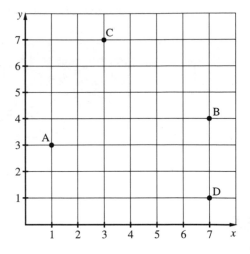

Pythagoras' theorem

Exercise 2

Find the side marked x. All lengths are in cm. Give answers correct to one decimal place.

1.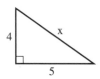

2.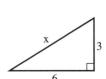

3.

4.

5.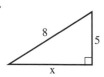

6.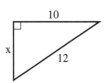

7.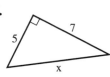

8.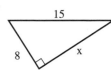

9.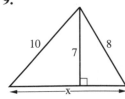

10.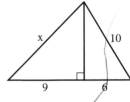

11.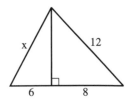

12. A ladder of length 4 m rests against a vertical wall, with its foot 2·2 m from the wall. How far up the wall does the ladder reach?

13. Calculate the length of the diagonal of a rectangle measuring 9 cm by 12 cm.

Pythagoras' theorem in circles

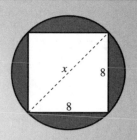

A circle is drawn through the corners of a square of side 8 cm. Find the shaded area.

Let the length of the diameter be x cm.
By Pythagoras', $\quad x^2 = 8^2 + 8^2$
$$x = 11 \cdot 313708$$
$\therefore \qquad \text{radius} = 5 \cdot 6568542$
$$\text{area of circle} = \pi \times 5 \cdot 6568542^2$$
$$= 100 \cdot 53096 \, \text{cm}^2$$
$$\text{area of square} = 64 \, \text{cm}^2$$
$$\text{shaded area} = 36 \cdot 5 \, \text{cm}^2 \text{ (3 s.f.)}$$

Notice that we have approximated to 3 s.f. only at the very end of the calculation.

Exercise 3

In Questions **1** and **2** find the shaded area. Lengths are in cm. All arcs are either semi-circles or quarter circles. You do not *always* have to use Pythagoras' theorem.

1.

2.

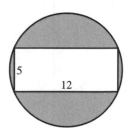

3. All arcs are semi-circles. Find the total area.

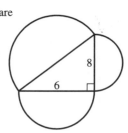

4. This diagram contains two semi-circles. Calculate the shaded area, given that the diameter of the larger semi-circle is 12 cm.

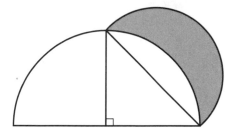

5. This diagram has one quarter circle and two semi-circles. Calculate the shaded area.

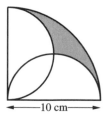

Transformations

Exercise 4

1. Draw each shape on a squared paper and then draw its reflection.

(a)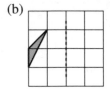

(b)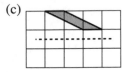

(c)

(d)

(e)

(f)

(g)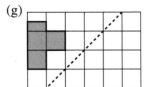

2. Write down the equation of the mirror line for each reflection.

   (a) $\Delta A \rightarrow \Delta B$

   (b) $\Delta A \rightarrow \Delta F$

   (c) $\Delta E \rightarrow \Delta D$

   (d) $\Delta B \rightarrow \Delta C$

   (e) $\Delta E \rightarrow \Delta F$

   (f) $\Delta F \rightarrow \Delta G$

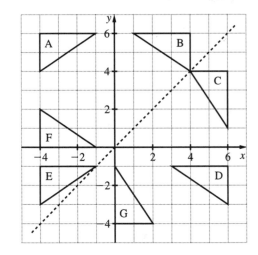

3. Draw each shape and its image under the rotation given.
   Take O as the centre of rotation in each case.

(a)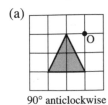

90° anticlockwise

(b)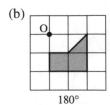

180°

(c)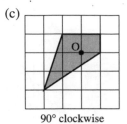

90° clockwise

(d)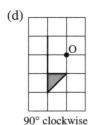

90° clockwise

(e)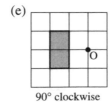

90° clockwise

(f)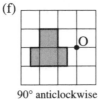

90° anticlockwise

4. Describe fully the rotations. (give the angle, direction and centre)

(a) $\Delta A \rightarrow \Delta B$

(b) $\Delta A \rightarrow \Delta C$

(c) $\Delta A \rightarrow \Delta D$

(d) $\Delta E \rightarrow \Delta D$

(e) $\Delta C \rightarrow \Delta E$

(f) $\Delta D \rightarrow \Delta F$

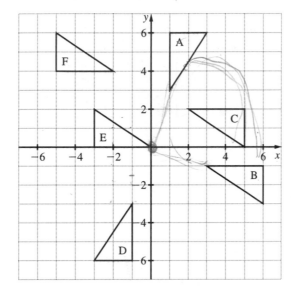

5. Copy each shape with its centre of enlargement. Then enlarge the shape by the scale factor given.

(a)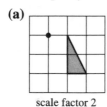

scale factor 2

(b)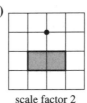

scale factor 2

(c)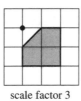

scale factor 3

(d)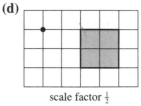

scale factor $\frac{1}{2}$

(e)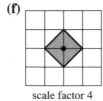

scale factor 3

(f)

scale factor 4

(g)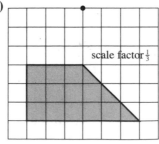

scale factor $\frac{1}{3}$

6. Describe fully each of the following enlargements

(a) $\triangle D \to \triangle C$

(b) $\triangle A \to \triangle B$

(c) $\triangle F \to \triangle E$

(d) $\triangle D \to \triangle E$

(e) $\triangle B \to \triangle D$

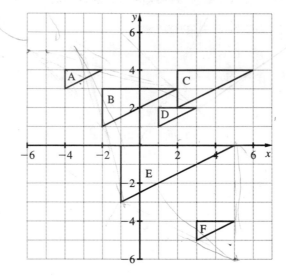

Exercise 5 (Miscellaneous)

1.

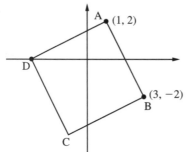

The diagram shows a square ABCD
Find the coordinates of C.

2. Many small cubes of side 1·2 are stuck together to make a large cube of volume 216 cm³.
How many cubes are needed?

3. (a) 24 unit cubes can be stuck together to make cuboids of different shapes. How many *different* cuboids can be made?
(b) How many different cuboids can be made with (i) 56 cubes?
(ii) 100 cubes?

4. Copy and complete

(a) 10 gallons ≈ ☐ litres (b) 3 kg ≈ ☐ pounds

(c) 8 km ≈ ☐ miles (d) 6 feet ≈ ☐ cm

(e) 9 litres ≈ ☐ gallons (f) 44 pounds ≈ ☐ kg

(g) 22 cm ≈ ☐ m (h) 1·6 cm ≈ ☐ mm

(i) 3·2 kg ≈ ☐ g

1 kg ≈ 2·2 pound
1 foot ≈ 30 cm
1 gallon ≈ 4·5 litres
1 km ≈ $\frac{5}{8}$ mile

3.2 Rounding, errors and estimating

Significant figures, decimal places

We have already seen how we can approximate a number to one decimal place or to two decimal places.

Reminder: 4·2$\overset{\uparrow}{8}$1 = 4·3   to one decimal place.

0·23$\overset{\uparrow}{5}$4 = 0·24   to two decimal places.

We look at the digit arrowed to see if it is '5 or more'.

Sometimes numbers are rounded off to a certain number of *significant figures* rather than decimal places.

For decimal places we started counting from the decimal point.
For significant figures we approach from the left and start counting as soon as we come to the first figure which is not zero. Once we have started counting we count any figure, zeros included.

(a) 52·7211 = 52·7 to 3 significant figures. (3 s.f.)

[Count 3 figures. The 'next' figure is 2, which is less than 5].
(b) 7·0264 = 7·03 to 3 significant figures.

(c) 0·0237538 = 0·0238 to 3 significant figures.

(d) 2475·6 = 2500 to 2 significant figures.

Notice that we need the two noughts after the '5' as the original number is approximately 2500.

Exercise 1

1. Write the following numbers correct to 3 significant figures
   (a) 1·0765   (b) 24·897   (c) 195·12   (d) 0·7648
   (e) 17·482   (f) 0·07666   (g) 28 774   (h) 2391·2
   (i) 0·8555   (j) 4258   (k) 0·01128   (l) 675899

2. Write the following numbers to the degree of accuracy indicated
   (a) 19·72 (2 s.f.)   (b) 8·314 (1 s.f.)   (c) 0·71551 (3 s.f.)
   (d) 1824·7 (3 s.f.)   (e) 23 666 (2 s.f.)   (f) 0·03476 (2 s.f.)

3. Work out the following on a calculator and write the answer correct to 3 significant figures.
   (a) 17 ÷ 3·1   (b) 0·13 × 0·11   (c) 2 ÷ 0·11   (d) 87 ÷ 19
   (e) 1·7 × 8·32   (f) 5 ÷ 0·753   (g) 19 ÷ 0·021   (h) 1 ÷ 0·7

Errors

Whenever a quantity is measured the measurement is never *exact*. If you measure the thickness of a wire with a ruler, you might read the thickness as 2 mm. If you use a more accurate device for measuring you might read the thickness as 2·3 mm. An even more accurate device might give the thickness as 2·31 mm. None of these figures is precise.

They are all approximations to the actual thickness. This means that there is always an error in making any kind of measurement such as length, weight, time, temperature and so on. An error of this kind is not the same as making a mistake in a calculation!

Bounds of accuracy

(a) Suppose the length of a book is measured at 22 cm to the nearest cm. The actual length could be from 21·5 to *almost* 22·5. We say 'almost' 22·5 because a length of 22·499 999 9.... would be rounded off to 22 cm. The number 22·499 999.... is effectively 22·5 and we take 22·5 as the *upper bound*.

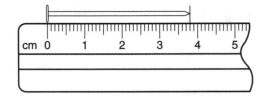

So in this case the *bounds of accuracy* are 21·5 cm and 22·5 cm. The maximum possible error is 0·5 cm.

(b) Using a ruler, the length of the nail shown is measured at 3·8 cm to the nearest 0·1 cm. In this case the bounds of accuracy are 3·75 cm and 3·85 cm.

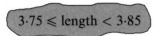

(c) Sometimes measurements are given 'to the nearest 10, 100, etc.' Suppose the length of a lake is measured at 4200 m to the nearest 100 m. The bounds of accuracy are 4150 m and 4250 m.

(d) Summary. In (a), (b) and (c) above the maximum possible error is always half of the level of accuracy.
In part (b) the level of accuracy is the nearest 0·1 cm. The maximum possible error is 0·05 cm.

(e) Here are some further examples:

	lower bound	upper bound
(i) The weight of an apple is 43 g to the nearest gram	42·5 g	43·5 g
(ii) The temperature of a room is 22·9 °C to one decimal place	22·85 °C	22·95 °C
(iii) The length of a road is 780 m to the nearest 10 m	775 m	785 m
(iv) The capacity of a mug is 115 ml to the nearest 5 ml	112·5 ml	117·5 ml
(v) The weight of a lorry is 23 000 kg to 2 s.f.	22 500 kg	23 500 kg

Exercise 2

1. Copy and complete each statement. Part (a) is done as an example.

   (a) A length d is 42 m, to the nearest m, so $41{\cdot}5 \leqslant d < 42{\cdot}.5$.

   (b) A volume V is 8 m³, to the nearest m³, so $7{\cdot}5 \leqslant V < \square$.

   (c) A mass m is 72 kg, to the nearest kg, so $\square \leqslant m < \square$.

   (d) A time t is 3·2 h, to the nearest 0·1 h, so $\square \leqslant t < 3{\cdot}25$.

   (e) A radius r is 5·8 cm, to the nearest 0·1 cm, so $\square \leqslant r < \square$

2. The height of a table is measured at 84 cm to the nearest cm write down the lower bound for the height of the table.

3. A postmaster weighs a parcel at 5·2 kg to the nearest 0·1 kg. Write down the upper bound for the weight of the parcel.

4. The length and width of a rectangle are measured to the nearest 0·1 cm, as shown.

   (a) Write down the upper bound for the length of the rectangle.

   (b) Write down the lower bound for the width of the rectangle.

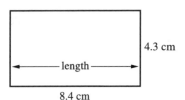

4.3 cm

length

8.4 cm

5. The height of a man is measured at 5 feet 8 inches, to the nearest inch. Write down the upper bound for the height of the man.

6. A scientist weighs a bird's egg at 3·7 g, correct to one decimal place. What is the least possible weight of the egg?

7. A book states that the distance from the Earth to the Sun is 93 million miles correct to two significant figures. What is the shortest possible distance?

8. In a 200 m race a sprinter is timed at 20·63 seconds to the nearest 0·01 seconds. Write down the least possible time.

9. Copy and complete the table:

   (a) length of nail = 5·6 cm, to nearest mm
   (b) height of lighthouse = 37 m, to nearest m
   (c) weight of insect = 0·27 mg, to 2 d.p.
   (d) temperature in oven = 230 °C, to nearest 10 °C
   (e) length of oil pipeline = 315 km, to nearest km

	lower bound	upper bound

10. The weight of a coin is 7 g, to the nearest gram. The weight lies between:

A	B	C
6 g and 8 g	6·9 g and 7·1 g	6·5 g and 7·5 g

11. Chuck and Dave each weigh a different frog and they both say that their frog weighs 27 grams to the nearest gram.
What is the greatest possible difference in the actual weights of the two frogs?

Estimation

- In some situations an estimate of a quantity is more helpful than the actual number. For example we may know that on January 1st 1996 the population of France is 61 278 514 and the population of Greece is 9 815 972. For purposes of comparison we could use 60 million for France and 10 million for Greece so that the population of France is *about* six times that of Greece.

- Find an estimate for the radius of a circular pond of area 150 m².

We know that $\pi \times (\text{radius})^2 = 150$
The value of π is about 3, so $3 \times (\text{radius})^2 \approx 150$
$$(\text{radius})^2 \approx 50$$
The square root of 50 is about 7
The radius of the pool is about 7 m.

- Estimate, correct to one significant figure

(a) $\dfrac{58 \cdot 2 \times 28 \cdot 4}{18 \cdot 27} \approx \dfrac{6\cancel{0} \times 30}{2\cancel{0}} \approx 90$

(b) $\dfrac{\sqrt{11\,213} \times 0 \cdot 0974}{52 \cdot 7} \approx \dfrac{100 \times 0 \cdot 1}{50} \approx 0 \cdot 2$

(c) 48% of £22 615 $\approx \dfrac{50}{1\cancel{0}\cancel{0}} \times 20\,0\cancel{0}\cancel{0} \approx £10\,000$

Exercise 3

In Questions **1** to **9** give your answer correct to one significant figure. Do *not* use a calculator.

1. A doctor is paid a salary of £49 450 per year. Work out a rough estimate for her weekly pay.

2. Estimate the mean weight of articles with the following weights:
4·9 kg, 0·21 kg, 0·72 kg, 25·1 kg, 0·11 kg.

3. In 2002 Helen's pay was £19 380 per year. In 2003 she receives a pay increase of 19·2%. Estimate the *monthly increase* in her pay.

4. Two people on a bike travel at an average speed of 98·7 km/h from 0810 until 1217. Roughly how far do they go?

5. Estimate the length of the diagonals of a square of side 7·2 cm.

6. A lorry can carry a maximum load of 30 tonnes. A copy of Elmwood's Almanac weighs 475 g. The manager of the delivery firm estimates that each lorry can take about 6000 copies of the book. Is this a reasonable estimate? If not suggest a better estimate. [1 tonne = 1000 kg]

7. In the grounds of his palace, the Sultan of Brunei has a circular pond with a surface area of $\frac{3}{4}$ hectare. Estimate the diameter of the pond in metres. [1 hectare = 10 000 m²]

8. Estimate the mean weight, in kg, of two wrestlers weighing 131 kg and 10 stones 4 pounds respectively.
[1 pound ≈ 0·45 kg, 1 stone = 14 pounds].

9. Give an estimate for each of the following calculations.

(a) $\dfrac{82·4 \times \sqrt{907·4}}{2·824}$

(b) $\dfrac{2848·7 - 1·94}{0·32 + 39·83}$

(c) 52% of 0·394 kg

(d) $\dfrac{3·15^2 + 30·63^2}{0·104^2}$

(e) $\frac{7}{15}$ of £3918.25

(f) $\dfrac{207·5 + 4·21 + 0·63}{109·4 + 293·2}$

(g) $\dfrac{5·13 \times 18·777}{0·952}$

(h) $\pi \times 9·73^2$

(i) $\frac{17}{31}$ of 12% of £2057

10. Decide whether or not the following are reasonable estimates. Write 'yes' or 'no' for each part.
(a) The total weight of thirty 14 year-olds = 1500 kg.
(b) The time taken by an international athlete to run 1 mile = 240 s.
(c) The total weight of 10 £1 coins = 1 kg.
(d) The top speed of your maths teacher's car = 150 km/h.
(e) The height of a four storey office building = 80 m.

11. The population of the Earth is about 6 billion. Estimate how many people share the same birthday as you.

12. When you multiply by a number greater than 1, you make it bigger.

When you multiply by a number less than 1, you make it smaller.

When you divide by a number greater than 1, you make it smaller.

When you divide by a number less than 1, you make it bigger.

E.g. $5\cdot7 \times 1\cdot2 > 5\cdot7$, $16\cdot8 \div 1\cdot2 < 16\cdot8$.
       $5\cdot7 \times 0\cdot8 < 5\cdot7$, $16\cdot8 \div 0\cdot8 > 16\cdot8$

Copy and complete the following with the correct sign ($>$ or $<$) instead of the box.

(a) $3\cdot58 \times 1\cdot3 \ \square\ 3\cdot58$ (b) $19 \times 0\cdot92 \ \square\ 19$ (c) $5\cdot5 \times 1\cdot04 \ \square\ 5\cdot5$

(d) $9\cdot2 \div 1\cdot5 \ \square\ 9\cdot2$ (e) $11\cdot2 \div 0\cdot87 \ \square\ 11\cdot2$ (f) $67 \div 1\cdot34 \ \square\ 67$

(g) $59 \times 0\cdot89 \ \square\ 59$ (h) $0\cdot42 \times 0\cdot73 \ \square\ 0\cdot42$ (i) $17 \div 0\cdot99 \ \square\ 17$

(j) $0\cdot2^2 \ \square\ 0\cdot2$ (k) $0\cdot061 \div 0\cdot41 \ \square\ 0\cdot061$ (l) $(0\cdot85)^3 \ \square\ 0\cdot85$

3.3 Area and volume

Important formulae

(a) 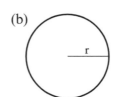 Triangle

Area $= \dfrac{b \times h}{2}$

(b) Circle

Area $= \pi r^2$

Circumference $= \pi d$

(c) 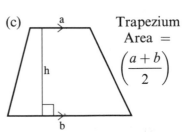 Trapezium

Area $= \left(\dfrac{a+b}{2}\right)$

(d) A prism is a solid with the same cross-section throughout its length

Volume $= A \times l$

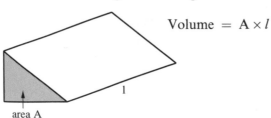

area A

(e) Cylinder

Volume $= \pi r^2 h$

[A cylinder is a prism.]

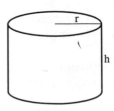

Exercise 1

[Give answers correct to 3 s.f., where necessary]

1. Find the area of each circle. All lengths are in cm.

(a)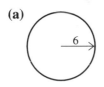
6

(b)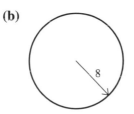
8

(c)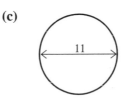
11

(d)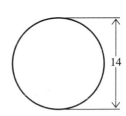
14

2. Find the circumference of each circle in Question 1.

3. Find the area of the shapes.

(a)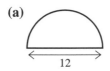
12

(b)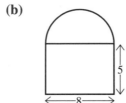
5
8

(c)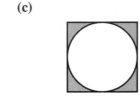
10

Find the shaded area.

4. Find the volume of each cylinder.

(a)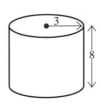
3
8

(b)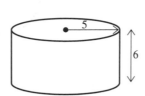
5
6

(c)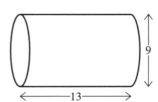
9
13

5. Find the volume of a cylinder of radius 5 m and height 8·2 m.
   State clearly the units for the answer.

6. Find the area of each shape. All lengths are in cm.

(a)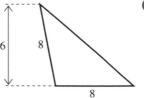
5
8

(b)
6
8
8

(c)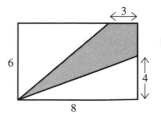
3
[Find the shaded area.]
6
4
8

7. A right angled triangle has sides of length 6 m, 8 m and 10 m.
   Sketch the triangle and then find its area.

8. A rectangle has area 24 cm² and perimeter 22 cm. Find the sides
   of the rectangle.

(a) Find the area of the trapezium

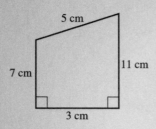

$$\text{Area} = \left(\frac{7 + 11}{2}\right) \times 3$$

$$= 45\,\text{cm}^2$$

[Notice that the length 5 cm is not used.]

(b) Find the volume of the prism

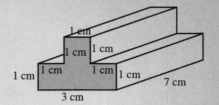

$$\text{Area of shaded end} = 4\,\text{cm}^2$$

$$\text{Volume} = 4 \times 7$$

$$= 28\,\text{cm}^3$$

Exercise 2

[Give answers correct to 3 s.f., where necessary]

leave out

1. Find the area of each shape. All lengths are in cm.

(a)

(b)

(c)

2. Find the area shaded.

(a)

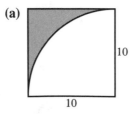

(b)

(c)

3. The diagonals of the kite shown are of length a and b and intersect at right angles.
Find an expression, in its simplest form, for the area of the kite in terms of a and b.

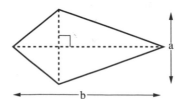

4. In some triangles you know the lengths of the three sides but you do not know the perpendicular height. Here is a famous formula which is used to calculate the area of a triangle when you know the three sides a, b and c.

$$\text{Area} = \sqrt{s(s-a)(s-b)(s-c)}, \quad \text{where} \quad s = \frac{a+b+c}{2}$$

(the semi-perimeter)

Use this formula to calculate the area of each triangle below, correct to 3 s.f.

(a)

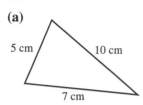

5 cm   10 cm

7 cm

(b)

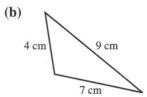

4 cm   9 cm

7 cm

5. Which of the solids below are prisms?

(a) 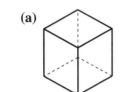   **(b)** 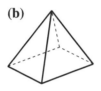   **(c)** 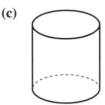   **(d)**    **(e)**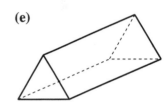

(f) 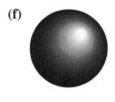   **(g)**    **(h)** 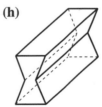   **(i)**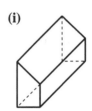

6. A long jump pit is 2·4 m wide by 18 m long and 20 cm deep. What volume of sand is required to fill it?

7. How many boxes of matches 10 cm by 2 cm by 6 cm will fit into a packing case 1 m by 80 cm by 48 cm?

8. How many boxes of cornflakes measuring 24 cm by 16 cm by 6 cm will fit into a packing case 1 m by 64 cm by 54 cm?

9. Find the volume of the bottle bank.

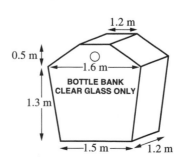

1.2 m

0.5 m

1.6 m

BOTTLE BANK
CLEAR GLASS ONLY

1.3 m

1.5 m   1.2 m

10. The total surface area of a cube is $121 \cdot 5 \, \text{cm}^2$. What is its volume?

11.

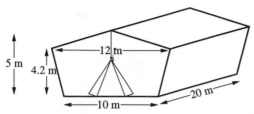

Find the internal volume of the marquee.

12. How much cement is required to make the octagonal floor tile shown?

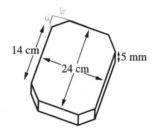

13. An ice rink with semi-circular ends is to be filled to a depth of 10 cm with ice. If the straight sides are 60 m long and 30 m apart how many cubic metres of ice will be needed?

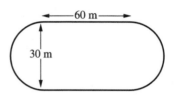

14. Rain falling onto a flat rectangular roof measuring $3 \cdot 2 \, \text{m}$ by $5 \cdot 5 \, \text{m}$ is drained off into a covered water tank with a square base 80 cm by 80 cm. If 5 mm of rain fell, by what depth would the water in the tank increase?

15. A railway tunnel $\frac{1}{2}$ km long is to be cut through a hillside. The cross-section of the tunnel consists of a rectangle and a semi-circle. How much earth will have to be removed?

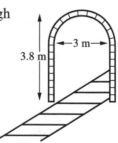

16. A solid cuboid has edges of lengths a, b, c. What is its surface area?

17. In the diagram a square of side a cm is surrounded by four equal isosceles triangles. Find the value of a is the area of the shape is $144 \, \text{cm}^2$.

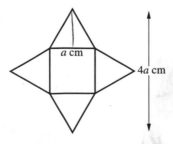

18. A triangle and a square are drawn on dotty paper with dots 1 cm apart. What is the area of the shaded region?

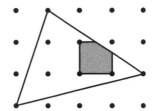

Finding the radius of a circle

Reminder: Circumference of a circle $= 2 \times \pi \times$ radius
(or $\pi \times$ diameter)
Area of a circle $= \pi \times$ (radius)^2

If we know the circumference or area of a circle we can find the radius by reversing these formulae.

Either $2\pi r = C$ or $\pi r^2 = A$

$$r = \frac{C}{2\pi} \qquad r = \sqrt{\frac{A}{\pi}}$$

(a) The circumference of a circle is 48 cm

$2\pi \times$ radius $= 48$

$$\text{radius} = \frac{48}{2\pi} = 7.64 \text{ cm (3 s.f.)}$$

(b) The area of a circle is 120 cm^2.

$\pi \times$ (radius)$^2 = 120$

$$(\text{radius})^2 = \frac{120}{\pi}$$

$$\text{radius} = \sqrt{\left(\frac{120}{\pi}\right)} = 6.18 \text{ cm (3 s.f.)}$$

(c) A cylinder of height 15 cm has a volume of 2250 cm^3. Find its diameter.

Area of top A $= 2250 \div 15 = 150$ cm^2

radius of top $= \sqrt{(150 \div \pi)} = 6.91$ cm

diameter of cylinder $= 2 \times$ radius $= 13.8$ cm (3 s.f.)

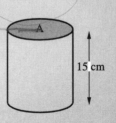

Exercise 3

Give all answers to 3 sig. fig.

1. Find the radius of a circle with circumference of:
   (a) 20 cm   (b) 64 m   (c) 120 cm

2. Find the radius of a circle with area of:
   (a) 16 m^2 (b) 9.2 cm^2 (c) 42 cm^2

$\pi r^2 \times l$

3. Find the diameter of each of the following cylinders:

(a)

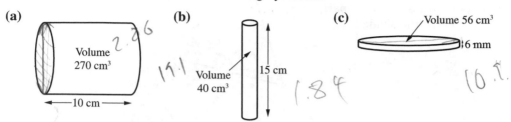

Volume
270 cm³

2.96

←— 10 cm —→

(b)

19.1

Volume
40 cm³

15 cm

1.84

(c)

Volume 56 cm³

6 mm

10.1

4. A litre of water is poured into a cylindrical glass jug. If the water in the jug is 8 cm deep, what is the diameter of the jug?
(1 litre = 1000 cm³)

5. Karen measures the girth of a tree trunk to be 1·8 metres. What is its diameter?

6. A trundle wheel is used by surveyors to measure distances along the ground.
It consists of a circular disc attached to a handle. One revolution of the wheel measures out exactly one metre. Find the diameter of the wheel.

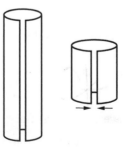

7. A block of marzipan measuring 10 cm by 12 cm by 3 cm is rolled out to cover the top of a circular cake. If the marzipan is to be 1·5 cm thick, what is the maximum radius of cake that can be covered?

8. A bar of bronze that has a volume of 90 cm³ is melted down to make 100 coins with a thickness of 3 mm. Find the diameter of the coins.

9. A circular paddling pool is filled to a depth of 25 cm. This takes 400 litres of water. How wide is the pool?

10. A rectangular piece of card 12 cm by 20 cm is rolled up to make a tube (with no overlap). Find the radius of the tube if
(a) the long sides are joined,
(b) the short sides are joined.

11. The point of the minute hand on a church clock travels 180 cm farther than the point of the hour hand in one complete revolution. If the hour hand is 60 cm long, how long is the minute hand?

12. The useable area on a CD is 10 000 mm². If the hole in the centre has a radius of 7·5 mm, what is the radius of the CD?

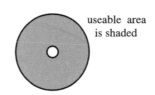

useable area is shaded

13. While on special offer, a tin of baked beans contains 25% extra free.
If the height of the tin is to remain the same and the area of the base of the original tin is 30 cm², find the diameter of the new tin.

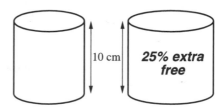

10 cm **25% extra free**

14. A running track consists of two straight sections with semi-circular ends. If the straight sections measure 100 metres and one complete lap on the inside of the track measures ½ km, what is the distance x between the two straights?

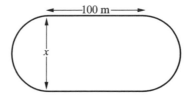

←——100 m——→

x

15. 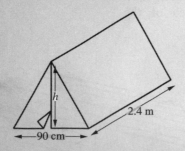 A rope 60 m long and 5 cm in diameter is coiled tightly as shown. Estimate, correct to one significant figure, the radius of the 'circle' formed.

Harder problems

A two man tent has an internal space of 0·864 m³

If the tent is 2·4 m long and 90 cm wide, find its height.

As the volume is in m³ change all measurements to metres.

End area $= \frac{1}{2} \times h \times 0.9 = 0.45h$

Volume $= 0.45h \times 2.4 = 1.08h$

$\therefore \quad 1.08h = 0.864$

$$h = \frac{0.864}{1.08} = 0.8 \text{ m or } 80 \text{ cm}$$

2·4 m

h

←—90 cm—→

Exercise 4

Give answers correct to 3 s.f. where necessary.

1. Find the missing lengths in the following prisms.

(a)

Volume = 88 cm³

(b)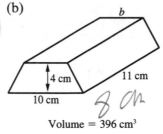

Volume = 396 cm³

(c)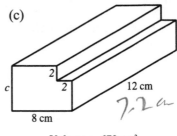

Volume = 672 cm³

2. Gary's car is 4·4 m long. His garage has an internal volume of 28·2 m³. Will his car fit in?

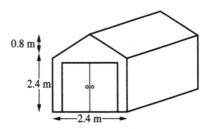

3. Carol cuts a circular Camembert cheese into 10 equal wedge shape pieces. If the volume of cheese in one of these pieces is 180 cm³ and the wedge is 5 cm thick, find the diameter of the original cheese.

4. The plastic guttering along the front of a house consists of a semi-circular prism 8 metres long. If it contains 35 litres of rain water before overflowing find the width, x, of the top of the guttering.

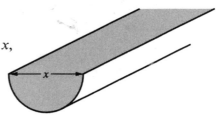

5. A barrel containing 50 litres of oil has been spilt. It has formed into two puddles each of a constant depth of 0·5 cm. The area of the larger puddle is exactly three times the area of the smaller one. Find the surface area of each puddle. (1 litre $\doteqdot$ 1000 cm³)

6. A pig sty is made from a sheet of corrugated steel bent into a semi-circular prism. If the internal volume is 3·6 m³ and it is 2·4 m wide at the front find the dimensions of the original piece of steel.

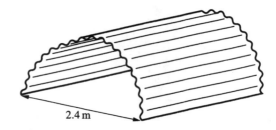

2.4 m

7. After harvesting Farmer Giles has $740\,m^3$ of hay.
This is stored as 180 cylindrical bales. If each bale
is $2 \cdot 3\,m$ long, what is its diameter?

8. The top view of the square tray in the bottom of a shower
cubical is shown below.
If it is designed to hold 46 litres of water
before overflowing, how deep is the tray?

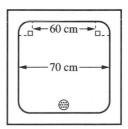

9.

cross section

A bath trim tile is a prism with cross
section as shown. If each tile is $15\,cm$
long andtakes $3 \cdot 6\,cm^3$ of plaster to make,
find the width x.

1.5 cm x

$$V = \frac{88cm^3}{8}$$

$$= 11\,ch$$

10. The diagram on the right consists of a
quarter circle with centre A and a
triangle. The shaded area is $200\,cm^2$.
Find the radius r.

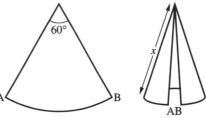

A r

44 $4.4 = A = 11ch$

$a?$ $15.36 = s$

11. A wizard's hat is made by rolling up a
sector of a circle into a cone as shown.
If the original piece of card has an area
of $470\,cm^2$, what will be the slant height,
x, of the cone? The arc length **AB** becomes
the circumference of the base of the cone.
What is the base diameter of the hat?

3.4 Interpreting graphs

Exercise 1

1. The step graph shows the cost of travelling on a bus. [Note that an open dot, o, means the overlap point is not included.]
Find the cost of travelling
(a) 7 miles
(b) 22 miles
(c) 10 miles

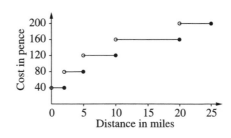

2. The graph below shows the depth of water at the centre of a puddle one summer day.

Describe what might be happening at each stage A–B, B–C, etc.

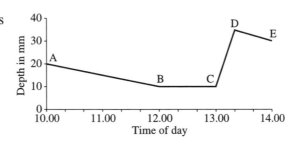

3. The graph shows the water level in a bath. Use the letters A, B, C etc to describe when the events below occurred. [For example: A → B '.....................']

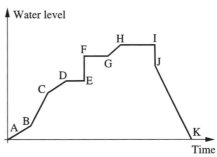

- John got out of bath
- Water drained from bath
- John got into bath
- Both taps on
- Hot tap on alone
- More hot water added when John was in bath
- John lies in bath, solving equations in his head.

4. Which of the graphs A to D below best fits the following statement: 'The price of paint is still rising, but by less each month.'

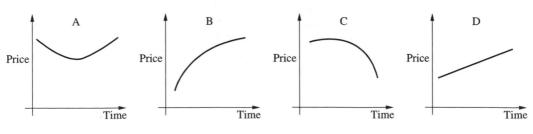

5. Which of the graphs A to D below best fits each of the following statements:
  (a) The examination pass rate, which has been rising steadily, is now beginning to fall.
  (b) The price of computers has fallen steadily over the last year.
  (c) The birthrate was falling but is now steady.
  (d) The cost of holidays, which rose slowly until 1998, is now rising fast.

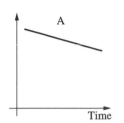 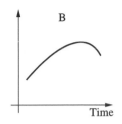 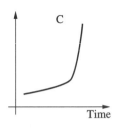 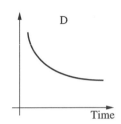

6. Water is poured at a constant rate into each of the containers A, B and C.
The graphs X, Y and Z shows how the water level rises.
Decide which graph fits each container.
State your reasons.

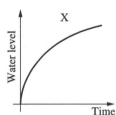 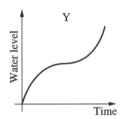 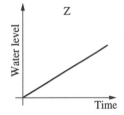

7. Water is poured at a constant rate into three different containers P, Q and R.
Draw sketch graphs, similar to those above, to show how the water level would rise in each one.

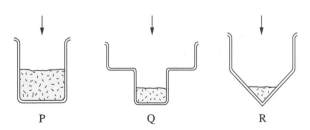

8.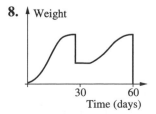

The line graph shows how the weight of an earthworm varies over the first 60 days of its life. Describe the main features of the graph and speculate about the possible causes of the main events.

Exercise 2

1. The charts show annual temperature and
rainfall for two cities.
Write one sentence about each chart to
describe the main features.

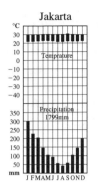

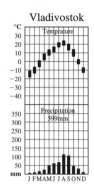

2.

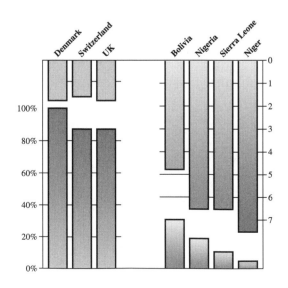

Here are population pyramids for
Turkey and Australia. The charts
show, for example, that about 4%
of the male population of Australia
is aged 0–4.

What are the main differences in
the two charts? Try to explain
why this might be so.

3. The upper chart shows the fertility rate,
which is the average number of children
borne per woman.
The lower chart shows the percentage of
females aged 12–17 in secondary education.

(a) What is the average number of children
borne per woman in Switzerland and in
Nigeria?

(b) Describe the main differences that the
graph shows for Denmark and Niger.
Why do you think these differences
exist?

4. The chart shows population growth rates in various parts of the world.
   (a) What was the growth rate in North America between 1960 and 1965?
   (b) Which region has seen an increase in growth rate?
   (c) Which areas currently have the highest and lowest growth rates? Try to think of reasons to explain the differences.

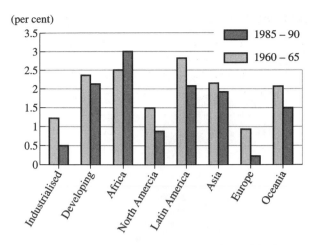

[SOURCE: United Nations Populations Division, World Population Prospects 1990, New York, 1991]

5. Describe briefly what each scatter graph shows.

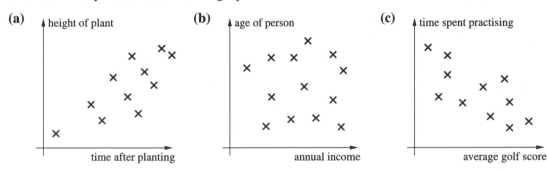

6. The sport of mud wrestling is best played when the ground is made soft by plenty of rainfall. The World Mudwrestling Association (W.M.A.) have to choose a venue for the 2005 championships. They have past rainfall data for the relevant month for two potential towns, Ortega and Pantena. Which venue would be more suitable? Explain your answer.

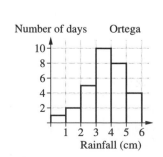

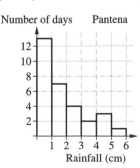

7. The pie chart on the left shows the proportion of votes cast for each of the main political parties in the 1987 general election. The pie chart on the right shows the proportion of seats won by each party.

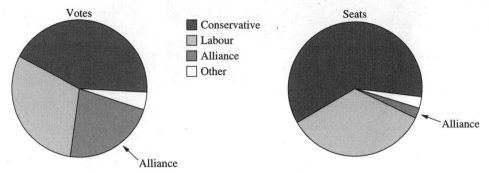

(a) There were 650 seats to be won in the election.
   (i) Estimate what percentage of the votes were cast for the Conservative party and estimate how many seats that party won.
   (ii) Repeat these two calculations for the votes cast and seats won by the Alliance party.

(b) Comment briefly on your answers.

Exercise 3

1. The graph shows a car journey from York to Harrogate and back.

   (a) When did the car arrive at Harrogate?

   (b) When did the car return to York?

   (c) At what speed did the car travel
      (i) between 0900 and 1000,
      (ii) between 1100 and 1200,
      (iii) between 1000 and 1030?

   (d) At what time was the car halfway between Harrogate and York on the return journey?

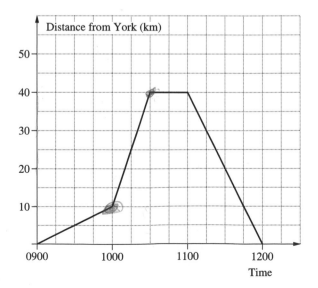

2. The travel graph below shows the progress of two cars, B and C, in a race from Leeds to Blackpool and back again.

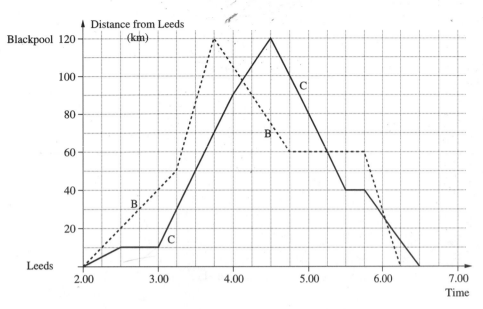

(a) At what speed, in km/h, did car B travel between
   (i) 2·00 and 3·15
   (ii) 5·45 and 6·15
   (iii) 4·45 and 5·45?
(b) Which car was leading in the race at
   (i) 3·30
   (ii) 4·15?
(c) What was the distance between the two cars at 4·45?
(d) What happened just after 6·00?
(e) Which car won the race?

3. At 0900 Kate leaves home and drives at a speed of 80 km/h. At 0930 she increases her speed to 100 km/h and continues to her destination which is 90 km from home. She stops for $\frac{3}{4}$ hour and then returns home at a speed of 90 km/h.
Draw a travel graph to show Kate's journey. Use the same scales as in Question **2**, showing 'Distance from home' on the vertical axis.
At what time did she return home?

4. A car leaves Nottingham at 3·00 p.m. and travels at 60 km/h for $\frac{1}{2}$ hour before stopping for $\frac{3}{4}$ hour. After that it continues towards York, which is 120 km from Nottingham, at 90 km/h.
Also at 3·00 p.m. a lorry leaves York travelling towards Nottingham. The lorry travels at 40 km/h for the first hour but then breaks down. After repairs lasting $\frac{3}{4}$ hour the lorry returns to York at a speed of 40 km/h.

Draw a travel graph to show the journeys of the car and the
lorry. Use the same scales as in Question **2**, showing 'Distance
from Nottingham' on the vertical axis.

Use your graph to answer the following:

(a) At about what time does the car overtake the lorry?

(b) At what time does the lorry arrive back in York?

(c) How far is the lorry from Nottingham at 3·45?

3.5 Statistical problems

What sort of problem?

In general we are concerned here with solving problems or
answering questions for which data is required. In particular we
can often use statistics to make predictions for the future. Here are
some examples:

- Is the R.S.P.C.A. the most popular charity in the country?

- How much T.V. do adults and children watch?

- Do first class letters arrive next day?

- Will people use trains if they are cheaper and run on time?

- Which subject do people find most difficult at school?

Many problems of a statistical nature are made more
clear when they are put in the form of a *conjecture*.
A conjecture is a statement which may or may not be true.
Here are some examples of conjectures:

- More money is donated to the R.S.P.C.A. than to any
  other charity.

- People aged 18 and over watch more T.V. than under
  18 year olds.

- 90% of first class letters arrive next day.

The data relevant to each might be obtained from:

- A questionnaire or survey of a sample of people

- Published tables or from computer databases

- The internet

Collecting data

When you design a data collection sheet you must think ahead and decide what exactly is the purpose of the survey and what information does each question provide. Think also about the *order* of the questions.

Here are several points to consider when designing a data collection sheet.

- Keep it as short and simple as possible.
    People are (quite rightly) not prepared to spend a long time filling in forms.

- Do not ask questions if they are not relevant.
    Do not ask for the person's name unless you have to. People are more likely to cooperate if their replies are anonymous.

- Try not to ask questions that require written replies.
    You may get a hundred different points of view which makes analysing the answers extremely difficult. It is much better to ask questions that can be answered with yes/no or by ticking an appropriate box. Do not *only* ask questions which can be answered yes/no.

- Try to avoid personal questions.
    If you ask someone their age, weight or income they will often be inclined to give you false information. A better approach would be to ask 'Which category do you fall into?'

| under 16 | 16–19 | 20–29 | 30–49 | 50 or over |

- Make sure you cover all possibilities.
    Do not leave a person thinking 'I don't belong to any of those categories'.

- Do not ask questions in such a way that the person feels forced to agree.

Example 1. Most people would find it difficult to say 'no' to a question such as 'Don't you agree that the cruel and inhumane way of transporting live animals should be abolished'.

Example 2. Do *not* ask: 'Do you agree that pupils in this school are given too much homework?'.

A better question is:

The amount of homework set to pupils in this school is:

Tick one box.

not enough	about right	too much	don't know

108

- Here are two data collection sheets: the first is well designed but the second contains several faults.

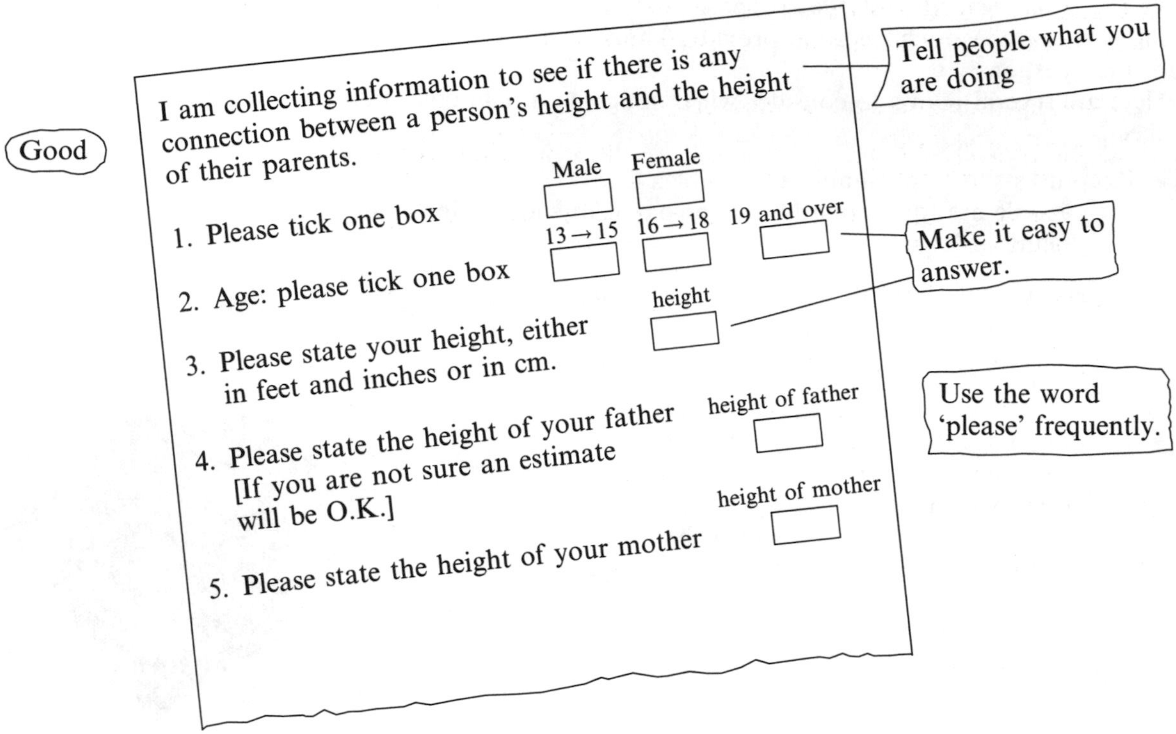

Good

I am collecting information to see if there is any connection between a person's height and the height of their parents.

Tell people what you are doing

1. Please tick one box

Male Female

2. Age: please tick one box

13 → 15   16 → 18   19 and over

Make it easy to answer.

height

3. Please state your height, either in feet and inches or in cm.

4. Please state the height of your father [If you are not sure an estimate will be O.K.]

height of father

Use the word 'please' frequently.

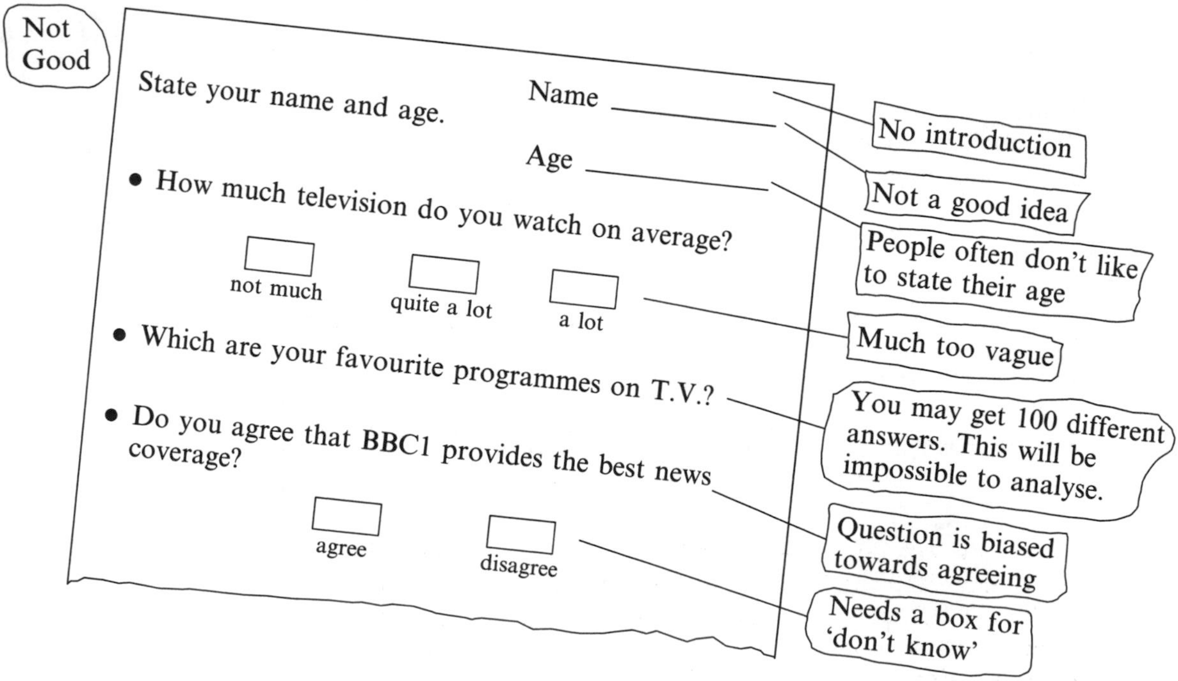

height of mother

5. Please state the height of your mother

Not Good

State your name and age.

Name _____

Age _____

No introduction

Not a good idea

People often don't like to state their age

- How much television do you watch on average?

not much   quite a lot   a lot

Much too vague

- Which are your favourite programmes on T.V.?

You may get 100 different answers. This will be impossible to analyse.

- Do you agree that BBC1 provides the best news coverage?

agree   disagree

Question is biased towards agreeing

Needs a box for 'don't know'

Exercise 1

In Questions **1** to **6** explain why the question is not suitable for a questionnaire. Write an improved question in each case.

1. How much do you earn per month?

| 0–£100 | £100–£200 | £200–£500 | £400–£700 | more than £700 |

2. Wouldn't you agree that the present government is doing an appalling job?

3. For how long do you watch the television each day?

| 2–3 hrs | 3–4 hrs | 5–6 hrs |

4. Do you think that the disintegration of theological suppositions is leading to ethical degeneration?

5. Which sort of holiday do you most enjoy?

6. Some of the money from the National Lottery goes to charities.
Tick one box:

The money going to charities is   ☐   ☐
                                    Too little   Too much

7. A group of pupils were asked to design a questionnaire to find out people's views about watching sport on television. Comment on the following two pupils' efforts. Design an improved questionnaire to find out people's opinions.

(a)
```
Name ............ Sex M/F

Age ...............

Do you like sport? ......... Y/N

Do you have satellite TV? ......
                            Y/N

Is there enough sport on TV?
                ......... Y/N
```

(b)
```
Do you like sport?
Not at all
Not much
A bit
Quite a lot
I love it

Do you have cable or satellite TV?
Yes/No

How often do you watch sport?
Every day
Up to three times a week
Less than twice a month

Should there be more sport on
television?
Yes/No
```

8. A new variety of soup, 'Cheese and Onion', is to be launched by a leading manufacturer. They wish to know if it will be popular and sell well. People are asked to try a free sample and comment on their impression.
Design a questionnaire to test people's opinions.

Bias

When a survey is conducted it is possible for the
results to be misleading because of bias.
Bias can be either *intentional* or *unintentional*.

For example a company selling food for dogs might
want to exagerate the popularity of its product.
It might conduct a survey but deliberately choose
people who already buy the product.

Similarly, a political party might choose to collect
a 'random' sample from visitors to the Chelsea Flower
Show on the assumption that its own supporters
would be more likely to visit the flower show.

Also the *wording* of a question can introduce bias
because it might lead the respondent to agree with
a certain statement.

Unintentional bias can occur in many ways:
In a recent large scale experiment, people were asked
to choose a 'representative' sample by selecting 20 stones
from a mixed collection of 1200 stones of varying sizes.
It was found that people tended to pick samples whose
mean weight was significantly higher than the mean weight
for the whole collection. This was true for 30 out of 36
samples. People used their own judgement to choose a
mixture of small, medium and large stones for their sample
but the 1200 stones in fact contained far more small stones.

In your own work you can easily introduce bias by choosing
a sample from your friends rather than across a whole
year group. If the question is relevant to both boys and girls,
you should ensure that your sample contains equal numbers
from both sexes.

Even in professionally conducted surveys people sometimes refuse
to answer questions like 'Which political party would you
vote for?' This can introduce bias because respondents
who hold 'unpopular' views might not be willing to express
them to a stranger and thus their views would not be
represented in the survey.

The best way to avoid bias in choosing a sample is to
select people using a random number table or, in simple
cases, by 'picking names from a hat.'

You own work, testing a conjecture

- A conjecture is a statement which may or may not be true.

  Examples: 'Spurs are the best team in the world.'

  'Tall people are less likely to wear glasses than short people.'

  'Most people in schools find French the hardest subject.'

  "People who are good at Maths are also good at Science.'

- A conjecture can often be tested by conducting a survey in which a large number of people respond to a questionnaire.
  When you design a questionnaire you should think ahead to how you will display your results. In general graphs or charts are easier for other people to understand than tables of numbers.

You might use:
Pie charts;
Bar charts;
Scatter graphs;
Frequency polygons.

 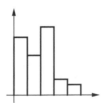  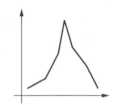

- *Do* use colour in your work and *do* write a short and clear summary of your results. Comment on whether your results support or do not support your conjecture.
  Don't produce page after page of repetitive, uninteresting results without any comments or observations.

- It is always a good idea to ask a few people to try out your questions in a *pilot survey*. Then if there are any problems with the questions these can be corrected. You might also get ideas for additional questions.

- You will almost certainly design a more interesting questionnaire if *you* choose the topic or the conjecture to be tested.

3.6 Mid-book review

Review exercise 1

1. Find the circumference and area of a circle of radius 6 cm.

2. Use the method of trial and improvement to find a solution to the following equation, giving your answer correct to one decimal place.

$$x(x + 5) = 70$$

3. Use differences to predict the next number in each of the sequences below.

(a) 8	(b) 4	(c) 1
18	12	7
30	24	25
44	40	61
⑦	60	121
	⑦	⑦

4. Work out, without using a calculator

(a) $\frac{2}{3} \times \frac{1}{5}$ (b) $\frac{2}{3} - \frac{1}{5}$ (c) $\frac{2}{3} \div \frac{1}{5}$

(d) $3 \cdot 2 \times 0 \cdot 5$ (e) $1 \cdot 24 \times 3 \cdot 1$ (f) $9 \cdot 64 \div 0 \cdot 4$

5. Find the mean and the median of the following data:
5, 9, 4, 20, 11, 4, 10, 15

6. Water flows into an empty cylinder of diameter and height 60 cm at the rate of 300 cm³/s. How long, to the nearest second, will it take to fill the cylinder?

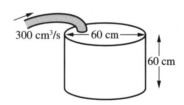

7. (a) Copy the table below and complete rows 4, 5 and 6.

Row			Sum of digits
1	$4^2 =$	16	7
2	$34^2 =$	1156	13
3	$334^2 =$	111556	19
4	$3334^2 =$	....	....
5	$33334^2 =$	....	....
6	$333334^2 =$	....	....

(b) Calculate the sum of the digits in the answer to 33333333334^2

8. A human brain has about 10 billion brain cells. [1 billion = 1000 million] Doctors estimate that a person loses 55 brain cells every time they sneeze. Narishta suffers from hay fever and on average she sneezes 100 times every day of the year.
   (a) How many brain cells, correct to one significant figure, will Narishta lose in a year?
   (b) How many of the original 10 billion brain cells are left after a year of sneezing?

9. As a publicity stunt the organisers of the National Lottery decide to make a huge pile of £10 notes to the value of £20 million. A £10 note measures 14 cm by 7·5 cm and a wad of ten £10 notes is 1 mm thick. The pile of notes is made into a cuboid whose base is a rectangle measuring 140 cm by 75 cm. How high will the pile be?

Review exercise 2

1. (a) Write the following numbers in standard form:
      (i) 56 000   (ii) 0·000 002   (iii) 250 million.
   (b) Give the answers to the following in standard form.
      (i) $(4·3 \times 10^4) \times (6·5 \times 10^{12})$
      (ii) $(3·6 \times 10^7) \div (2 \times 10^{11})$
      (iii) $(4·8 \times 10^{-3}) \times (2 \times 10^{-8})$

2. The diagram consists of a rectangle inside a semi-circle.
   Find the shaded area, correct to 3 significant figures.

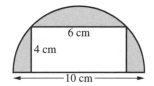

3. Do not use a calculator for this question.
   (a) The square root of 73 lies between which two whole numbers?
   (b) The cube root of 20 lies between which two whole numbers?
   (c) Estimate the value of $\dfrac{\sqrt{897·2} \times 10·93}{\sqrt{16·75}}$.

4. Solve the equations
   (a) $\dfrac{x}{3} = \dfrac{3}{4}$ (b) $3(x + 4) = 2(1 - x)$

5. Find the length x, correct to 3 significant figures.

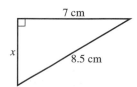

6. For a medical survey 12 children had the span of their right hand and the length of their right foot measured. These are the results:

handspan (cm)	16·5	15	14	12·5	12	11	24	24	21	21	20
length of foot (cm)	20	23	18	19	17	14	28	24·5	27·5	23	25

(a) Draw a scatter graph, plotting handspan on the horizontal axis and length of foot on the vertical axis. Take values from 10 to 28 on both axes.

(b) Describe the results in one sentence.

(c) One girl had her leg in plaster so her foot length could not be measured. Her handspan was 17·5 cm. Draw a line of best fit on your scatter graph and use it to estimate the likely length of her foot.

7. The rectangle shown has an area of 155 cm².

(a) Write an equation involving x.

(b) Use trial and improvement to find the value of x, correct to one decimal place.

8. A barrel of water is initially $\frac{7}{10}$ full. After 243 litres of water are removed, the barrel is $\frac{1}{4}$ full. How many litres does the barrel hold when it is full?

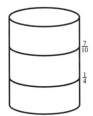

9. (a) A solid metal cylinder of radius 5 cm and height 8 cm is melted down and recast as a solid cube. Find the length of each side of the cube.

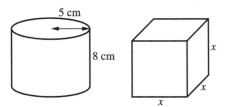

(b) The cube is then melted down and made into a cylinder of height 1 cm. Calculate the radius of the cylinder.

10. Evaluate the following, with $a = 3$, $b = -2$, $c = 5$.

(a) $2a + b$ (b) $b^2 + c^2$ (c) $3c - b$

(d) $ab + c$ (e) $a^2 - b$ (f) abc

11. A class of 30 pupils obtained the following marks in English and Mathematics tests. Draw frequency polygons for both subjects on the same set of axes and comment on the differences between the two sets of results.

Mark	0–10	11–20	21–30	31–40	41–50	51–60	61–70	71–80	81–90	91–100
English	0	0	0	3	4	12	8	2	1	0
Maths	0	1	2	5	1	6	6	5	2	2

Review exercise 3

1. Professor Gibson has calculated that in 100 000 years from now the Earth will collide with a seriously large flat object and will be transformed into a flat circular disc of thickness 1 km.
If the volume of the earth is $1·08 \times 10^{12}\,\text{km}^3$, calculate the radius of the 'new' Earth.

2. Solve the equations

(a) $4(y - 1) + 3(y + 2) = 5(y - 4)$

(b) $\dfrac{4}{x + 1} = 3$

3. This is a scatter graph of the marks of 15 pupils in a history test and the length of time they spent revising for the test.

What can you deduce from the graph?

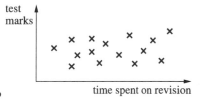

4. The two rectangles have the same area.
(a) Write down an equation involving x.
(b) Solve your equation and hence give the dimensions of each rectangle.

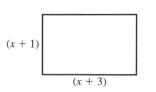

5. Find the length x in each diagram, correct to 3 s.f.

(a)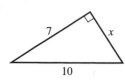

(b)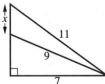

6. The rectangle shown has length
$(2x + 1)$ cm and perimeter $(6x + 8)$ cm.
(a) Find an expression, in terms of x,
for the width of the rectangle.
(b) Given that the area of the
rectangle is 103 cm^2, use trial
and improvement to find the
value of x correct to 1 decimal
place.

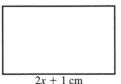

7. Thirteen people managed to squeeze into
a 'Smart' car.
(a) Without a calculator, work out how
many cars would be needed for 1000
similarly minded people.
(b) You can see just the legs of one
person. What is she saying?

8. (a) The point of the minute hand of a clock travels 21 cm in 20
minutes. How long is the minute hand?
(b) The point of the hour hand travels 3 cm in one hour. How
long is the hour hand?

9.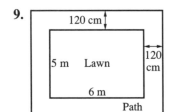

A concrete path, measuring 120 cm wide, is
made to surround a lawn measuring 6 m
by 5 m. If 4.824 m^3 of concrete is used, how
thick is the path?

10. A kitchen roll consists of 144 sheets
    of absorbent paper, each measuring
    24 cm by 24 cm and 0·02 cm thick.
    These sheets are wound onto a cardboard
    tube 4 cm in diameter. Find the diameter
    of the finished roll of kitchen towels.
    Give the answer correct to 3 s.f.

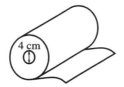

11. A boat sails from point A on a bearing 040° to reach point B,
    which is 22 km from A. The boat then changes course and sails
    35 km on a bearing 130° to reach point C. Draw a diagram to
    show the journey and hence *calculate* the distance between
    point A and point C.

12. (a) The cross below has four lines of
        symmetry. Find its area in terms of
        l and w.

    (b) Find the area of the shaded region
        in terms of p, q, r and s.

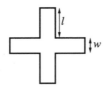

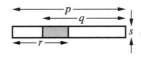

13. Cyril eats x slices of toast in y days.
    How many does he eat in a week?

14. The Isle of Wight has a land area of 380 km². In a violent storm
    6 cm of rain fell over the entire island.
    Calculate the volume (in m³) of water which fell in the storm.

Part 4

4.1 Transformations

Translation

In a translation an object 'shifts' from one position to another. There is no turning or reflection and the object stays the same size. A translation is described completely by its *vector*.

In the diagram:

(a) $\triangle A$ is mapped onto $\triangle B$ by the translation with vector $\begin{pmatrix} 3 \\ 2 \end{pmatrix}$.

(b) $\triangle A$ is mapped onto $\triangle C$ by the translation with vector $\begin{pmatrix} 5 \\ -2 \end{pmatrix}$.

(c) $\triangle C$ is mapped onto $\triangle B$ by the translation with vector $\begin{pmatrix} -2 \\ 4 \end{pmatrix}$.

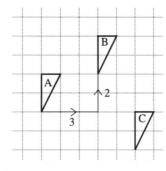

When performing a translation, concentrate your attention on *one* vertex of the shape.

The top number of a vector gives the number of units across (positive to the right). The bottom number gives the number of units up or down (positive upwards).

So $\begin{pmatrix} 5 \\ 2 \end{pmatrix}$ is $\begin{matrix} 5 \text{ right} \rightarrow \\ 2 \text{ up} \uparrow \end{matrix}$, $\begin{pmatrix} 3 \\ -1 \end{pmatrix}$ is $\begin{matrix} 3 \text{ right} \rightarrow \\ 1 \text{ down} \downarrow \end{matrix}$

Exercise 1

1. Look at the diagram shown. Write down the vector for each of the following translations:

(a) $\triangle H \rightarrow \triangle P$ (b) $\triangle E \rightarrow \triangle A$
(c) $\triangle R \rightarrow \triangle S$ (d) $\triangle W \rightarrow \triangle C$
(e) $\triangle Y \rightarrow \triangle L$ (f) $\triangle U \rightarrow \triangle F$
(g) $\triangle T \rightarrow \triangle A$ (h) $\triangle W \rightarrow \triangle G$
(i) $\triangle O \rightarrow \triangle Y$ (j) $\triangle U \rightarrow \triangle I$

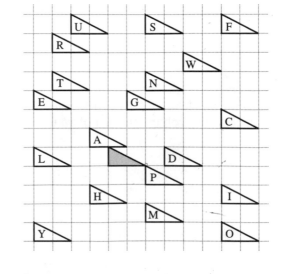

2. Using the diagram in Question **1** the vector $\begin{pmatrix} 2 \\ 7 \end{pmatrix}$ translates the shaded triangle onto △S. Similarly the vectors $\begin{pmatrix} -3 \\ 4 \end{pmatrix}$, $\begin{pmatrix} 6 \\ -4 \end{pmatrix}$, $\begin{pmatrix} 2 \\ -1 \end{pmatrix}$ translate the shaded triangle onto △T, △O and △P. So the four vectors $\begin{pmatrix} 2 \\ 7 \end{pmatrix}$, $\begin{pmatrix} -3 \\ 4 \end{pmatrix}$, $\begin{pmatrix} 6 \\ 4 \end{pmatrix}$, $\begin{pmatrix} 2 \\ -1 \end{pmatrix}$ translate the shaded triangle onto the letters of the word 'STOP'.

(a) What word is given when the shaded triangle is translated using the vectors $\begin{pmatrix} -1 \\ 1 \end{pmatrix}$, $\begin{pmatrix} 2 \\ -1 \end{pmatrix}$, $\begin{pmatrix} 2 \\ -1 \end{pmatrix}$, $\begin{pmatrix} -4 \\ 0 \end{pmatrix}$, $\begin{pmatrix} -4 \\ 3 \end{pmatrix}$?

(b) Write down the vectors which translate the shaded triangle onto the letters of the word 'LAMP'.

3. Write the sentence given when the shaded triangle is translated using the vectors below.

(a)

$\begin{pmatrix} 4 \\ 5 \end{pmatrix} \begin{pmatrix} -1 \\ -2 \end{pmatrix} \begin{pmatrix} -1 \\ 1 \end{pmatrix} \begin{pmatrix} -3 \\ 4 \end{pmatrix} * \begin{pmatrix} 3 \\ 0 \end{pmatrix} \begin{pmatrix} 6 \\ -4 \end{pmatrix} * \begin{pmatrix} -4 \\ -4 \end{pmatrix} \begin{pmatrix} 6 \\ -4 \end{pmatrix} \begin{pmatrix} -2 \\ 7 \end{pmatrix} * \begin{pmatrix} 6 \\ 2 \end{pmatrix} \begin{pmatrix} -1 \\ 1 \end{pmatrix} \begin{pmatrix} -4 \\ 0 \end{pmatrix} \begin{pmatrix} -4 \\ 0 \end{pmatrix} * \begin{pmatrix} -1 \\ 1 \end{pmatrix} *$

$\begin{pmatrix} 2 \\ -3 \end{pmatrix} \begin{pmatrix} -1 \\ 1 \end{pmatrix} \begin{pmatrix} 2 \\ 4 \end{pmatrix} * \begin{pmatrix} 4 \\ 5 \end{pmatrix} \begin{pmatrix} 6 \\ -2 \end{pmatrix} \begin{pmatrix} -3 \\ 4 \end{pmatrix} \begin{pmatrix} -1 \\ -2 \end{pmatrix} * \begin{pmatrix} -1 \\ 1 \end{pmatrix} * \begin{pmatrix} 4 \\ 5 \end{pmatrix} \begin{pmatrix} 6 \\ -4 \end{pmatrix} \begin{pmatrix} 6 \\ -4 \end{pmatrix} \begin{pmatrix} 3 \\ 0 \end{pmatrix} \begin{pmatrix} -4 \\ 3 \end{pmatrix} \begin{pmatrix} 2 \\ 4 \end{pmatrix} *$

$\begin{pmatrix} -1 \\ -2 \end{pmatrix} \begin{pmatrix} -4 \\ 3 \end{pmatrix} \begin{pmatrix} -1 \\ 1 \end{pmatrix} \begin{pmatrix} 3 \\ 0 \end{pmatrix} * \begin{pmatrix} -4 \\ 3 \end{pmatrix} \begin{pmatrix} 3 \\ 0 \end{pmatrix} \begin{pmatrix} 4 \\ 5 \end{pmatrix} \begin{pmatrix} -1 \\ 1 \end{pmatrix} \begin{pmatrix} -3 \\ 6 \end{pmatrix} \begin{pmatrix} 3 \\ 0 \end{pmatrix} . *$

(b)

$\begin{pmatrix} -1 \\ -2 \end{pmatrix} \begin{pmatrix} 6 \\ -4 \end{pmatrix} \begin{pmatrix} 4 \\ 5 \end{pmatrix} * \begin{pmatrix} 3 \\ 0 \end{pmatrix} \begin{pmatrix} 6 \\ -4 \end{pmatrix} * \begin{pmatrix} -4 \\ -4 \end{pmatrix} \begin{pmatrix} 6 \\ -4 \end{pmatrix} \begin{pmatrix} -2 \\ 7 \end{pmatrix} * \begin{pmatrix} 2 \\ 7 \end{pmatrix} \begin{pmatrix} 2 \\ -1 \end{pmatrix} \begin{pmatrix} -4 \\ 3 \end{pmatrix} \begin{pmatrix} -4 \\ 0 \end{pmatrix} \begin{pmatrix} -4 \\ 0 \end{pmatrix} *$

$\begin{pmatrix} -1 \\ -2 \end{pmatrix} \begin{pmatrix} -2 \\ 7 \end{pmatrix} \begin{pmatrix} 2 \\ 4 \end{pmatrix} \begin{pmatrix} 1 \\ 3 \end{pmatrix} \begin{pmatrix} -3 \\ 6 \end{pmatrix} \begin{pmatrix} -4 \\ -4 \end{pmatrix} * \begin{pmatrix} -1 \\ -2 \end{pmatrix} \begin{pmatrix} 6 \\ -4 \end{pmatrix} \begin{pmatrix} -3 \\ 6 \end{pmatrix} \begin{pmatrix} 2 \\ 7 \end{pmatrix} \begin{pmatrix} -4 \\ 3 \end{pmatrix} \begin{pmatrix} 2 \\ 7 \end{pmatrix} * \begin{pmatrix} 6 \\ -2 \end{pmatrix} \begin{pmatrix} 2 \\ 4 \end{pmatrix} *$

$\begin{pmatrix} 6 \\ 7 \end{pmatrix} \begin{pmatrix} 6 \\ -4 \end{pmatrix} \begin{pmatrix} -2 \\ 7 \end{pmatrix} \begin{pmatrix} -3 \\ 6 \end{pmatrix} * \begin{pmatrix} -4 \\ 0 \end{pmatrix} \begin{pmatrix} -4 \\ 3 \end{pmatrix} \begin{pmatrix} -3 \\ 4 \end{pmatrix} \begin{pmatrix} -3 \\ 4 \end{pmatrix} \begin{pmatrix} -4 \\ 3 \end{pmatrix} \begin{pmatrix} -3 \\ 6 \end{pmatrix} \begin{pmatrix} 2 \\ 7 \end{pmatrix} *$

$\begin{pmatrix} 2 \\ -3 \end{pmatrix} \begin{pmatrix} -3 \\ 4 \end{pmatrix} \begin{pmatrix} 1 \\ 3 \end{pmatrix} \begin{pmatrix} 1 \\ 3 \end{pmatrix} . *$

4. Under a certain translation, the image of the point (5, −2) is (3, −6). Find the image of the point (−2, 10) under the same translation.

5. Under a certain translation, the image of the point (−2, 0) is (6, −5). What point has (3, 3) as its image under the same translation?

120

Combined transformations

So far in Book 8 and Book 9 you have studied four basic transformations. A full description of each transformation requires the information below.

- To describe a *reflection* you need the equation of the mirror line.
- To describe a *rotation* you need the angle, the direction and the centre of the rotation.
- To describe an *enlargement* you need the scale factor and the centre of the enlargement.
- To describe a *translation* you need the vector.

In the diagram the transformations are as follows:

$\triangle 1 \rightarrow \triangle 2$: Rotation 90° clockwise, centre (0, 0)

$\triangle 1 \rightarrow \triangle 3$: Reflection in $y = x$

$\triangle 1 \rightarrow \triangle 6$: Translation $\begin{pmatrix} 3 \\ -1 \end{pmatrix}$

$\triangle 4 \rightarrow \triangle 5$: Enlargement, scale factor 3, centre (3, −3)

$\triangle 1 \rightarrow \triangle 4$: Reflection in $y = 1\frac{1}{2}$

$\triangle 2 \rightarrow \triangle 6$: Rotation 90° anti-clockwise, centre (2, 1)

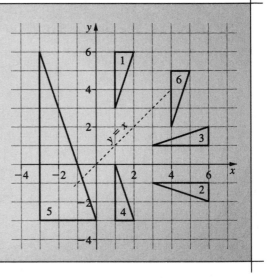

Exercise 2

[Tracing paper will be helpful in this exercise.]

1. Copy the diagram so that you can draw construction lines.

   Describe fully each of the following transformations:
   (a) $\triangle 1 \rightarrow \triangle 2$
   (b) $\triangle 2 \rightarrow \triangle 3$
   (c) $\triangle 3 \rightarrow \triangle 4$
   (d) $\triangle 1 \rightarrow \triangle 5$
   (e) $\triangle 4 \rightarrow \triangle 6$

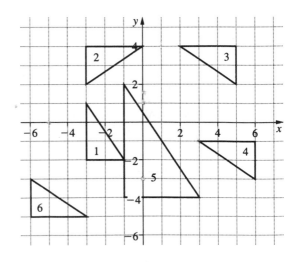

2. (a) Draw axes with x and y from -6 to $+6$.
   (b) Plot and label $\triangle 1$ with vertices at $(-6, -2)$, $(-6, -5)$, $(-5, -2)$.
   (c) Draw $\triangle 2$, $\triangle 3$, ... $\triangle 7$ as follows:
      (i) $\triangle 1 \rightarrow \triangle 2$ Reflection in $y = x$
      (ii) $\triangle 2 \rightarrow \triangle 3$ Rotation $180°$, centre $(0, -5\frac{1}{2})$
      (iii) $\triangle 3 \rightarrow \triangle 4$ Reflection in $y = -x$
      (iv) $\triangle 3 \rightarrow \triangle 5$ Rotation $90°$ anticlockwise, centre $(0, -3)$
          [Check that the right angle is at $(2, -1)$]
      (v) $\triangle 5 \rightarrow \triangle 6$ Enlargement, scale factor 3, centre $(4, 0)$
      (vi) $\triangle 5 \rightarrow \triangle 7$ Translation $\begin{pmatrix} -6 \\ 4 \end{pmatrix}$
   (d) Describe fully each of the following single transformations:
      (i) $\triangle 7 \rightarrow \triangle 6$
      (ii) $\triangle 1 \rightarrow \triangle 4$
      (iii) $\triangle 2 \rightarrow \triangle 5$

3. (a) Draw axes with x and y from -7 to $+7$.
   (b) Plot and label $\triangle 1$ with vertices at $(0, 0)$, $(0, 2)$, $(3, 2)$.
   (c) Draw $\triangle 2$, $\triangle 3$,...$\triangle 7$ as follows:
      (i) $\triangle 1 \rightarrow \triangle 2$ Reflection in $y = 0$ (the x axis)
      (ii) $\triangle 2 \rightarrow \triangle 3$ Reflection in $y = x$
      (iii) $\triangle 1 \rightarrow \triangle 4$ Translation $\begin{pmatrix} -6 \\ 2 \end{pmatrix}$
      (iv) $\triangle 4 \rightarrow \triangle 5$ Translation $\begin{pmatrix} 4 \\ 3 \end{pmatrix}$
      (v) $\triangle 4 \rightarrow \triangle 6$ Reflection in $y = 0$
      (vi) $\triangle 6 \rightarrow \triangle 7$ Reflection in $y = x$
   (d) Describe each of the following single transformations:
      (i) $\triangle 1 \rightarrow \triangle 3$
      (ii) $\triangle 1 \rightarrow \triangle 5$
      (iii) $\triangle 1 \rightarrow \triangle 7$

4.

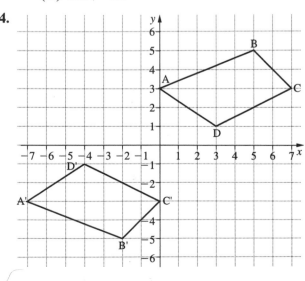

ABCD is mapped onto A′B′C′D′ by a reflection followed by a translation parallel to the x axis.
(a) Describe these two transformations as fully as possible.
(b) Would the image be the same if the translation was completed before the reflection?

5. How could ABCD be transformed
onto A′B′C′D′ by
(a) a single reflection,
(b) a reflection after a rotation
of 90° anticlockwise about (0, 0)?
(c) Would the image be the same
if the order of the rotation
and reflection were reversed?

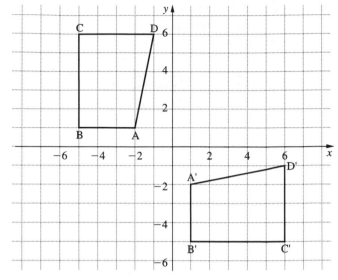

6. Draw axes for both x and y between -8 and $+8$.
Plot the points (1, 1), (3, 1), (3, 2), (2, 2), (2, 4) and (1, 4) and
join up to make an 'L' shape.
This is mapped onto the points $(-2, -2)$, $(-2, -6)$, $(-4, -6)$,
$(-4, -4)$, $(-8, -4)$, $(-8, -2)$ by *two* transformations; an
enlargement with centre (0, 0) followed by a reflection. Describe
these transformations as fully as possible.

7. Draw axes for both x and y between -5 and $+5$.
Plot and label the points A (1, 1), B (3, 1), C (5, 3) and D (1, 2).
Join these up to make a quadrilateral.
The images of these points after a translation parallel to the
y-axis followed by a reflection are A′ (0, 3), B′ $(-2, 3)$, C′ $(-4, 5)$
and D′ (0, 4). Plot A′B′C′D′ on the same set of axes. Describe
fully the translation and reflection required.

8.

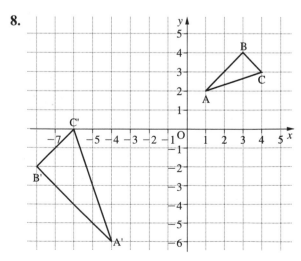

Three transformations are required to map
ABC onto A′B′C′, an enlargement centre
(0, 0) followed by a translation parallel to
the x axis and lastly a rotation about (0, 0).
Describe these transformations as fully as
possible.

4.2 3D Shapes

Exercise 1

1. 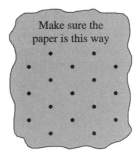 Here is a cube made from eight 1 cm cubes.
Draw a cuboid with a volume of 12 cm^3.

Make sure the paper is this way

2. (a) Make this shape using cubes.
   (b) Draw two other isometric views of the shape.

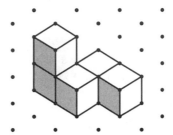

3. The S-shape falls over onto the shaded face.
Draw the shape after it has fallen over.

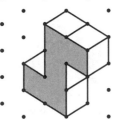

4. You need 16 cubes. Make the two shapes shown and then arrange them into a $4 \times 4 \times 1$ cuboid by adding a third shape, which you have to find. Draw the third shape on isometric paper. There are *two* possible shapes.

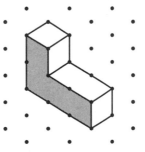 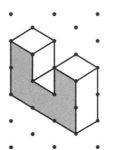

5. (a) Make the S-shape from Question 3 and the two shapes from Question 4.
   (b) Join the three shapes together and add a fourth shape to make a $4 \times 4 \times 1$ cuboid. Describe the fourth shape.

6. Here are two possible nets to make a cube.
   For each net decide which face is opposite the shaded face in the cube.

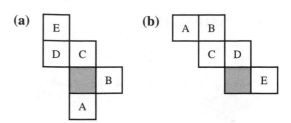

7. The net for a tetrahedron consists of four equilateral triangles.
   On isometric paper draw two possible nets for a tetrahedron.

8. Draw an accurate net for a square-based pyramid where the vertex is directly above the centre of the base.

9. The diagrams below show four side-views of the model.
   Which side-view does each diagram show?

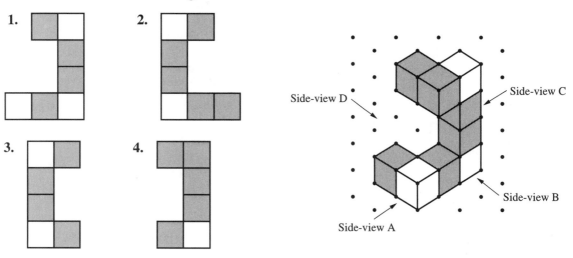

10. The diagram shows a model made with 9 cubes, 5 grey and 4 white.

    Draw 5 diagrams to show the side-views A, B, C and D and also the plan view.

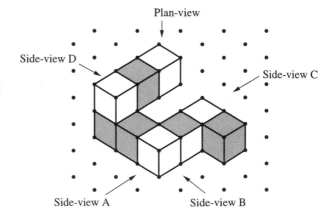

Planes of symmetry

- A plane of symmetry divides a 3-D shape into two congruent shapes. One shape must be a mirror image of the other shape.

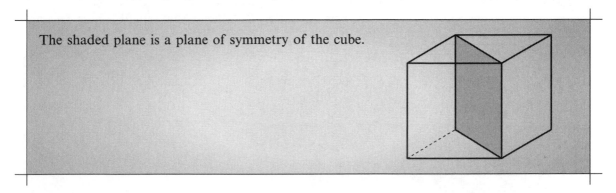

The shaded plane is a plane of symmetry of the cube.

Exercise 2

1. Here is a cuboid and a triangular prism (whose cross-section is an equilateral triangle).

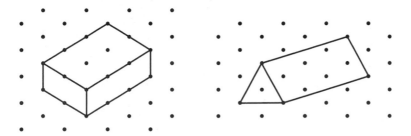

   How many planes of symmetry does each shape have?

2. Here are two shapes made from four cubes. There are eight different shapes which can be made using four cubes.

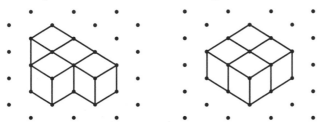

   Make the eight shapes, using cubes, and draw them on isometric paper. Identify any planes of symmetry.

3. Visualise and describe all the planes of symmetry of:
   (a) a square-based pyramid
   (b) a cylinder
   (c) a regular tetrahedron.

126

4.3 Finding a rule

For the sequence 3, 8, 13, 18, ... the rule is 'add 5'. We draw a mapping diagram with a column for 5 times the term number (i.e. $5n$)

n	$5n$	term
1	5	3
2	10	8
3	15	13
4	20	18

We see that each term is 2 less than $5n$.

So, the 10th term is $(5 \times 10) - 2 = 48$
the 20th term is $(5 \times 20) - 2 = 98$
the nth term is $5 \times n - 2 = 5n - 2$

Exercise 1

1. Look at the sequence 5, 8, 11, 14, ...

   The difference between terms is 3.
   Copy the table, which has a column for $3n$.
   Copy and complete: 'The nth term of the
   sequence is $3n + \boxed{}$.'

n	$3n$	term
1	3	5
2	6	8
3	9	11
4	12	14

2. Look at the sequence and the table underneath. Find the nth term in each case.

   (a) Sequence 5, 9, 13, 17, ...

n	$4n$	term
1	4	5
2	8	9
3	12	13
4	16	17

   nth term = $\boxed{}$

   (b) Sequence 2, 8, 14, 20, ...

n	$6n$	term
1	6	2
2	12	8
3	18	14
4	24	20

   nth term = $\boxed{}$

3. In the sequence 6, 11, 16, 21, ...
   the difference between terms is 5.
   Copy and complete the table and
   write an expression for the
   nth term of the sequence.

n	$\boxed{}$	term
1	$\boxed{}$	6
2	$\boxed{}$	11
3	$\boxed{}$	16
4	$\boxed{}$	21

4. Look at the sequence 6, 10, 14, 18, ...
   Write down the difference between terms.
   Make a table like the one in Question **3** and use it to find an
   expression for the nth term.

5. Write down each sequence in a table and then find the nth term.
   (a) 5, 7, 9, 11, ...
   (b) 3, 7, 11, 15, ...
   (c) 2, 8, 14, 20, ...

6. Make a table for each sequence and write the nth term.
   (a) 2, 10, 18, 26, ...
   (b) 7, 10, 13, 16, ...
   (c) 21, 30, 39, 48, ...

7. Here is a sequence of triangles made from a number of
   matches m.

n	m
1	3
2	5
3	7
4	

$n = 1$ $n = 2$ $n = 3$
$m = 3$ $m = 5$ $m = 7$

   Draw the next diagram in the sequence and write the values for
   n and m in a table. How many matches are in the nth term?

8. Crosses are drawn on rectangular 'dotty' paper. The diagram
   number of the cross is recorded together with the total number
   of dots d on each cross.

 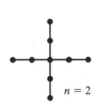 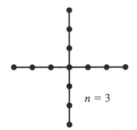

n	d
1	5
2	9
3	13

$n = 1$ $n = 2$ $n = 3$

   Find a formula connecting n and d.
   Write it as '$d = ...$'.

9. Look at the tables below. In each case, find a formula
   connecting the two letters.

(a)
n	h
2	10
3	13
4	16
5	19

write '$h = $

(b)
n	p
3	12
4	17
5	22
6	27

write '$p = $

(c)
n	s
2	4
3	$4\frac{1}{2}$
4	5
5	$5\frac{1}{2}$

write '$s = ...$'

10. In each diagram below, a number of white squares w surrounds a rectangle of black squares. The length of each rectangle is one unit more than the height h.

$n = 1$
$w = 10$

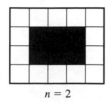
$n = 2$

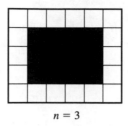
$n = 3$

n	w
1	10

Make a table of values of n and w use it to find a formula connecting n and w. Write it as '$w = \ldots$'

11. In a sequence of diagrams similar to the one in Question **5**, white squares surround a rectangle but this time the length of the black rectangle is twice the height. The diagram with $n = 2$ is shown.

Draw the sequence of diagrams and make a table of values of n and w.

Write the formula connecting n and w in the form '$w = \ldots$'

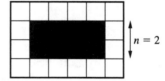
$n = 2$

12. Open 'boxes' are drawn on rectangular dotty paper.

$h = 1$

$h = 2$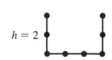

$h = 3$

Count the number of dots d in each diagram and find a formula for d in terms of h (the height of the box).

13. Look at the tables below and in each case find a formula for z in terms of n. Write the formula as '$z = \ldots$'

Notice that in part (a) the values of n are not consecutive.

(a)

n	z
2	7
3	13
5	25
6	31

(b)

n	z
0	15
1	12
2	9
3	6

14. In these diagrams 4 triangles are joined either at a vertex or along a whole side. We are counting the number of common edges c [shown bold] and the perimeter of the shape p.

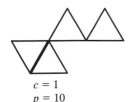 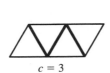 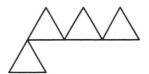 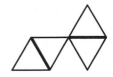

$c = 1$
$p = 10$

$c = 3$

Make a table of values of p and c and find a formula for p in terms of c [i.e. '$p = \ldots$']

15. In each diagram below a 'V' is formed by shading squares inside a rectangle of height h and width w.

 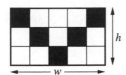 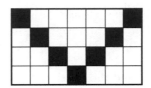

(a) Record the number of shaded squares s and the height h of each rectangle. Find a formula for s in terms of h [i.e. '$s = \ldots$']
(b) Find the width w for each value of h and hence find the number of *unshaded* squares in a rectangle with $h = 10$.

16. A chain of pentagons can be made from matches, as shown.
(a) How many matches are needed to make a chain of 5 pentagons?
(b) How many matches are needed to make a chain of n pentagons?

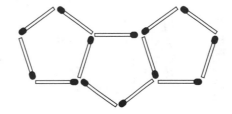

17. In each diagram there are w white squares and s shaded squares. How many white squares are there in the diagram which has n shaded squares?

18. For each sequence find (i) the 10th term
(ii) the nth term.

(a) 5, 10, 15, 20,
(b) 2, 4, 6, 8,
(c) $\frac{1}{2}, \frac{2}{3}, \frac{3}{4}, \frac{4}{5}$,
(d) $\frac{1}{4}, \frac{2}{5}, \frac{3}{6}$,
(e) 1, 4, 9, 16,
(f) 1, 10, 100, 1000,
(g) 4×3, 5×3^2, 6×3^3, 7×3^4,
(h) 101, 201, 301, 401

Quadratic sequences

- In the sequence below we have written the first and second differences.

Sequence ⟶ 9   15   25   39   57
First difference   6   10   14   18
Second difference   4   4   4

- If the second difference is constant it tells us about terms involving n^2.

    +2   tells us it is n^2
    +4   tells us it is $2n^2$
    +6   tells us it is $3n^2$

We see that the nth term of the sequence is $2n^2 + 7$.

- Make a table

n	$2n^2$	Sequence
1	2	9
2	8	15
3	18	25
4	32	39

Exercise 2

Use differences to help you find the nth term of these sequences.

1. 3, 9, 19, 33, 51, ...

2. 4, 7, 12, 19, 28, ...

3. 1, 7, 17, 31, 49, ...

4. 7, 16, 31, 52, 79, ...

5. 4, 16, 36, 64, 100, ...

6. 7, 13, 23, 37, 55

In the sequence below we have written the first and second differences

Sequence   11   21   33   47   63
First difference   10   12   14   16
Second difference   2   2   2

For *any* quadratic sequence, nth term $= an^2 + bn + c$

The second difference above is 2, so we know that $a = 1$

So the nth term is now $n^2 + bn + c$

when $n = 1$, $1 + b + c = 11$

when $n = 2$, $4 + 2b + c = 21$

Solving the simultaneous equations, we obtain $b = 7$, $c = 3$
The nth term of the sequence is $n^2 + 7n + 3$

Exercise 3

Use the method above to find the nth term of each sequence.

1. 2, 7, 14, 23, 34 ...   **2.** 5, 11, 19, 29, 41 ...   **3.** 2, 3, 6, 11, 18 ...

4. 4, 11, 22, 37 ...   **5.** 7, 16, 31, 52 ...   **6.** 2, 10, 20, 32, 46 ...

7. 1, 3, 6, 10, 15 ...   **8.** 4, 5, 8, 13, 20 ...

9. In these diagrams 'steps' are made from sticks.

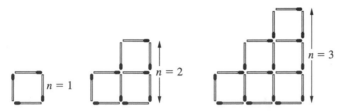

(a) Draw the next diagram in the sequence.
(b) Count the number of sticks s for each value of n, the height of the steps.
(c) Find the number of sticks in the nth term of the sequence.

4.4 Percentage change

Suppose the price of a car was increased from £8000 to £8100 and the price of a computer was increased from £200 to £300.
The *actual* increase of £100 is the same for both items but the increase is far more significant for the computer!
A good way of comparing price changes (up or down) is to work out the *percentage* change.
For an increase use the formula,

$$\text{percentage increase} = \left(\frac{\text{actual increase}}{\text{original value}}\right) \times 100$$

For the car above, percentage increase $= \left(\dfrac{100}{8000}\right) \times 100 = 1\frac{1}{4}\%$

For the computer, percentage increase $= \left(\dfrac{100}{200}\right) \times 100 = 50\%$

132

(a) Waitrose reduce the price of their own label cheesecake from £1·60 to £1·12. Find the percentage decrease.

The actual decrease = £0·48

Percentage decrease = $\left(\dfrac{0·48}{1·60}\right) \times 100$

$= 30\%$

(b) The owner of a sports shop buys tennis rackets for £32 and sells them for £69·99. Find the percentage profit.

The actual profit = £37·99.

Percentage profit = $\left(\dfrac{37·99}{32}\right) \times 100$

$= 118·7\%$ (1 d.p.)

Exercise 1

Give answers correct to 1 decimal place, where necessary.

1. Find the percentage increase when the price of a house goes up from £120 000 to £144 000.

2. Vijay's wages were increased from £115 per week to £130 per week. What was the percentage increase?

3. Calculate the percentage increase or decrease in each case.

	Original price	Final price
(a)	£160	£176
(b)	£200	£206
(c)	£410	£630
(d)	£240	£210
(e)	$880	$836
(f)	$22·50	$18·00

4. One year a leading dancer from the Royal Ballet earned £39 600. In the year after she returned from dancing in Paris and Rome, she was paid £65 000. Calculate her percentage increase in pay.

5. During a season when Liverpool were near the top of the league, their average crowd was 31 750. In the following season, they suffered a loss of form and the average attendance went down to 27 430. Calculate the percentage fall in the attendance.

6. A man bought a car in an auction for £6350 and then quickly sold it for £7295. Calculate the percentage profit.

7. A cube originally had sides of length 40 cm. All the sides were then increased by 10%.
 (a) *Without* doing any accurate calculations, estimate what you think the percentage increase in the volume of the cube was.
 (b) Now work out the actual percentage increase in the volume.

8. A sports centre recorded the number of girls and boys who were admitted in 1995 and 1996.

	1995	1996	Total
Girls	22 414	20 904	43 318
Boys	18 715	27 404	46 119
Total	41 129	48 308	89 437

 (a) What percentage of the admissions in 1995 were girls?
 (b) What percentage of the total admissions over the two years were boys?
 (c) What was the percentage increase in the number of boys admitted between 1995 and 1996?
 (d) What was the overall percentage increase in admissions between 1995 and 1996?

9. A box has a square base of side 20 cm and height 10 cm. Calculate the percentage increase in the volume of the box after the length and width of the base are both increased by 20% and the height is increased by 15%.

10. The monthly rent for a town house went up from £900 to £1050. Calculate the percentage increase.

11. One year a supermarket sold 'Hawaiian Crunch' in a 1·2 kg bag for £1·56. Next year they sold the same product in 1·5 kg bags for £2·04. Calculate the percentage increase or decrease in the price per gram of the cereal.

Reverse percentages

After an increase of 4%, the price of a railway season ticket is £998·40. What was the price before the increase?

A common mistake here is to work out 4% of £998·40. This is wrong because the increase is 4% of the *old price*, not 4% of the new price.

$$104\% \text{ of the old price} = £998·40$$

$$\therefore \quad 1\% \text{ of the old price} = \frac{998·40}{104}$$

$$\therefore \quad 100\% \text{ of the old price} = \frac{998·40}{104} \times 100$$

$$\text{The old price} = £960$$

Exercise 2

1. After an increase of 7%, the price of a squash racket is £58·85. Find the price of the racket before the increase.

2. After being heated, the volume of a metal ingot is increased by 3%. Find the volume of the unheated ingot, if the volume after being heated is 463·5 cm^3.

3. After a 75% pay rise, the salary of the chairman of British Gas was £441 000. What was his salary before the increase?

4. Between 1980 and 1990 the population of a town fell by 4%. Find the population of the town in 1980 if it was 252 960 in 1990.

5. As it descends, ballast is rapidly thrown overboard from a hot air balloon to reduce its weight by 3%. After the ballast is thrown the weight is 339·5 kg. Find the weight of the balloon before.

6. In a restaurant V.A.T., at 17·5%, is added to the cost of a meal. The total cost of a meal is £42·30 including V.A.T. Find the cost of the meal before the V.A.T. was added.

7. Tescos have a special offer on its own brand pizza. Find the missing number.

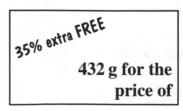

35% extra FREE

432 g for the price of

8. In May the price of a magazine went up by 10% and then in August the new price went up by a further 4%. After the second increase, the price of the magazine was £2·86. What was the price of the magazine before the first increase?

9. The diagram shows two rectangles. The length of rectangle B is 20% greater than the length of rectangle A. The width of rectangle B is 15% greater than the width of rectangle A. Use the figures given to find the length and width of rectangle A.

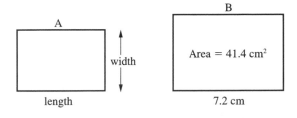

10. In the first week after waking up from its hibernation, a squirrel increases its weight by 2%. In the second week it increases its new weight by a further 10% so that it then weighs 5·61 kg. Find the weight of the squirrel when it first awoke from hibernation.

11. Businessmen use the '747 Rule' to work out the V.A.T. at $17\frac{1}{2}$% which has been added to give the total price of goods. The rule to find the V.A.T. is 'Multiply by 7 and divide by 47'.

(a) Use the rule to calculate the V.A.T. on a CD which cost £112·80, including V.A.T.

(b) Check that the rule works by calculating $17\frac{1}{2}$% of the price without the V.A.T.

Mixed percentage questions

Exercise 3

1. Compared to last year, the number of cars on the roads went up by 3·2%. This corresponded to an increase of 635 200 cars. How many cars were on the roads last year?

2. In 1995 the prison population was 2% higher than in the previous year. What was the prison population in 1994, if the increase was 1040 prisoners?

3. One day a sports centre conducted a survey to find information about the people who were using its facilities.

Ages	Males	Females	Totals
under 10	68	23	91
10 → 14	215	347	562
14 → 18	307	269	576
18 and over	164	98	262

(a) What percentage of the 10–14 group was female?
(b) What percentage of the people using the sports centre were 18 and over?

4. A cuboid made of special plastic has a square base of side 15 cm and height 25 cm. After immersion in water the sides of the base and the height all increase by 5·5%.
Find the volume of the enlarged cuboid.

5. A FAX machine costs £329 including V.A.T. at $17\frac{1}{2}$%. How much V.A.T. is paid?

6. When 240 litres are removed from a tank of fuel, the original quantity of fuel is reduced by 16%. What was the final quantity of fuel left in the tank?

7. When Alex drives to work at an average speed of 15 m/s, her journey takes 20 minutes.
(a) How far is her journey to work?
(b) How much longer does her journey take when roadworks cause her average speed to be reduced by 8%? Give your answer to the nearest second.

8. Mrs Hawke's salary in 1995 is £20 000 per year. Every year her salary is increased by 4%.
In 1996 her salary will be 20 000 × 1·04 = £20 800
In 1997 her salary will be 20 000 × 1·04 × 1·04 = £21 632
In 1998 her salary will be 20 000 × 1·04 × 1·04 × 1·04 = £22 497·28
And so on.
(a) What will her salary be in 2001?
(b) What will her salary be in 2006?

[Hint. Use the x^y button on a calculator]

9. Mrs Hawke's daughter was paid £10 000 per year in 1995 but her salary is increased by 15% every year?
   (a) What will be her salary in 1997?
   (b) What will be her salary in 2006?
   (c) (More difficult) In what year will Mrs Hawke be paid less than her daughter for the first time? [See Question **8**]

4.5 Simultaneous equations

Up to now the equations you have solved have had just one unknown. For example $3x - 1 = 1 - 4x,$

$$5(1 - x) = 2(3x + 1),$$

$$x(x + 1) = 100.$$

The equation $3x + y = 8$ involves two variables x and y. There are many pairs of values of x and y which satisfy the equation.
For example, if $x = 1$ and $y = 5$, $(3 \times 1) + 5 = 8$
   or, if $x = 4$ and $y = -4$, $(3 \times 4) + (-4) = 8.$

There is in fact an infinite number of pairs of solutions. Similarly the equation $2x + 5y = 1$ is satisfied by an infinite number of pairs of solutions.

When we solve a *pair* of *simultaneous* equations we find the one pair of values of x and y which satisfy *both* equations simultaneously.
Confirm that the equations $3x + y = 8$ and $2x + 5y = 1$ are both satisfied by $x = 3$ and $y = -1$.
These are the solutions of the simultaneous equations.

Graphical solution of simultaneous equations

The equations $x + y = 7$ and
$$2x - y = -1$$

can be represented by straight lines as shown.

Since both lines pass through the point (2, 5), the solutions of the simultaneous equations

$$x + y = 7$$

$$2x - y = -1$$

are $x = 2$, $y = 5$.

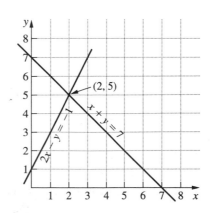

Solve the simultaneous equations

$$2x + y = 6$$
$$x - 2y = -2.$$

(a) Draw the line $2x + y = 6$.
   When $x = 0$, $y = 6$
   When $y = 0$, $x = 3$
   When $x = 1$, $y = 4$

(b) Draw the line $x - 2y = -2$.
   When $x = 0$, $y = 1$
   When $y = 0$, $x = -2$
   When $x = 6$, $y = 4$

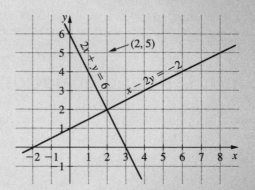

(c) The lines intersect at $(2, 2)$ so the solutions are $x = 2$, $y = 2$.

Exercise 1

1. Use the graph to solve the simultaneous equations.

   (a) $2x + y = 8$
       $x + y = 5$

   (b) $x - y = -5$
       $x + y = 5$

   (c) $2x + y = 8$
       $x - y = -5$

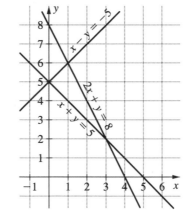

2. Use the graph to solve the simultaneous equations.

   (a) $x + y = 11$
       $x + 3y = 13$

   (b) $2x - y = -2$
       $x + y = 11$

   (c) $x + 3y = 13$
       $2x - y = -2$

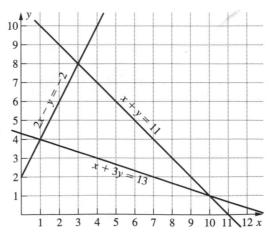

In Questions **3** to **8** solve the simultaneous equations by drawing graphs.

3. $x + y = 6$

$y = x + 3$

Draw axes with x and y from 0 to 6.

4. $x + 2y = 11$

$2x + y = 13$

Draw axes with x and y from 0 to 13.

5. $3x + 4y = 24$

$3x + 2y = 18$

Draw axes with x and y from 0 to 9.

6. $x + y = 5$

$y = x + 2$

Draw axes with x and y from 0 to 5.

7. $y = 3x + 6$

$x + y = 4$

Draw axes with x and y from -2 to 6.

8. $2x + 5y = 17$

$2x - 3y = -3$

Draw axes with x and y from 0 to 6.

[Give your answers correct to 1 d.p.]

9. Use the graph to solve the equations below. Give your answers correct to 1 d.p. where necessary.

(a) $x + y = 9$

$y = 2x - 3$

(b) $x + 3y = 5$

$x + y = 9$

(c) $x + 3y = 5$

$y = 2x - 3$

(d) $y = 2x - 3$

$5y = 4x + 18$

(e) $5y = 4x + 18$

$x + 3y = 5$

(f) $x + y = 9$

$5y = 4x + 18$

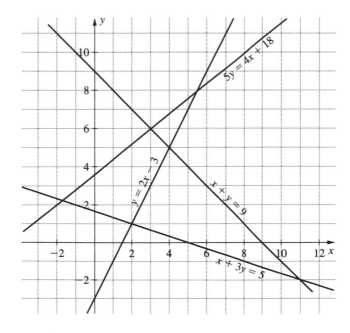

10. The simultaneous equations $x + 2y = 10$ and $x + 2y = 15$ have no solutions. What can you say about their graphs?

Algebraic solution of simultaneous equations

(a) Consider the simultaneous equations $5x + y = 21$ [1]

$$3x + y = 13 \qquad [2]$$

If we subtract equation [2] from equation [1] we eliminate the y terms.

We obtain $2x = 8$

$$x = 4$$

Now substitute $x = 4$ into equation [1] (or equation [2]).

$$(5 \times 4) + y = 21$$

$$y = 1$$

The solution is $x = 4$, $y = 1$

(b) Consider the simultaneous equations $x - y = 4$ [1]

$$4x + y = 31 \qquad [2]$$

If we *add* equation [1] to equation [2] we eliminate the y terms.

We obtain $5x = 35$

$$x = 7$$

Now substitute $x = 7$ into equation [1] (or equation [2]).

$$7 - y = 4$$

$$y = 3$$

The solution is $x = 7$, $y = 3$.

(c) Why can we add equations like this?
Equations are like scales which balance.

Equation [1]   Equation [2]

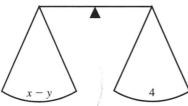 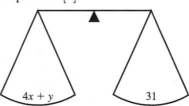

Both sets of scales balance. If we add the contents of the scales they will still balance.

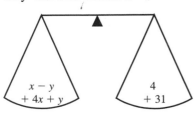

So $5x = 35$
$$x = 7$$

Solve the simultaneous equations

(a) $x + 2y = 7$ [1]
    $x - y = 4$ [2]
    Label the equations [1] and [2]

[1] − [2] gives $2y - (-y) = 3$
                   $3y = 3$
                    $y = 1$
Substitute $y = 1$ in [1]
   $x + (2 \times 1) = 7$
           $x = 5$
The solution is $x = 5$, $y = 1$.

(b) $3x + 2y = 10$ [1]
    $5x - 2y = 14$ [2]
    In this case to eliminate the y terms
    we *add* the equations.
[1] + [2] gives $8x = 24$
                 $x = 3$
Substitute $x = 3$ in [1]
   $9 + 2y = 10$
      $2y = 1$
       $y = \frac{1}{2}$
The solution is $x = 3$, $y = \frac{1}{2}$.

Remember: 'If the signs in front of the letter to be eliminated are the *same* we *subtract*, but if the signs are different we add.'

Be careful with negative numbers when using this method. Look carefully at the following examples:

$2 - (-2) = 2 + 2$
       $= 4$

$3y - (+8y) = -5y$

$3y + (-3y) = 3y - 3y$
            $= 0$

$-2x - (-2x) = -2x + 2x$
                 $= 0$

$-11 - (-3) = -11 + 3$
           $= -8$

$-4y + (-4y) = -4y - 4y$
                 $= -8y$

Exercise 2

1. Simplify
   (a) $-3 + (-4)$
   (d) $2y - (-2y)$
   (g) $-3x - (-7x)$
   (j) $4y + (-8y)$

   (b) $-3 - (-2)$
   (e) $-8x - (-8x)$
   (h) $a + (-a)$
   (k) $-5p - (-p)$

   (c) $x + (-3x)$
   (f) $5 + (-6)$
   (i) $8n - (-2n)$
   (l) $3p - (5p)$

Solve the simultaneous equations.

2. $5x + y = 22$
   $2x + y = 10$

3. $6x + y = 31$
   $3x + y = 16$

4. $5x + 2y = 16$
   $x + 2y = 4$

5. $7x + 4y = 17$
   $3x + 4y = 5$

6. $x + 3y = 11$
   $x + 2y = 9$

7. $3x + 5y = 21$
   $3x - y = 3$

8. $4x + 5y = 9$
   $4x - 2y = 2$

9. $x - 2y = 8$
   $x - 5y = 17$

10. $4x + 3y = -5$
    $7x + 3y = -11$

In Questions **11** to **16** add the equations to eliminate the y terms.

11. $3x + y = 14$
$\quad\;\; 2x - y = 6$

12. $5x + 2y = 16$
$\quad\;\; 3x - 2y = 8$

13. $7x - 3y = 24$
$\quad\;\; 2x + 3y = 3$

14. $5x - y = -7$
$\quad\;\; x + y = -5$

15. $6x - y = -26$
$\quad\;\; 5x + y = -18$

16. $\quad x + 3y = -4$
$\quad\;\; 2x - 3y = -11$

In Questions **17** to **28** either add or subtract to eliminate terms.

17. $3x + 2y = -1$
$\quad\;\; 3x - y = 5$

18. $\quad a + b = 3$
$\quad\;\; 3a - b = 17$

19. $2a - b = 6$
$\quad\;\; 3a + b = 14$

20. $5a - 2b = 4$
$\quad\;\; 3a + 2b = 12$

21. $\quad 5x + y = -7$
$\quad\;\; 5x - 2y = -16$

22. $3x + y = 14$
$\quad\;\; 3x - y = 10$

23. $\quad m - 2n = 0$
$\quad\;\; 9m + 2n = 30$

24. $3x - y = 16$
$\quad\;\; 6x - y = 31$

25. $3x - 2y = 11$
$\quad\;\; 7x - 2y = 27$

26. $4x - 5y = -17$
$\quad\;\; 2x - 5y = -16$

27. $3x = y + 10$
$\quad\;\; 3x - 2y = 4$

28. $x = 3y + 15$
$\quad\;\; 5x + 3y = 3$

Sometimes we cannot eliminate either x or y terms unless we multiply one equation or both equations by a suitable number or numbers. Examples (a) and (b) illustrate the method.

(a) $3x + y = 14$ $\qquad\qquad$ [1]
$\quad\; x + 2y = 3$ $\qquad\qquad$ [2]

Multiply equation [1] by 2.

[1] $\times$ 2: $6x + 2y = 28$ $\qquad$ [3]

[3] $-$ [2]: $\quad\;\; 5x = 25$

$\qquad\qquad\quad\;\; x = 5$

Substitute $x = 5$ in [1] (or [2])

$(3 \times 5) + y = 14$

$\qquad\qquad y = -1$

The solution is $x = 5$, $y = -1$

(b) $5x + 2y = 23$ $\qquad\qquad$ [1]
$\quad\; 2x + 3y = 18$ $\qquad\qquad$ [2]

Multiply both equations.

[1] $\times$ 3: $15x + 6y = 69$ $\qquad$ [3]

[2] $\times$ 2: $\quad 4x + 6y = 36$ $\qquad$ [4]

[3] $-$ [4]: $\qquad 11x = 33$

$\qquad\qquad\qquad x = 3$

Substitute $x = 3$ in [1] (or [2])

$(5 \times 3) + 2y = 23$

$\qquad\qquad y = 4$

The solution is $x = 3$, $y = 4$

Exercise 3

Solve the simultaneous equations.

1. $\quad 4x + y = 14$
$\quad\;\; 5x + 2y = 19$

2. $\quad 2x + y = 5$
$\quad\;\; 5x + 3y = 12$

3. $4x + 3y = 25$
$\quad\;\; x + 5y = 19$

4. $7a + 2b = 22$
$\quad\;\; 3a + 4b = 11$

5. $5m + 3n = 11$
$\quad\;\; 4m + 6n = 16$

6. $2x + 3y = 20$
$\quad\;\; x + 5y = 31$

In Questions **7** to **9** alter one of the equations and then add to eliminate the y terms.

7. $3x + 2y = 19$
   $4x - y = 29$

8. $5x - y = 8$
   $7x + 4y = 22$

9. $8x - 3y = 30$
   $3x + y = 7$

In the remaining questions alter either one or both equations before eliminating the x or y terms.

10. $2x + 3y = 12$
   $5x + 4y = 23$

11. $3x + 2y = 14$
   $2x + 7y = 15$

12. $9a + 5b = 15$
   $3a - 2b = -6$

13. $2x + 5y = 5$
   $4x + 3y = 3$

14. $3x - 2y = 21$
   $4x + 3y = 11$

15. $6x + 5y = 20$
   $5x + 2y = 21$

16. $7x + 5y = 32$
   $3x + 4y = 23$

17. $x - y = -1$
   $2x - y = 0$

18. $y - x = -1$
   $3x - y = 5$

19. $5x - 7y = 27$
   $3x - 4y = 16$

20. $3x + 2y = 7$
   $2x - 3y = -4$

21. $4x + 5y = -19$
   $6x - 3y = 24$

22. $2x + 3y = 5$
   $5x - 2y = -16$

23. $7a - 5b = 10$
   $9a + 11b = -22$

24. $10x + 5y = 2\frac{1}{2}$
   $7x - 2y = \frac{1}{10}$

Solving problems with simultaneous equations

Exercise 4

Solve the problems by forming a pair of simultaneous equations.
In Questions **1** to **4** there are two numbers to be found.

1. Find two numbers whose sum is 9 and which have a difference of 6. [Let the numbers be x and y.]

2. Twice one number plus the other number adds up to 13. The sum of the numbers is 10.

3. Double the larger number plus three times the smaller number makes 19. The difference between the numbers is 2.

4. The mean of the two numbers is 11. The larger number is one more than twice the smaller number.

5. Angle A is 12° greater than angle C. Find the angles of the triangle.

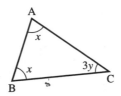

6. In the squares shown the sum of the numbers in each row and each column is given. Find the value of P and the value of Q in each case.

(a)

P	Q	P	Q	76
P	Q	P	P	92
Q	P	Q	Q	60
P	P	Q	Q	76
92	76	76	60	

(b)

P	Q	P	Q	P	25
P	P	P	Q	P	30
Q	P	Q	P	Q	20
P	P	P	P	Q	30
P	Q	P	Q	Q	20
30	25	30	20	20	

7. In this square there are three letters to be found.
[Hint: Find A and B first.]

A	B	A	17
B	A	A	17
C	B	B	15
13	19	17	

8. 76 football fans need to be transported to an away match. A minibus can take 12 people and a car can take 5 people. How many of each are needed if 11 vehicles are taken?
[Let the number of minibuses be m and let the number of cars be c].

9. A theatre sold 470 tickets at two different prices. A total of £5770 was made when x seats were sold at £15 and y seats were sold at £11. Find the values of x and y.

10. Stephen bought 4 cassettes and 2 CD's which came to a total of £69 while Amanda bought 3 cassettes and 3 CD's for a total of £66. Assuming that all cassettes are the same price and all CD's are the same price find the cost of each.

11. A box of 6 eggs costs 46p but a box of 12 eggs costs only 82p. If a total of 78 eggs are bought for a cost of £5.38, how many of each size box were bought?

12.* The six numbers around each shaded hexagon add up to 100. Find a, b and c, given that $b + c = 29$.

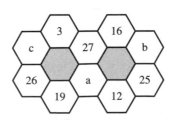

4.6 Puzzles and problems

Puzzles

1. The sum of three prime numbers is 50. What is the smallest number?

2. A six-digit telephone number can start with any digit apart from zero. The other five digits can be any number. How many different six-digit numbers are there?

327814 921487

862103

3. Fill in the space in words so that it is correct:
'*This sentence has* _____ *letters.*'

4. The symbols $*$, $\bigcirc$, $\triangle$, $\square$ represent weights. Use the information in (i), (ii), (iii) to answer part (iv).

  (a)   (i) $* + \triangle = \square$
         (ii) $* = \triangle + \bigcirc$
        (iii) $* + * + \triangle = \square + \bigcirc + \bigcirc$
        (iv) $\triangle =$ How many $\bigcirc$'s?

  (b)   (i) $\bigcirc + \bigcirc + \square = * + \bigcirc$
        (ii) $* + * = \bigcirc + \bigcirc + \bigcirc$
       (iii) $\square + * = \bigcirc + \bigcirc$
       (iv) $* =$ How many $\square$'s?

5. PQRS is a rectangle in which PQ $=$ 2QR. Point E is such that PQE is an equilateral triangle which overlaps rectangle PQRS. M is the mid point of EQ. Find the size of angle QMR.

6. Show how the cross can be cut along the broken lines and the pieces rearranged to make a square.

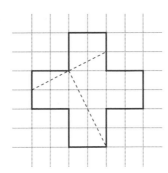

7. What is the sum of all the digits in the number $10^{30} - 90$?

8. The whole numbers from 1 to 789 are alternately added and subtracted:
$$1 - 2 + 3 - 4 + 5 - 6 + \ldots + 787 - 788 + 789.$$
What is the result?

9. The formula for converting degrees Celsius ($^\circ$C) to degrees Fahrenheit ($^\circ$F) is $F = \frac{9}{5}C + 32$.
At which temperature do both scales have the same reading?

10. Using square 'dotty' paper, squares are drawn with their corners on dots. On the right are the three different squares which can be drawn inside a 2×2 grid. How many different size squares can be drawn inside a 10 × 10 grid?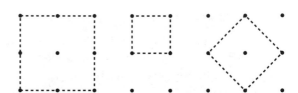

11. The circle has a radius of 1 unit. Find the total length of the arcs in the diagram. Give your answer as a multiple of π.

12. The *factorial* notation uses an exclamation mark to show a product of decreasing integers. For example $4! = 4 \times 3 \times 2 \times 1$ and $7! = 7 \times 6 \times 5 \times 4 \times 3 \times 2 \times 1$. How many zeros are at the end of 20!?

13. What is the radius of a circle whose area is $\dfrac{1}{\pi}$ square units?

14. Find the diameters of the circles if PQ = 9, PR = 7, QR = 5.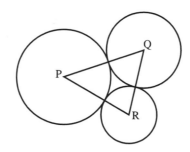

15. The Sun is 60° above the horizon. A vertical tree, 80 feet high, casts its shadow straight down a 30° slope. How long is the shadow?

16. The diagram shows a circle of radius 1 unit touching two sides of a square. Find the radius of the largest circle which could be drawn in the space between the circle and the corner of the square.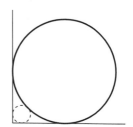

17.* The Humber Bridge is seriously big! Its span is 1·37 miles and its two 533 ft towers are set almost 2 inches out of parallel to allow for the curvature of the Earth. Use the above information to calculate an estimate for the radius of the Earth.

How many dots?

1. The diagram shows a 5 × 5 square of dots.
   There are 16 dots on the perimeter
   and 9 dots inside the square.
   (a) Draw a 3 × 3, a 4 × 4 and a 6 × 6
       square of dots. For each diagram, count
       the number of dots on the perimeter and
       the number of dots inside the square.
   (b) For a 100 × 100 square of dots, how many dots are on the
       perimeter?
   (c) For a 57 × 57 square of dots, how many dots are inside the
       square?

2. Rectangles are drawn so that the width is always 1 unit more
   than the height. The number of dots on the perimeter and the
   number of dots inside the rectangle are counted.
   (a) How many dots are on the perimeter of a 101 × 100
       rectangle?
   (b) How many dots are inside a 9 × 8 rectangle?
   (c) (Much harder) How many dots are inside a 52 × 51
       rectangle?

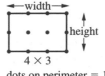

4 × 3
dots on perimeter = 10
dots inside = 2

General knowledge quiz

The answer to each question is a number.

Quiz A
1. Hills of Rome.
2. Faces on a Dodecahedron.
3. James Bond.
4. Links in a Chain.
5. Birdie.
6. British standard voltage.
7. Sextant.
8. Greenwich meridian.
9. Tchaikovsky overture.
10. Trafalgar.
11. Green bottles.
12. Octave.
13. Major planets.
14. Trilogy.
15. Pleiades.
16. Visually handicapped rodents
17. Novel by George Orwell.
18. Marathon.
19. Unlucky.
20. Four score and ten.

Part 5

5.1 Similar shapes

In everyday use the word 'similar' merely describes things which are 'alike', 'of the same kind' or 'resembling one another'. For example the taste of an orange is similar to the taste of a tangerine.

In mathematics objects are described as *similar* only if they are exactly the same shape. When two shapes are similar one is an enlargement of the other. Corresponding angles are equal and corresponding lengths are in the same proportion.

The shapes A and B *are* similar. All the corresponding angles are the same and all the sides in shape B are twice as long as the corresponding sides in shape A.

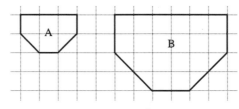

The shapes P and Q are not similar. The ratio $\frac{4}{2}$ does not equal the ratio $\frac{5}{3}$.

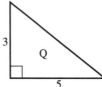

Picture A is enlarged to fit frame B. Find the length x.

Method 1. The two rectangles are similar.

$$\therefore \quad \frac{x}{10} = \frac{11 \cdot 2}{7}$$

$$x = \frac{11 \cdot 2}{7} \times 10 = 16$$

Method 2. The scale factor of the enlargement is $\frac{10}{7}$.

$$\therefore \quad x = \frac{10}{7} \times 11 \cdot 2$$

$$= 16$$

Exercise 1

1. Which of the rectangles A, B, C, D, E, F, G, H are similar to rectangle R?

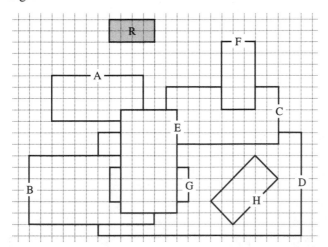

In Questions **2** to **7** you are given two similar shapes. Find the lengths marked with letters. All lengths are in cm.

2.

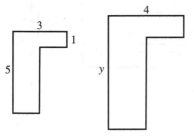

3.

4.

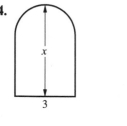

5.

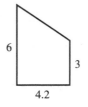

6.

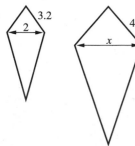

7.

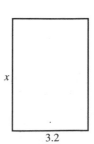

8. The photo in frame Q is either reduced or enlarged to fit exactly into frames P, R and S. Find the lengths x, y and z.

P

x

2

5.4

3

R

9

y

S

z

8

9. The diagram shows 3 similar rectangles. Find the lengths marked m and n.

10. Decide which of the following are *always* similar. Write 'yes' or 'no'.
(a) Any two squares
(b) Any two circles
(c) Any two right-angled triangles
(d) Any two semi-circles
(e) Any two rectangles
(f) Any two isosceles triangles.

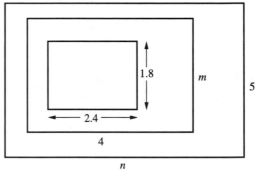

1.8

m

5

2.4

4

n

Triangles

Two triangles are similar if they have the same angles.

Triangles ABC and PQR have two angles the same, as shown. Since the angles in a triangle add up to 180°, the triangles must have the same three angles and are similar.

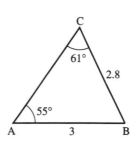

C

61°

2.8

55°

A   3   B

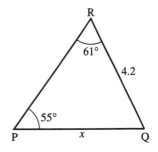

R

61°

4.2

55°

P x Q

To find the length x, use corresponding ratios.

[x and 3 are opposite the 61° angles.] $\quad \dfrac{x}{3} = \dfrac{4\cdot2}{2\cdot8}$ [4·2 and 2·8 are opposite the 55° angles.]

$$x = 4\cdot5$$

Exercise 2

1. Decide whether or not the pair of triangles are similar. Write 'yes' or 'no' for each pair.

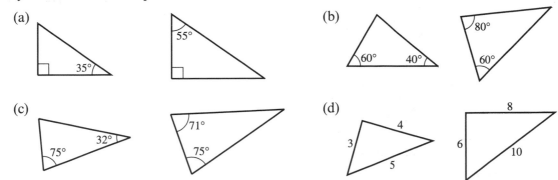

(a)

(b) 80° 60° 40° 60°

(c) 32° 75° 71° 75°

(d) 4 3 5 8 6 10

In Questions **2** to **11** the shapes are similar. Find the sides marked with letters.

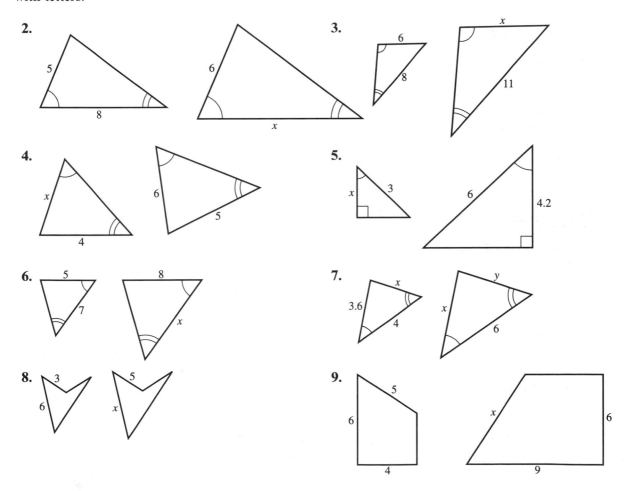

2. 5 8 6 x

3. 6 8 x 11

4. x 4 6 5

5. x 3 6 4.2

6. 5 7 8 x

7. 3.6 x 4 y x 6

8. 3 6 5 x

9. 5 6 4 x 6 9

10.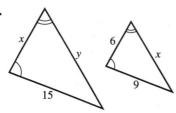

11.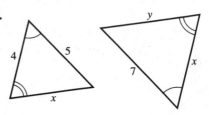

12. One sunny afternoon when Jane, who is 150 cm tall, is in Paris she notices her shadow measures 125 cm. She estimates that the shadow thrown by the Eiffel Tower is approximately 250 metres long. Roughly how high is the Eiffel Tower?

Exercise 3 (more difficult)

1. Triangles ADE and ABC are similar
Copy and complete:

$$\frac{DE}{BC} = \frac{AE}{AC}$$

$$\frac{x}{4} = \frac{3}{\Box}$$

$$x = \Box.$$

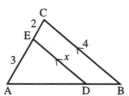

In Questions **2** to **7** use similar triangles to find the lengths marked with letters.

2.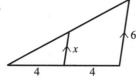

3.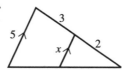

4.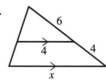

5.

6.

7.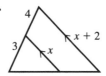

8. The two sides of a step ladder are each 2 metres long. A cross strut 1 metre long is attached 70 cm from the foot of each side. How far apart are the feet of the ladder?

9. A photograph measuring 8 cm by 12 cm is mounted on white card with margins 3 cm wide at the side and 4·5 cm wide top and bottom.
Are the two rectangles similar?

10. A simple musical instrument consists of 4 strings attached to a triangular wooden frame. If the shortest string P measures 10 cm, find the lengths of the other three strings.

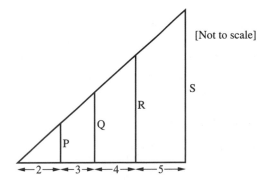

[Not to scale]

11. (a) Name two similar triangles.
(b) Calculate the length x.

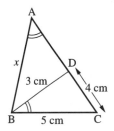

12. The sides of triangle ABC are each increased by 1 cm to form triangle DEF.
Are triangles ABC and DEF similar?

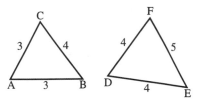

13.* In the diagram $A\widehat{B}E = A\widehat{D}C$.
Find the length x.

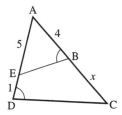

14.* When the large rectangle is folded in half along PQ, each of the smaller rectangles is similar to the large rectangle.
Form an equation and use trial and improvement to find x, correct to 1 d.p.

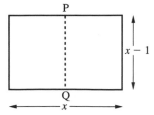

5.2 Drawing graphs

Draw the graph of $y = 2x - 2$ for x from -2 to 3.

Method 1   Draw a flow chart.

$$x \rightarrow \boxed{\times 2} \rightarrow \boxed{-2} \rightarrow y$$

x	-2	-1	0	1	2	3
y	-6	-4	-2	0	2	4

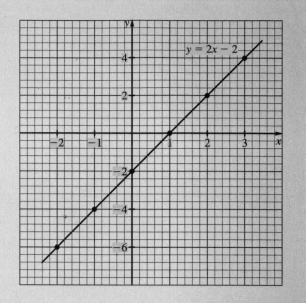

Method 2. Make a table of values.

x	-2	-1	0	1	2	3
$2x$	-4	-2	0	2	4	6
-2	-2	-2	-2	-2	-2	-2
y	-6	-4	-2	0	2	4

} add these numbers

Many people use method 2 because we use that method for curved graphs. (see next page)

Exercise 1

1. (a) Copy and complete the table for $y = 2x + 1$.

x	0	1	2	3	4	5
$2x$	0	2	4	6		
$+1$	1	1	1	1		
y	1	3	5	7.	9	

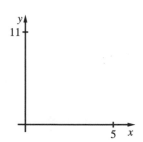

(b) Draw the graph using the axes shown.

2. (a) Make a table similar to the one above for the graph of $y = 2x - 3$. Take x from 0 to 5.
   (b) Draw the graph of $y = 2x - 3$.
   (c) Write down the coordinates of the point where the line cuts the x axis.

3. (a) Copy and complete the table for $y = 3x - 2$.

x	-2	-1	0	1	2	3
$3x$	-6	-3				
-2	-2	-2			-2	
y	-8					

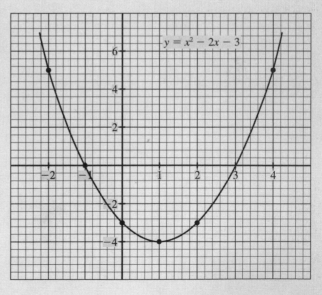

(b) Draw the graph using the axes shown.

In Questions **4** to **8** draw the graph for the values of x given.

4. $y = 3x + 1$; x from -3 to 3.

5. $y = 2x + 5$; x from -1 to 5.

6. $y = 4x - 7$; x from -2 to 3.

7. $y = 10 - x$; x from 0 to 10.

8. $y = 2(x - 3)$; x from -1 to 4.

Curved graphs

Draw the graph of $y = x^2 - 2x - 3$, taking values of x from -2 to 4.

Here is a table of values

x	-2	-1	0	1	2	3	4
x^2	4	1	0	1	4	9	16
$-2x$	4	2	0	-2	-4	-6	-8
-3	-3	-3	-3	-3	-3	-3	-3
y	5	0	-3	-4	-3	0	5

All functions of the form $y = ax^2 + bx + c$ are quadratic and are symmetrical about a vertical axis. In this example the line of symmetry is the line $x = 1$.

156

Exercise 2

1. (a) Copy and complete the table for $y = x^2 + 2$.

x	-3	-2	-1	0	1	2	3
x^2	9	4					
$+2$	2	2	2				
y	11	✓	✓	✓	✓	✓	✓

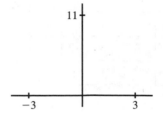

(b) Draw the graph using the axes shown.

2. (a) Copy and complete the table for $y = x^2 + 2x$.

x	-4	-3	-2	-1	0	1	2
x^2	16						4
$2x$	-8	-6					4
y	8						8

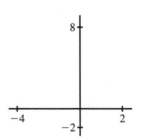

(b) Draw the graph using the axes shown.

3. (a) Make a table like the one above for the curve $y = x^2 - 3$, for x from -3 to 3.
   (b) Draw the curve and write down the coordinates of the two points where the curve cuts the x axis.

4. (a) Copy and complete the table for $y = x^2 + 2x - 5$.

x	-3	-2	-1	0	1	2	3
x^2	9			0			
$2x$	-6			0			
-5	-5	-5	-5	-5			
y	-2			-5			

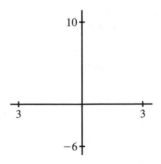

(b) Draw the graph.
(c) What is the equation of the line of symmetry?

5. Draw the graph of $y = x^2 - 3x + 1$ for values of x from -2 to 5. What is the equation of the line of symmetry?

6. Draw the graph of $y = x^2 - 4x - 3$ for values of x from -1 to 5.

In Questions **7** to **12** draw the graph for the values of x given.

7. $y = 2x^2 - 5$; x from -3 to 3.

8. $y = 2x^2 + x$; x from -3 to 2.

9. $y = x^3$; x from -3 to 3.

10. $y = x^3 - 4x$; x from -3 to 3.

11. $y = \dfrac{12}{x}$; x from 1 to 12.

12. $y = \dfrac{20}{x}$; x from 1 to 20.

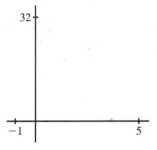

Remember:
$2x^2 = 2(x^2)$

13. (a) Copy and complete the table for $y = 2^x$.

x	-1	0	1	2	3	4	5
y	0·5	1	2				

(b) Draw the curve using the axes shown.

14. (a) Copy the graph of $y = x^2 - 2x - 3$.
(b) Draw the graph of $y = x - 1$
(c) Write down the coordinates of the two points of intersection.

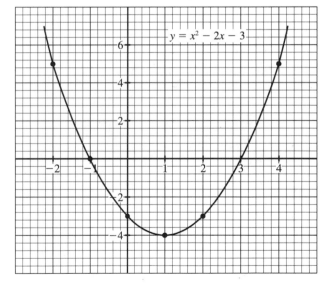

$y = x^2 - 2x - 3$

15. (a) Draw the graph of $y = \dfrac{8}{x}$ for x from 0 to 8.

(b) Draw the graph of $y = \dfrac{x+4}{2}$ for the same values of x.

(c) Write down the coordinates of the point of intersection.

Inverse functions

- With the function $x \to 2x$ 1 is 'mapped onto' 2,
  2 is mapped onto 4,
  3 is mapped onto 6 and so on.

The *inverse* function is $x \to \dfrac{x}{2}$

- A linear function is a function whose graph is a straight line.

  For example $x \to 5x + 8$, $x \to 1 - 7x$, $x \to \dfrac{x+4}{2}$

  We can find the inverse of a linear function using a flow diagram.

Here is a flow diagram
for $x \to 3x + 2$

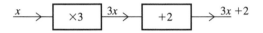

Now draw the flow diagram with
inverse operations.

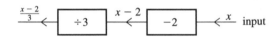

The inverse is found using x as
the input and going through the
diagram from right to left.

Here is another example.

The inverse of $x \to 5(x + 2)$ is $x \to \dfrac{x}{5} - 2$

Exercise 3

Find the inverse function

1. $x \to 4x + 1$
2. $x \to 5x - 3$
3. $x \to 7x + 1$

4. $x \to 5(x + 7)$
5. $x \to 10(x - 4)$
6. $x \to \dfrac{x+7}{3}$

7. $x \to \dfrac{x-4}{2}$
8. $x \to \dfrac{1}{2}x - 6$
9. $x \to \dfrac{1}{3}x + 11$

10. $x \to 3(2x - 1)$
11. $x \to \dfrac{4x+1}{5}$
12. $x \to 7\left(\dfrac{1}{2}x - 5\right)$

13. Functions of the form $x \to c - x$ are *self inverse*.
    So the inverse of $x \to c - x$ is the *same* function.
    Find the inverse functions:

    (a) $x \to 12 - x$
    (b) $x \to 30 - x$.

    Use different inputs to show that your answers are correct.

5.3 Compound measures

Speed

When a windsurfer moves at a constant speed of 30 metres per second, it means that he moves a distance of 30 metres in 1 second. In 2 seconds he moves 60 metres. In 3 seconds he moves 90 metres and so on. We see that the distance moved is equal to the speed multiplied by the time taken.

Remember: $\left(\text{distance} = \text{speed} \times \text{time}\right)$ ...①

We obtain two other formulas from ①:

Divide both sides by time: $\left(\dfrac{\text{distance}}{\text{time}} = \text{speed}\right)$ ...②

Divide both sides by speed: $\left(\dfrac{\text{distance}}{\text{speed}} = \text{time}\right)$ ...③

These three important formulas can be remembered using a triangle as shown. [D is at the top]

To find S: cover S, and you have $\dfrac{D}{T}$

To find T: cover T, and you have $\dfrac{D}{S}$

To find D: cover D, and you have $S \times T$

Note: The above formulas can only be used for objects moving at a constant speed.

The units used for speed, distance and time in a question must be compatible.

- If the speed is in miles per hour, the distance must be in miles and the time must be in hours.
- If the speed is in metres per second, the distance must be in metres and the time must be in seconds.

(a) A car is travelling at a steady speed of 25 m/s.
   (i) How far does the car travel in 3·2 s?
   (ii) How long does it take to travel a distance of 11 m?

   (i) distance travelled = speed × time
$$= 25 \times 3 \cdot 2$$
$$= 80 \text{ m}$$
   (ii) time taken $= \dfrac{\text{distance}}{\text{speed}}$
$$= \tfrac{11}{25} = 0 \cdot 44 \text{ s}$$

(b) A bird flies at a speed of 8 m/s for 10 minutes. How far does it fly?

Change 10 minutes into 600 seconds.

distance = speed × time
$$= 8 \times 600$$

The bird flies 4800 m.

(c) A train travels 15 000 m in 20 minutes. Find the speed of the train in km/h.

Change 15 000 m into 15 km.

Change 20 minutes into $\frac{1}{3}$ hour.

speed of train $= \dfrac{\text{distance}}{\text{time}}$
$$= \frac{15}{\frac{1}{3}}$$
$$= 45 \text{ km/h}$$

Exercise 1

1. A tram travels a distance of 200 m at a speed of 25 m/s. How long does it take?

2. A man runs at a speed of 7·5 m/s. How far will he run in 4 seconds?

3. An arctic tern flies a distance of 245 km in 9 hours. How fast does it fly?

4. A steamroller takes 180 seconds to travel 60 m. What is its speed, in m/s?

5. How long does it take a train to travel 270 km at a constant speed of 90 km/h?

6. A partridge flies 3 miles in 15 minutes. What is its speed in m.p.h.?

7. An aircraft flies at a speed of 940 km/h.
   How far does it fly in $2\frac{1}{2}$ hours?

8. If a train travels 60 km in 20 minutes, how far does it go in one hour at the same speed?

9. A horse runs for $1\frac{1}{2}$ hours at a speed of 8 m.p.h. How far does it run?

10. A cyclist takes 30 minutes to travel 11 miles. At what speed does he cycle in m.p.h.?

11. Eurostar goes 420 km from London to Paris in just 3 hours. Find the average speed of the train.

12. Find the distance travelled:
    (a) 65 m.p.h for 2 hours
    (b) 8 cm/day for 5 days
    (c) 5 m/s for 1 minute [units!]

13. A car takes 15 minutes to travel 20 miles. Find the speed in m.p.h.

14. A greyhound runs for 20 s at a speed of 22 m/s. How far does it run?

15. In the 1996 Olympics Donovan Bailey won the 100 m in 9·81 seconds and Michael Johnson won the 200 m in 19·37 seconds. Who ran at the faster average speed?

16. Find the time taken:
    (a) 260 km at 20 km/h
    (b) 2 km at 10 m/s
    (c) 4 miles at 8 m.p.h.

17. A T.G.V. travels 567 km from Bordeaux to Paris at an average speed of 252 km/h. Find the arrival time in Paris, if it leaves Bordeaux at 1410.

18. A boat sails at a speed of 13 knots for 2 days. How far does it travel? [1 knot = 1 nautical mile per hour].

19. In a grand prix, the winning car passed the chequered flag 0·3 seconds ahead of the next car. Both cars were travelling at 84 m/s. What was the distance between the two cars?

20.* (a) Sam drives from Liverpool to York at an
average speed of 30 m.p.h.
How long will it take in hours and minutes?
(b) Mike takes $2\frac{1}{2}$ h to drive from Hull to
Newcastle. What was his average speed?
(c) Nikki drives from Preston to Newcastle at
an average speed of 42 m.p.h. and the
journey takes 2 h 40 min. What is the
distance from Preston to Newcastle?

126	Liverpool			
122	170	Newcastle		
121	29		Preston	
38	100	84	83	York

(Hull)

21.* A train leaves London at 0815 and arrives in York, 193 miles
away, at 1100. Find the average speed of the train.

Other compound measures

Exercise 2

In Questions **1** to **7** use
the exchange rates for
foreign currency shown.

Country	Rate of exchange
France (franc)	F 8·8 = £1
Germany (mark)	DM 2·65 = £1
Spain (peseta)	Pta 220 = £1
Italy (lire)	lire 2600 = £1
U.S.A. (dollar)	$ 1·6 = £1

1. Change the pounds into the foreign currency stated.
   (a) £10 [marks]   (b) £1000 [lire]   (c) £20 [dollars]
   (d) £100 [francs]   (e) £4 [pesetas]   (f) £1 million [marks]

2. A lorry costs £35 000 in Britain.
   What is the price in marks?

3. A bottle of a certain wine costs
   1100 pesetas in Spain and £6·99 in
   Britain. In which country is the
   wine cheaper?

4. A C.D. costs £13·99 in Britain
   and $16 in the United States.
   How much cheaper, in British
   money, is the C.D. when bought
   in the USA?

5. (a) Change DM 265 into pounds.
   (b) Change DM 1 into pounds, to the nearest penny.

6. (a) Change $5000 into pounds, to the nearest penny.
   (b) Change Lire 10 000 into pounds, to the nearest penny.

7. A motorist is fined 1000F in France for speeding. Can he pay
   the fine if he has £150?

In Question **8** to **10**
use the formulas shown. $\left(\text{Density} = \dfrac{\text{Mass}}{\text{Volume}} \right)$ or $\left(\text{Mass} = \text{Density} \times \text{Volume} \right)$

8. Find the density of a metal if $100\,\text{cm}^3$ weighs 800 grams.

9. The density of copper is $9\,\text{g/cm}^3$. Find the mass of a copper bar of volume $20\,\text{cm}^3$.

10. A silver ring has a volume of $3\,\text{cm}^3$ and a mass of 36 grams. Find the density of the silver.

Questions **11** to **17** involve a variety of compound measures.

11. Heavy duty cable costs £1·50 per m. Find the cost of laying 3000 m of this cable.

12. A powerful mainframe computer can be hired at £55 per second. How much will it cost to hire the computer for 1 hour?

13. Gold plating costs £6 per cm^2. How much will it cost to plate this lid?

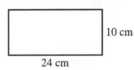

10 cm

24 cm

14. A gambler lost $3·2 million in one year. On average how much did the gambler lose per day? Give your answer to the nearest thousand dollars.

15. Good farmland is sold at £4000 per hectare (1 hectare $= 10\,000\,\text{m}^2$). Bacon farm has a rectangular field measuring 300 m by 80 m. Find the cost of the field.

16. The open box shown is made from metal weighing $5\,\text{g/cm}^2$. Find the weight of the box.

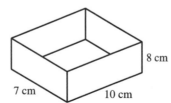

8 cm

7 cm   10 cm

17. The table shows the land area and population for four countries.
(a) Work out the number of people per km^2 for Ireland.
(b) Which country has the *most* people per km^2?
(c) Suppose all the people in Portugal had an equal area of land. How much would each person have in m^2? [$1\,\text{km}^2 = 1\,000\,000\,\text{m}^2$].

Country	Area in km^2	Population
Italy	301 000	58·3 million
Portugal	91 600	10·7 million
Ireland	68 900	3·4 million
Brazil	8 510 000	122·6 million

5.4 Mixed problems

Exercise 1

1. Copy and complete the following bill.

$5\frac{1}{2}$ kg of carrots at 64p per kg = £ ▢

2 kg of meat at ▢ per kg = £9·70

▢ jars of marmalade at 85p per jar = £5·95

Total = £ ▢

2. A ship's voyage started at 20.30 on Monday and finished at 07.00 on the following Wednesday. How long was the journey in hours and minutes?

3. Twenty articles cost £50. How many of these articles could be bought for £7·50?

4. How many apples at 16p each would be a fair exchange for 48 oranges costing 11p each?

5. Work out, without using a calculator
(a) 0·4 − 0·04   (b) 0·03 × 1000   (c) 0·31 ÷ 10
(d) 8·7 − 4   (e) 3% of £500   (f) $\sqrt{(11\cdot38 + 13\cdot62)}$

6. Write down *two* possible answers for the missing digits. Ask a friend to check your solutions.

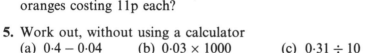 ▢3▢ ▢0▢ × ▢▢ ÷ ▢ = 120

7. (a) Increase £60 by 10%.
(b) Decrease £900 by 20%.
(c) Increase £2000 by 2%.

8. A man starts work each day at 07.30 and works until 16.00. He stops working for one hour at lunchtime. How many hours does he work in a 5-day week?

9. Copy each pattern and write down the next line
(a) $2^2 = 1^2 + 3$ (b) $1 + 9 \times \quad 0 = \quad 1$
    $3^2 = 2^2 + 5$ $2 + 9 \times \quad 1 = \quad 11$
    $4^2 = 3^2 + 7$ $3 + 9 \times \quad 12 = \quad 111$
    $5^2 = 4^2 + 9$ $4 + 9 \times 123 = 1111$

10. A 20p coin is 1·2 mm thick. What is the value of a pile of 20p coins which is 21·6 cm high?

Exercise 2

1. Use a calculator to work out 11^2, 111^2 and 1111^2. Use your answers to predict the values of $11\,111^2$ and $111\,111^2$.

2. The canoeists are concentrating on two numbers n and m. The product of n and m is 204 and their sum is 29.
   Find the two numbers.

3. At a party there are 116 people and there are 6 more boys than girls.
   How many boys are there?

4. Mark uses 14 screws in each of the model aircraft which he makes.
   How many *complete* aircraft can he make using a box of 360 screws?

5. The numbers 1 to 12 are arranged on the star so that the sum of the numbers along each line is the same.

   Copy and complete the star.

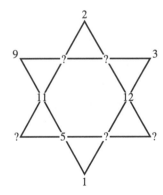

6. A jar with 8 chocolates in it weighs 160 g. The same jar with 20 chocolates in it weighs 304 g. How much does the jar weigh on its own?

7. Use the clues to find the mystery number
   - the sum of the digits is 18
   - the number reads the same forwards as backwards
   - the number is less than 2000
   - the number has four digits

8. Which bag of potatoes is the better value:
Bag A, 6 kg for £4·14 or
Bag B, 2·5 kg for £1·80?

9. An aeroplane was due to take off from Heathrow airport at 18:42 but it was 35 min late. During the flight, thanks to a tail wind, the plane made up the time and in fact landed 16 min before its scheduled arrival time of 00:05. (Assume that the plane did not cross any time zones on its journey.)
(a) What time did the aeroplane take off?
(b) What time did it land?

10. It rained so hard that a 4 cm deep egg cup was filled in 20 minutes.
How much rain fell between 07:30 and 13:50?

Exercise 3

1. Find the missing digits

(a)
```
    □ 4 □
  + 1 □ 8
  ───────
    4 1 4
```

(b)
```
    □ □ 9
  ×     4
  ───────
  1 3 9 □
```

(c) □ 4 × 2 □ = 1512

2. A wall measuring 3 m by 2 m is covered with square tiles of side 10 cm.
(a) How many tiles are needed?
(b) If the tiles cost £3·40 for ten, how much will it cost?

3. A journey by helicopter takes 3 hours 35 minutes.
How long will it take at half the speed?

4. A woman hires a car from a car hire firm which charges £15 per day plus 7p per km travelled.

£15 per day
7p per km

(a) How much does it cost to hire a car for four days and drive 200 km?
(b) A woman hired a car for two days and had to pay £65. How far did she drive?

5. Forty girls were asked to name their favourite
lipstick with the following results:

Chanel 12, Almay 5, Estée Lauder 10,
Maybelline 4, Rimmel 9

Display this information on a pie chart, showing
the angles corresponding to each.

6. Find the distance travelled by light in 1 hour, given that the
speed of light is 300 000 kilometres per second. Give the answer
in km in standard form.

7. A solid block of chocolate measuring 1·5 cm by 15 cm by 8 cm is
melted down and spread out to make a square layer of chocolate
2 mm thick. How long is the side of the square?

8.

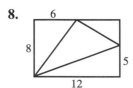

A rectangle is divided into
four triangles as shown.
Find the area of the biggest
of the triangles.

9. A garden 9 m by 12 m is to be treated with fertilizer. One cup of
fertilizer covers an area of 3 m² and one bag of fertilizer is
sufficient for 18 cups.
(a) Find the area of the garden.
(b) Find the number of bags of fertilizer needed.

10.

A prize-winning sand castle was built by
15 people in ten hours.
How long would it take 4 people to build
the sand castle if they worked at the same
speed and with equal skill?

Exercise 4

1. If $x = 3$, $y = -4$ and $z = -5$, work out

    (a) $x + z$ (b) $3y + x$ (c) $yz + x$

2. Use a calculator to evaluate the following, correct to 3 s.f.

    (a) $\dfrac{(3 \cdot 2^2 - 7)}{7(6 \cdot 5^2 + 1)}$ (b) $\dfrac{8 \cdot 2 + 5 \cdot 9}{\sqrt{(7 \cdot 1 - 1 \cdot 3^2)}}$ (c) $\dfrac{7 \cdot 3}{1 \cdot 5} - \dfrac{3 \cdot 6}{1 \cdot 31^2}$

3. Small cubes of side 1 cm are stuck together to form a large cube of side 4 cm. Opposite faces of the large cube are painted the same colour, but adjacent faces are different colours. The three colours used are red, black and green.

    (a) How many small cubes have just one red and one green face?

    (b) How many small cubes are painted on one face only?

    (c) How many small cubes have one red, one green and one black face?

    (d) How many small cubes have no faces painted?

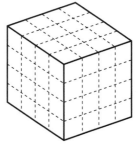

4. A sales manager reports an increase of 20% in sales this year compared to last year.

The increase was £70 800.

What were the sales last year?

5. The diagram shows a rectangle. Work out x and then find the area of the rectangle.

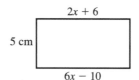

6. That's the way the money goes: used banknotes, chopped up and compressed, are dumped for the Bank of England at a landfill site near Tilbury. The bank has to dispose of seven tonnes a day. To avoid pollution they are no longer burned, but selling them as novelty firelighters is among proposals being investigated.

Estimate the value of the banknotes which are dumped each day.

Make the following assumptions:

    (a) All the notes dumped are £10 notes.

    (b) each note weighs 0·87 grams,

[1 tonne = 1000 kg]

7. How many points inside and outside the square are the same distance from B and C and are also 5 cm from A?

8. The pie chart shows how the price of a C.D. costing £14·99 can be broken down.
   (a) Work out the angle of the V.A.T. sector.

   (b) What is the total royalty paid to the artist if 500 000 C.D.s are sold?

   (c) Tax from the sale of C.D.s is collected in three ways:
   (i) as V.A.T. (ii) 40% of the Artist's royalty (iii) 40% of shop's profit.
   Calculate the total amount of tax paid when 500 000 C.D.'s are sold.

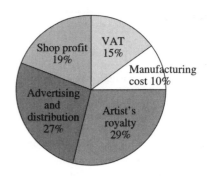

9. Three consecutive whole numbers can be expressed as x, $x+1$ and $x+2$. If four times the largest number is added to twice the middle number the answer is seven times the smallest number. Find the three numbers.

10. Bronze is made up of zinc, tin and copper in the ratio $1:4:95$. A bronze statue contains 120 g of tin. Find the quantities of the other two metals required and the total weight of the statue.

Exercise 5

1. Find the missing digits

   (a) $\boxed{}\,7 \times 1\,\boxed{} = 611$

   (b) $8)\overline{\boxed{}\,9\,\boxed{}\,8}$ with quotient $3\ 6\ 6$

   (c) $\boxed{}\,6 \times 1\,\boxed{} = 442$

   (d)
   $$\begin{array}{r} 6\ \boxed{}\ 1 \\ -\ \boxed{}\ 7\ \boxed{} \\ \hline 2\ 6\ 3 \end{array}$$

   (e)
   $$\begin{array}{r} \boxed{}\,\boxed{}\ 5 \\ \times\ \ \ 9 \\ \hline 2\ 5\ 6\ \boxed{} \end{array}$$

   (f) $7)\overline{\boxed{}\,3\,\boxed{}\,1}$ with quotient $4\ 8\ 3$

2. A pound coin has radius 1·1 cm and thickness 3 mm.
   Calculate the volume of a pile of pound coins of total value £1000.
   [Give your answer in cm^3.]

3. The volume of toothpaste in a tube is 150 cm^3. If this paste is squirted out in a straight line through a circular hole of diameter 5 mm, how long will this line be?

4.

Dinky's high price

A Dinky Toy model of a Bentalls Kingston-on-Thames delivery van which cost 6d ($2^1/_2$p) in 1936, fetched a record £12,650 at a Christie's auction.

Calculate the percentage profit made on the sale of the toy in the newspaper cutting. Give your answer correct to 3 significant figures.

5. A shooting target consists of four rings of radii 3 cm, 6 cm, 9 cm and 12 cm. Find the percentage of the target that is shaded.

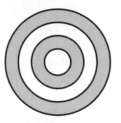

6.  North

P•

Draw a small sketch showing the possible position of points Q and R given that:
(a) the bearing of point Q from P is 200°
(b) the bearing of point P from R is 300°.

7. The bullet from a rifle travels at a speed of 3×10^4 cm/s. Work out the length of time in seconds taken for the bullet to hit a target 54 m away.

8. A sewing machine cost £162·40 after a price increase of 16%. Find the price before the increase.

9. To get the next number in a sequence you double the previous number and subtract two. The fifth number in the sequence is 50. Find the first number.

10. A code uses 1 for A, 2 for B, 3 for C and so on up to 26 for Z. Coded words are written without spaces to confuse the enemy, so 18 could be AH or R. Decode the following message.

208919 919 1 2251825 199121225 31545

Exercise 6

1. In the diagram $\frac{5}{6}$ of the circle is shaded and $\frac{2}{3}$ of the triangle is shaded.
   What is the ratio of the area of the circle to the area of the triangle?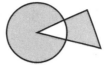

2. Find the exact answer to the following by first working out a rough answer and then using the information given. Do *not* use a calculator.
   (a) If $142\cdot3 \times 98\cdot5 = 14\,016\cdot55$ find $140\cdot1655 \div 14\cdot23$
   (b) If $76\cdot2 \times 8\cdot6 = 655\cdot32$ find $6553\cdot2 \div 86$
   (c) If $22\cdot3512 \div 0\cdot268 = 83\cdot4$ find $8340 \times 26\cdot8$
   (d) If $1\cdot6781 \div 17\cdot3 = 0\cdot097$ find $9700 \times 0\cdot173$

3. When the lid is left off an ink bottle, the ink evaporates at a rate of $2\cdot5 \times 10^{-6}\,\text{cm}^3/\text{s}$. A full bottle contains $36\,\text{cm}^3$ of ink. How long, to the nearest day, will it take for all the ink to evaporate?

4. Convert $3\cdot35$ hours into hours and minutes.

5. In quadrilateral ABCD, $\widehat{BAD} = \widehat{BCD} = 90°$, $AD = 10$, $BC = 4$, $CD = 12$. Find AB.

6. When I think of a number, multiply it by 6 and subtract 120, my answer is -18. What was my original number?

7. Solve the equations
   (a) $3(x + 6) = 2(6 - 3x)$ (b) $\dfrac{x + 6}{4} = \dfrac{3x - 3}{7}$

8. The diagram shows the frame for the roof of a house. Calculate the length x.

9. The area of the square exceeds the area of the rectangle by $13\,\text{m}^2$. Find y.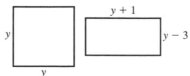

10. When a car is driven at a steady speed of 64 m.p.h., it travels 48 miles per gallon of petrol. If petrol costs £2·70 per gallon, work out the cost per minute of driving the car.

11. For an advertising photo, men were asked to bring their children and to stand 3 m apart next to a road of length 10 miles. How many men were needed? [1 km = 0·625 mile]

12. The table gives approximate stopping distances for cars at different speeds.

Speed (km/h)	40	60	80	100
Stopping distance (m)	18	33	50	74

Assume that cars are 4 m long and that they are driven at a steady speed, leaving a gap between cars equal to the stopping distance for that speed.

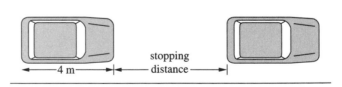

(a) How many cars, all travelling at 60 km/h, will there be on each kilometre of a single lane road?

(b) How many cars, travelling at 60 km/h, will pass a fixed point in one hour?

(c) On a 3 lane motorway, cars travel in the inside land at 60 km/h, in the middle lane at 80 km/h and in the outside lane at 100 km/h. How many cars altogether will pass a fixed point in one hour?

5.5 Changing the subject of a formula

The method for changing the subject of a formula is generally the same as the method for solving an equation. The examples below are written side by side to make comparison easy.

(a) Solve the equation

$$3(x - 1) = 5$$

$$3x - 3 = 5 \quad \text{[Multiply out the brackets]}$$

$$3x = 5 + 3 \quad \text{[Get the } x \text{ term on its own]}$$

$$x = \frac{8}{3} \quad \text{[Divide by the coefficient of } x\text{]}$$

(b) Make x the subject of the formula

$$a(x - b) = t$$

$$ax - ab = t$$

$$ax = t + ab$$

$$x = \frac{t + ab}{a}$$

A formula for the distance moved by an accelerating teacher is $s = ut + \frac{1}{2}at^2$.
Rearrange the formula to make a the subject

$$s = ut + \frac{1}{2}at^2$$

$$s - ut = \frac{1}{2}at^2 \quad \text{[Subtract } ut \text{ from both sides.]}$$

$$2(s - ut) = at^2 \quad \text{[Multiply both sides by 2.]}$$

$$\frac{2(s - ut)}{t^2} = a \quad \text{[Divide both sides by } t^2\text{.]}$$

This formula can now be used to calculate the value of a if we know the values of s, u and t.

Exercise 1

In Questions **1** to **12** make x the subject.

1. $x - a = e$

2. $x + t = h$

3. $a + b = x - g$

4. $v + x = m^2$

5. $h + x = 2h + n$

6. $s - t = t + x$

7. $x - y^2 = y$

8. $x - pq = m$

9. $n = x - mn$

10. $ax = c$

11. $mx + c = y$

12. $bx = a + c$

In Questions **13** to **24** make y the subject.

13. $my - c = n$

14. $5b = ay + b$

15. $a + c = ky - c$

16. $e + d = b + cy$

17. $t^2 + ty = p^2$

18. $ay - z = z$

19. $-m = fy$

20. $pqy = \pi r^2$

21. $aby = m + n$

22. $c^2 + d^2y = a^2$

23. $mty + c = d$

24. $xyz - p^2 = q^2$

In Questions **25** to **36** make the letter in brackets the subject.

25. $a + tb = e$ $[t]$

26. $ab + kn = a^2$ $[k]$

27. $n + mw = 2n$ $[w]$

28. $s(y + a) = b$ $[y]$

29. $p(a + x) = b$ $[x]$

30. $z(c + d) = e$ $[z]$

31. $m(r + s) = t$ $[m]$

32. $b = a(m + n)$ $[n]$

33. $b^2 = w(y - a)$ $[y]$

34. $s = (u + v)t$ $[u]$

35. $m^2(a + e) = n^2$ $[e]$

36. $ab(a + x) = c$ $[x]$

37. A formula involving the number of steps, n, on a spiral staircase is
$$n = \pi(2r + h)$$
Make h the subject

38. Using the formula $t^2 = z(a + c + d)$,
(a) Make c the subject
(b) Make z the subject.

39. Using the formula $(y + z)m = c + d$
(a) Make m the subject
(b) Make y the subject.

Formulae involving fractions

(a) Make x the subject.

(i) $\dfrac{m}{x} = e$

$m = ex$ [Multiply both sides by x.]

$\dfrac{m}{e} = x$ [Divide both sides by e.]

(ii) $\dfrac{x}{t} = a + b$

$x = t(a + b)$ [Multiply both sides by t.]

(b) Make p the subject

$\dfrac{h}{p - t} = a$

$h = a(p - t)$

$h = ap - at$

$h + at = ap$

$\dfrac{h + at}{a} = p$

Exercise 2

1. For the formula $p = \dfrac{m}{x}$,

(a) Make m the subject
(b) Make x the subject.

2. For the formula $\dfrac{a}{x} = t$

(a) Make a the subject
(b) Make x the subject.

In Questions **3** to **17** make x the subject.

3. $\dfrac{x}{m} = n$

4. $a = \dfrac{x}{t}$

5. $\dfrac{x}{c} = a + b$

6. $a = \dfrac{x}{m + n}$

7. $\dfrac{x}{2} = ab$

8. $c = \dfrac{x}{c}$

9. $\dfrac{a}{x} = d$

10. $\dfrac{y}{x} = t$

11. $a + b = \dfrac{c}{x}$

12. $(a + b) = \dfrac{(c + d)}{x}$

13. $\dfrac{e + f}{x} = a^2 + b$

14. $\dfrac{x}{m} = \dfrac{a}{b}$

15. $\dfrac{x}{t} = \dfrac{m}{n}$

16. $\dfrac{ax}{p} = \dfrac{s}{t}$

17. $\dfrac{b}{a} = \dfrac{ax}{b}$

In Questions **18** to **32** make a the subject.

18. $\dfrac{h}{a} = p^2$

19. $h = \dfrac{w + z}{a}$

20. $c - d = \dfrac{d + b}{a}$

21. $\dfrac{t^2}{r} = \dfrac{mn}{a}$

22. $\dfrac{\pi}{h} = \dfrac{a}{e - f}$

23. $\dfrac{a(e + k)}{b} = b$

24. $\dfrac{m}{a + b} = c$

25. $\dfrac{p}{a - c} = d$

26. $\dfrac{h}{x + a} = y$

27. $p = \dfrac{d}{a - e}$

28. $t + w = \dfrac{m^2}{a}$

29. $\dfrac{f}{g} = \dfrac{e}{a - b}$

30. $\dfrac{z}{a(p + q)} = t$

31. $\dfrac{y}{a} = \sin 20°$

32. $\tan 48° = \dfrac{x}{a}$

Formulae with negative x terms

Make x the subject of the formulae.

(a) $m - tx = c$

$$m = c + tx \dots [\text{A}]$$
$$m - c = tx$$
$$\dfrac{m - c}{t} = x$$

(b) $a(a - x) = t$

$$a^2 - ax = t$$
$$a^2 - t = ax \dots [\text{A}]$$
$$a^2 - t = ax$$
$$\dfrac{a^2 - t}{a} = x$$

Notice that in line [A], in both examples, the x term is taken to the other side of the equation to make it positive. Most people find it easier to work with a positive x term.

Exercise 3

In Questions **1** to **12** make x the subject.

1. $b - x = e$

2. $t^2 = h - x$

3. $z^2 - x = n^2$

4. $a + b = c - x$

5. $4q - x = 2q$

6. $d = a + m - x$

7. $t - ax = b$

8. $e = u - gx$

9. $w^2 = u^2 - ux$

10. $p = h^3 - tx$

11. $a + c - x = ac$

12. $3b - a^2x = b$

In Questions **13** to **21** remove the brackets and then make x the subject.

13. $c(m - x) = n$

14. $h(a - x) = g$

15. $k = a(a - x)$

16. $t^2 = p(q - x)$

17. $a = p(p + q - x)$

18. $w = m(n - mx)$

19. $v(u + t - x) = w$

20. $t(t^2 - p^2x) = a$

21. $ab(a - x) = d$

Formulae involving squares and square roots

(a) (i) Solve the equation

$$x^2 + 5 = 9$$
$$x^2 = 9 - 5 \quad \text{[Get the } x^2 \text{ term on its own.]}$$
$$x = \pm 2 \quad \text{[Take the square root of both sides. The answer can be positive or negative.]}$$

(ii) Make x the subject

$$x^2 - b = t$$
$$x^2 = t + b$$
$$x = \pm\sqrt{t + b}$$

(b) (i) Solve the equation

$$\sqrt{x + 2} = 7$$
$$x + 2 = 7^2 \quad \text{[Square both sides.]}$$
$$x = 49 - 2 \quad \text{[Get } x \text{ on its own.]}$$
$$= 47$$

(ii) Make x the subject

$$\sqrt{x - c} = m$$
$$x - c = m^2$$
$$x = m^2 + c$$

Exercise 4

In Questions **1** to **12** make x the subject.

1. $\sqrt{x} = c$

2. $\sqrt{x + a} = t$

3. $m = \sqrt{x - c}$

4. $a\sqrt{x} = k$

5. $a + b = m\sqrt{x}$

6. $\sqrt{ax} = c$

7. $p = \sqrt{\dfrac{x}{m}}$ **8.** $\sqrt{\dfrac{x}{a}} = c$ **9.** $\sqrt{x} = \dfrac{a}{b}$

10. $\sqrt{\dfrac{d}{x}} = k$ **11.** $q = \sqrt{\dfrac{e}{x}}$ **12.** $\sqrt{\dfrac{x}{n}} = \dfrac{a}{b}$

In Questions **13** to **24** make a the subject.

13. $a^2 + b = c$ **14.** $ma^2 = e$ **15.** $a^2 + f = g$

16. $(a + d)^2 = m$ **17.** $(a - y)^2 = h$ **18.** $ta^2 - n = c$

19. $h = \dfrac{(a - z)^2}{t}$ **20.** $\dfrac{ea^2}{m} = t$ **21.** $\dfrac{za^2}{n} + p = q$

22. $(ma - c)^2 = y$ **23.** $(t + ab)^2 = w$ **24.** $m - a^2 = n$

Exercise 5

1. To convert from Fahrenheit to Celsius we can use the formula
$C = \frac{5}{9}(F - 32)$

(a) Convert the following temperatures to Celsius
(i) $77\,°F$, (ii) $50\,°F$
(b) Make F the subject of the formula
(c) Convert the following temperatures to Fahrenheit
(i) $100\,°C$ (ii) $60\,°C$

2. Area of a trapezium, $A = \frac{1}{2}h(a + b)$
(a) Rearrange the formula to make h the subject.
(b) Find h if $A = 340\,cm^2$, $a = 7\,cm$, $b = 10\,cm$
(c) Rearrange the formula to make b the subject.
(d) Find b if $A = 136\,cm^2$, $a = 12\,cm$, $h = 8\,cm$.

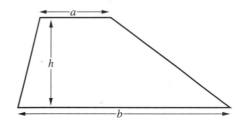

3.* A challenge! Here is part of a famous formula in mathematics

$$x = \dfrac{-b + \sqrt{b^2 - 4ac}}{2a}.$$

Rearrange the formula to make c the subject.

5.6 Mathematical reasoning, proof

Crossnumbers

(a) Copy out the crossnumber pattern.
(b) Fit all the given numbers into the correct spaces. Tick off the numbers from the lists as you write them in the square.

1.

2 digits	3 digits	4 digits	5 digits	6 digits
14	173	1615	14798	443205
16	202	1624	23641	533245
19	222	1824	31241	815713
21	227	3112	43641	885724
30	235	4076	46015	961723
32	302	4271	60111	
44	377	4284	60318	
47	378	4289	62078	
55	456	4875	71341	
56	532	5381		
57	628	5623		
58	732	5673		7 digits
58	770			1402224
63	828			6133335
73	853			
80				

2.

2 digits		3 digits	4 digits	5 digits	6 digits
11	53	111	2905	10752	523416
12	63	134	3072	12282	538222
17	66	499	3141	15216	762214
25	70	525	3333	18253	
28	73	571	4951	25837	
29	74	576	7364	26275	
30	78	611	9362	31785	
32	81	773	9591	43567	
35	82	817		47907	7 digits
38	83			50078	2308712
41	85			69073	4284173
44	91			77527	
47	99			83114	
				95392	

Diamonds and triangles

In this task you will draw rectangles on triangular dotty paper (make sure you have the paper the right way up!)

In each diagram you have:

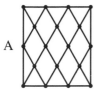

equilateral triangles (e),

isosceles triangles (i),

diamonds (d).

In all rectangles each corner must be on a dot.

This is correct.

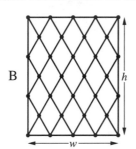

This is not allowed.

Each rectangle has width w and height h.
In rectangle A $w = 3$, $h = 2$
In rectangle B $w = 4$, $h = 3$
Both w and h must be whole numbers.

(a) Count the number of equilateral triangles e in diagrams A and B and in rectangles of your own.
   Can you find a rule connecting e and w or a rule connecting e and h?

(b) Count the number of isosceles triangles i in your rectangles.
   Can you find a rule connecting i with either w or h?

(c) The rule connecting d with w and h is more difficult to find.
   Be systematic by putting your results in tables.
   First keep w the same and change only h.
   For example:

(i)

w	h	d
2	2	4
2	3	?
2	4	?
2	5	?

(ii) Change to $w = 3$

w	h	d
3	2	?
3	3	?
3	4	?
3	5	?

(iii) Change to $w = 4$ etc.

Hints: As you look for a connection try the following:

in (i) write a column in the table for $3h$
in (ii) write a column in the table for $5h$
in (iii) write a column in the table for $7h$

Can you see a rule connecting, w, h and d for each of the different widths?
Try to write '$d =$ '

Now add a column for $w \times h \times 2$.
Can you now see a rule that works for *any* diagram you could draw?

Connect the transformations

The triangle ABC is mapped onto triangle A'B'C' by a rotation followed by a translation.

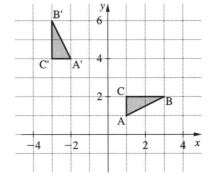

For example: Rotation 90° anticlockwise about (1, 1)

followed by translation $\begin{pmatrix} -3 \\ 3 \end{pmatrix}$.

or   Rotation 90° anticlockwise about (3, 0)

followed by translation $\begin{pmatrix} -4 \\ 6 \end{pmatrix}$.

Is there a connection between the centre of the rotation and the vector of the translation?

This is not an easy question to answer. You need to work methodically and to record your results in a table.

Suggestions:
(a) Take the following points as the centres of the rotation:
(0, 0), (1, 1), (2, 2), (3, 3) etc.

Record the results in a table.

Write down any connection you notice between the centre of rotation and the vector of the translation.

centre	translation
(0, 0)	$\begin{pmatrix} -1 \\ 3 \end{pmatrix}$
(1, 1)	$\begin{pmatrix} -3 \\ 3 \end{pmatrix}$

(b) Now take a different set of points for the centres of the rotation:
(0, 0), (1, 0), (2, 0), (3, 0), etc.

Again write down any connections you notice.

(c) Can you use your results from (a) and (b) above to *predict* the vector of the translation if the centre of the rotation is (7, 7) or (10, 0)?

(d) Investigate other sets of points for the centre of rotation. Can you find a general rule which predicts the vector of the translation for *any* centre of rotation?

In search of π

You have been using the fact that the circumference of a circle $= \pi \times$ diameter, where π is some value a bit more than 3. You may also have been told that π is an *irrational* number which means it does not have an exact decimal value, and that it has been calculated to many hundreds of decimal places. So how can we be sure this value is correct?

Firstly find the perimeter of a regular pentagon where the distance from the centre to the vertices is 0·5 cm.

A pentagon is made up of five isosceles triangles.

$z = 360° \div 5 = 72°$

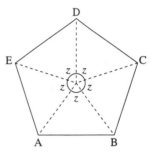

By splitting triangle AOB into two right angled triangles we can find AX, where X is the mid-point of AB.

$AX = 0·5 \sin 36°$
$AB = 2 AX = 2(0·5 \sin 36°)$
$AB = \sin 36° = 0·5877852523$ (10 d.p.)
So perimeter of pentagon $= 5 \times 0·5877852523$.

In a similar way find the perimeters of the following regular polygons with the same distance from the centre to the vertices.

(a) an octagon (8 sides)
(b) a decagon (10 sides)
(c) a 20 sided polygon
(d) a 100 sided polygon
(e) a 1000 sided polygon!

The more sides we take the closer our shape resembles a circle with a diameter of 1 cm and the nearer our perimeter gets to the circumference of a circle of diameter 1 cm.

182

Proof

- In the field of science a theory, like Newton's theory of graviation, can never be proved. It can only be considered highly likely using all the evidence available at the time. The history of science contains many examples of theories which were accepted at the time but were later shown to be untrue when more accurate observation was possible.

- A mathematical proof is far more powerful. Once a theorem is proved mathematically it will *always* be true. Pythagoras proved his famous theorem over 2500 years ago and when he died he knew it would never be disproved.

  A proof starts with simple facts which are accepted. The proof then argues logically to the result which is required.

For example, in Book 8 we used alternate angles to prove that the angle sum of any triangle is 180°.

We then *used* that result to prove that the angle sum of a quadrilateral is 360°.

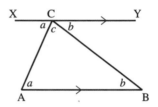

It is most important to realise that a result *cannot* be proved simply by finding thousands or even millions of results which support it.

Exercise 1

Questions **1**, **2**, **3** require a knowledge of the conditions for triangles to be congruent [i.e. SSS, SAS, ASA or RHS see section 2·2]

1. Copy and complete a proof that the opposite sides of a parallelogram are equal.

ABCD is a parallelogram

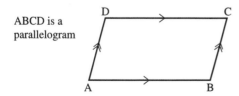

Draw diagonal AC

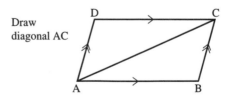

$\widehat{BAC} = \widehat{DCA}$ and $\widehat{DAC} = \widehat{BCA}$ (alternate angles)

AC is common to triangles ABC and DCA.

∴ Triangles ABC and ▢ are congruent (A.S.A.)

∴ AB = ▢ which proves that opposite sides of a parallelogram are equal.

2. To prove that the two base angles of an isosceles triangle are equal.

Triangle ABC is isosceles with AB = AC

Draw AD, the perpendicular from A, to meet BC at D

Prove that triangles ABD and ACD are congruent. [Hint: 'RHS']

Hence prove that the two base angles of an isosceles triangle are equal.

3. Draw any rhombus ABCD with four equal sides and opposite sides parallel.

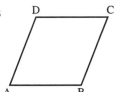

Draw diagonals AC and BD and introduce angles x and y.

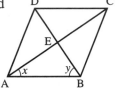

Use alternate angles and congruent triangles to prove that the diagonals of a rhombus bisect each other at right angles.

4. Triangle PQR is isosceles. Prove that $R\widehat{Q}S = 2 \times R\widehat{P}Q$.

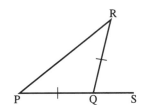

5. Prove that the answer to every line of the pattern below is 8.

$$3 \times 5 - 1 \times 7$$
$$4 \times 6 - 2 \times 8$$
$$5 \times 7 - 3 \times 9$$
$$\vdots \qquad \vdots$$

Hint: Write an expression for the nth line of the pattern.

6. Any three numbers [e.g. 2, 3, 7] are written at the corners of a triangle.

Each corner number is increased by 4 and the answer is written on the side opposite.

Sum of corner numbers $= 2 + 3 + 7 = 12$
Sum of side numbers $= 11 + 6 + 7 = 24$

What do you notice?

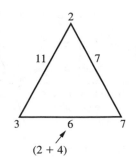

Draw a triangle with letters a, b, c at the corners and repeat the calculations.

What do you notice? Is the sum of the side numbers always twice the sum of the corner numbers?

7. (a) Draw a square and write four numbers at the corners and a fifth number in the middle. Four triangles are formed.

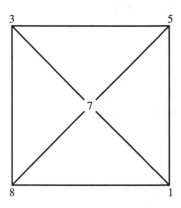

(b) Add the numbers at the corners of each triangle and write the answer inside the triangle.

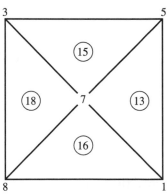

(c) Add the numbers inside *opposite* triangles: $15 + 16 = 31$
$18 + 13 = 31.$

(d) Is the sum of the numbers inside opposite triangles always the same?

Draw and label a square with letters a, b, c, d, e.

Part 6

6.1 Locus

A locus is the set of points which fit a certain description. Sometimes a locus can be described in words, sometimes it is better to draw a diagram. The plural of locus is loci.

(a) Suppose television reception is 'good' within 100 km of a transmitter T. The diagram shows the locus of points where the reception is 'good'.

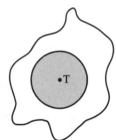

Here the locus is the boundary and all the points inside the circle.

(b) In this diagram the shaded region shows the locus of points inside a room which are within 1 m of a wall.

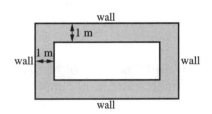

(c) Find the locus of points which are an equal distance from the points A and B. (we say 'equidistant' from A and B).

A•

•B

> This is an important and common locus construction.

Take a pair of compasses and set the radius at more than half the length AB. With centre A draw two arcs. With the same radius and centre B draw two more arcs. Draw a straight line through the points where the arcs cut. This is the locus of points equidistant from A and B. (shown with a broken line).

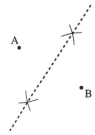

Exercise 1

1. Draw the locus of a point P which moves so that it is always 4 cm from a fixed point A.

2. Draw points B and C 6 cm apart. Draw the locus of a point P which moves so that it is equidistant from B and C.

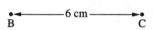

3. Draw the square KLMN. A tiny spider wanders around inside the square so that it is always nearer to corner K than to corner L. Shade the region to show the locus of the spider.

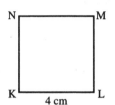

4. A newt crawls across a rectangular garden so that it is always at an equal distance from the two stone walls. Draw a sketch to show the locus of the newt.

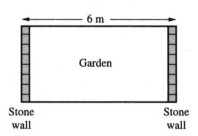

5. (a) Describe in words the locus of M, the tip of the minute hand, as the time changes from 3 o'clock to 4 o'clock.
   (b) Sketch the locus of H, the tip of the hour hand, as the time changes from 3 o'clock to 6 o'clock.

6. The diagram shows a rectangular room ABCD. Draw three diagrams with a scale of 1 cm to 1 m to illustrate the following loci:
   (a) Points in the room up to 3 m from A
   (b) Points in the room up to 2 m from E, the centre of the room.
   (c) Points in the room equidistant from A and B.

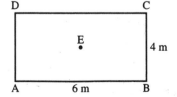

7. A snake's cage is built against a wall, as shown. The public are not allowed to be within one metre of the cage.
Sketch the cage and show the locus of points where the public are not allowed.

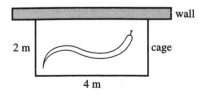

A submarine is known to be within 26 km of port P. The submarine is also known to be within 15 km of port Q. Show the region where the submarine must be.

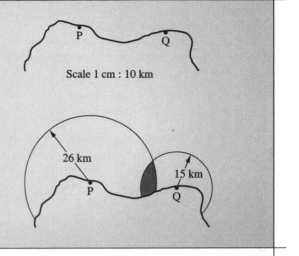

Scale 1 cm : 10 km

(a) Draw an arc of radius 2·6 cm with centre P.
(b) Draw an arc of radius 1·5 cm with centre Q.
(c) The submarine must lie inside both arcs so it lies in the shaded region.

Exercise 2

1. Inspector Clouseau has put a radio transmitter on a suspect's car, which is parked somewhere in Paris. From the strength of the signals received at points R and P, Clouseau knows that the car is
   (a) not more than 40 km from R, and
   (b) not more than 20 km from P.

   Make a scale drawing [1 cm ≡ 10 km] and show the possible positions of the suspect's car.

2. A treasure is buried in the rectangular garden shown. The treasure is: (a) within 4 m of A and (b) more than 3 m from the line AD.
   Draw a plan of the garden and shade the points where the treasure could be.

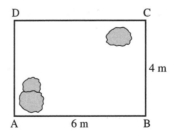

3. Draw four copies of square KLMN and show the locus of points *inside the square* which are:
   (a) within 3 cm of the mid point of KL,
   (b) equidistant from K and M,
   (c) nearer to M than to K,
   (d) more than 5 cm from N.

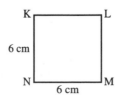

4. A goat is tied to one corner on the outside of a barn.
The diagram shows a plan view.
Sketch a plan view of the barn and show the locus of points where the goat can graze if the rope is 4 m long.

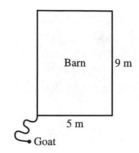

5. Draw a line AB of length 10 cm. With AB as base draw a triangle ABP so that the *area* of the triangle is 30 cm².
Describe the locus of P if P moves so that the area of the triangle ABP is always 30 cm².

6. A conker is hanging motionless on a string.
I move a finger so that its tip is always 20 cm from the conker. Describe the locus of my finger tip.

7. A rectangular paving slab is rotated 90° about corner A as shown.
(a) Copy the diagram and use a pair of compasses to draw the locus of X during the first rotation.
(b) The slab is then rotated a further 90° clockwise, this time about the corner B. Draw the new position of the slab. Use compasses to draw the path of X during this second rotation.

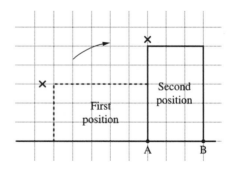

8. Draw two points A and B 10 cm apart.

Place the corner of a piece of paper (or a set square) so that the edges of the paper pass through A and B.
Mark the position of corner C.
Slide the paper around so the edges still passes through A and B and mark the new position of C. Repeat several times and describe the locus of the point C which moves so that angle ACB is always 90°.

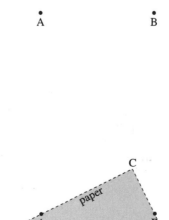

In a rectangle ABCD, AB = 4 cm and BC = 3 cm.
Find the points inside the rectangle which are:
(a) equidistant from lines AB and AD,
(b) nearer to line AD than to line AB.

(a) Construct the line which bisects angle BAD.
The broken line is the required locus.

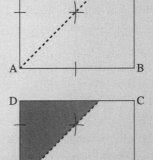

(b) Use the line drawn above and shade the points above the
broken line. Points on the line are *not* included in the locus
as the question asks for points *nearer* to AD than to AB.

Exercise 3

1. Draw two triangles ABC as shown.
In each triangle construct the locus
of points which are equidistant
from lines AB and AC.

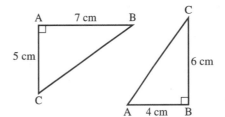

2. Draw full size the rectangle PQRS.
(a) Construct the locus of points which
are equidistant from lines SP and SR.
(b) Construct the locus of points which are
equidistant from lines RP and RQ.

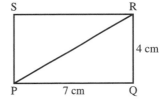

3.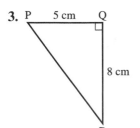

Draw one copy of triangle PQR and show on it:
(a) the locus of points equidistant from P and Q,
(b) the locus of points equidistant from lines PQ and PR,
(c) the locus of points nearer to PR than to PQ.

6.2 Probability

Methods of estimating probability

The probability of an event is a measure of the chance of it happening. Probability is measured on a scale from 0 to 1. An event which is impossible has a probability of 0. An event which is certain has a probability of 1.

There are four different ways of estimating probabilities.

Method A
Use symmetry

- The probability of rolling a 3 on a fair dice is $\frac{1}{6}$.
- This is because all the scores 1, 2, 3, 4, 5, 6 are equally likely.
- Similarly the probability of getting a head when tossing a fair coin is $\frac{1}{2}$.

Method B
Conduct an experiment or survey to collect data

- Suppose I wanted to estimate the probability of a drawing pin landing point upwards when dropped onto a hard surface. I could not use symmetry for obvious reasons but I could conduct an experiment to see what happened in, say, 500 trials.

- I might want to know the probability that the next car going past the school gates has only one occupant.
  I could conduct a survey in which the number of people in cars is recorded over a period of time.

Method C
Look at past data

Suppose I wanted to estimate the probability that there will be snow in the ski resort to which a school party is going in February next year. I could look at weather records for the area over the last 10 or 20 years.

Method D

Make a subjective estimate

We have to use this method when the event is not repeatable. It is not really a 'method' in the same sense as are methods A, B, C.

- We might want to estimate the probability of England beating France in a soccer match next week. We could look at past results but these could be of little value for all sorts of reasons. We might consult 'experts' but even they are notoriously inaccurate in their predictions.

Exercise 1

In Questions **1** to **14** state which method A, B, C or D you would use to estimate the probability of event given.

1. The probability of drawing a 'king' from a pack of playing cards.

2. The probability that it will rain every day at the site where the school party is going on a camping holiday next year.

3. The probability that a person selected at random would vote 'Conservative' in a general election tomorrow.

4. The probability that your maths teacher will pick the winning six numbers in the National Lottery next week. [There are 13 983 816 ways of choosing 6 numbers from 1 to 49.]

5. The probability that a letter posted 'first class' at 8.00 a.m. today will arrive at its destination tomorrow.

6. The probability that the England cricket team will win the toss in their next three test matches.

7. The probability that someone in your class will be the parent of twins within the next 20 years.

8. The probability that you will throw a 'double' when you roll a pair of fair dice.

9. The probability of spinning a '10' on a roulette wheel which is suspected of being biased.

10. The probability that sometime this week your mother will ask you to tidy your bedroom (unnecessarily!).

Relative frequency

- In Book 8 probabilities were worked out using equally likely outcomes. This is sometimes called the principle of *symmetry* (not to be confused with 'line symmetry' or 'rotational symmetry').

- In many situations this argument of symmetry cannot be applied. For example it is not easy to *work out* the probability of spinning a 5 on the spinner shown, which has unequal sectors.

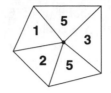

- When a drawing pin is dropped onto a hard surface, it will come to rest either point up or point down. You might think that the probability of the pin landing point up is $\frac{1}{2}$ because it must land either point up or point down. But a drawing pin is not a regular shape like a coin or a dice.

Often the best way to find an estimate of the probability of an event, which cannot be predicted, is to perform an experiment.

Experiment: 'Spinning a five'

A spinner, with unequal sectors, is spun 10 times and the number of 5's obtained is recorded. This procedure is repeated several times and the results are recorded in a table. The relative frequency of spinning a 5 is given by:

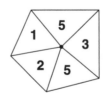

$$\text{Relative frequency of spinning a 5} = \left(\frac{\text{number of 5's obtained so far}}{\text{number of trials so far}}\right)$$

For simplicity use $\sqrt{}$ for 'spinning a 5' and $\times$ for 'not spinning a 5'.

Results	Number of 5's obtained so far	Number of trials so far	Relative frequency of spinning a 5
$\sqrt{}\times\times\sqrt{}\times\times\times\times\times\times$	2	10	$\frac{2}{10} = 0{\cdot}2$
$\times\sqrt{}\sqrt{}\sqrt{}\times\sqrt{}\sqrt{}\sqrt{}\times\sqrt{}$	9	20	$\frac{9}{20} = 0{\cdot}45$
$\sqrt{}\times\times\sqrt{}\sqrt{}\times\sqrt{}\times\times\sqrt{}$	14	30	$\frac{14}{30} = 0{\cdot}467$ (3 d.p.)
...	...	...	...

The experiment is continued until the number in the relative frequency column settles down to a fairly constant value.

A graph shows the progress of the experiment very clearly.

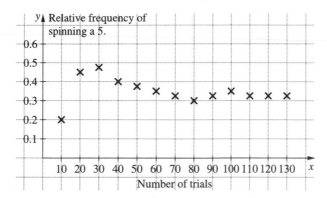

The graph may start by going up and down but after many trials the relative frequency settles down to a fairly constant number.

We can take the *relative frequency* of an event occurring as an estimate of the *probability* of that event occurring. The estimate improves as the number of trials is increased.

Exercise 2

1. Karim randomly selects a card from a pack and notes whether it is a Heart, Spade, Diamond or Club. Here are his results:

   S H D S S C H C C S D H H C S
   C H C D S D H C D S H S S C H

   (a) What was the relative frequency of selecting a Heart?
   (b) What was the relative frequency of selecting a Diamond?

2. In an experiment Tom drops 12 drawing pins onto a hard floor. He does the experiment 10 times and counts how many pins land 'point up'. His results were

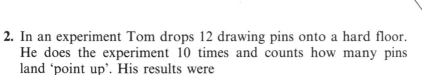

Number of the 12 drawing pins that landed 'point up'									
3	5	6	2	4	7	3	3	4	5

   (a) Use Tom's data to work out the probability that a *single* drawing pin will land point up.
   (b) Tom continues the experiment until he has dropped the 12 drawing pins 100 times.
   About how many drawing pins in total would you expect to land point up?

3. Four friends are using a spinner for a game and they wonder if it is perfectly fair. They each spin the spinner several times and record the results.

	Number of	Results		
Name	spins	0	1	2
Alan	30	12	12	6
Keith	100	31	49	20
Bill	300	99	133	68
Ann	150	45	73	32

(a) Whose results are most likely to give the best estimate of the probability of getting each number?

(b) Make a table and collect together all the results.
Use the table to decide whether you think the spinner is biased or unbiased.

(c) Use the results to work out the probability of the spinner getting a '2'.

4. The ⟨RAN#⟩ button on a calculator generates random numbers between ·000 and ·999. It can be used to simulate tossing three coins. We could say any *odd* digit is a *tail* and any *even* digit is a head. So the number ·346 represents THH

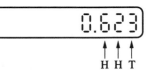

Use the ⟨RAN#⟩ button to simulate the tossing of three coins

'Toss' the three coins 100 or 200 times and work out the relative frequency of getting three heads.

Compare your result with the value that you would expect to get theoretically.

5. **(Practical).** To find the relative frequency of a drawing pin landing pointing up.

Drop a drawing pin (or perhaps 10 drawing pins) onto a hard surface and count the number of times it lands point up. Record the results in groups of 10 trials in a table. Use √ for 'point up' and ⨯ for 'point down'.

Draw a graph of relative frequency against number of trials, similar to the one above, and state the relative frequency of the event occurring after a large number (say 200) trials. (Combine results with other people).

Working out probabilities

Exercise 3

1. One card is picked at random from a pack of 52.
   Find the probability that it is
   (a) the Jack of diamonds
   (b) a seven
   (c) a heart.

2. A bag contains 9 balls: 3 red, 4 white and 2 yellow.
   (a) Find the probability of selecting a red ball.
   (b) The 2 yellow balls are replaced by 2 white balls.
       Find the probability of selecting a white ball.

3. Mark played a card game with Paul. The cards were dealt so
   that both players received two cards. Mark's cards were a five
   and a four. Paul's first card was a six.

Mark   Paul

   Find the probability that Paul's second card was
   (a) a five
   (b) a picture card [a King, Queen or Jack].

4. One ball is selected at random from the bag
   shown and then replaced. This procedure is
   repeated 400 times. How many times would you
   expect to select:
   (a) a blue ball,
   (b) a white ball?

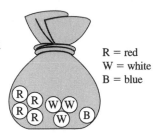

R = red
W = white
B = blue

5.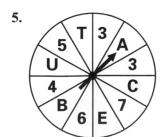

A spinner, with 12 equal sectors, is spun 420 times.
How often would you expect to spin:
(a) an E,
(b) an even number,
(c) a vowel?

10. Heena puts 4 white balls and 1 black ball in a bag. She then takes out one ball without looking.

(a) Heena asks her parents about the probability of getting a black.

Her mum says, 'It is $\frac{1}{4}$ because there are 4 whites and 1 black.'

Her dad says, 'It is $\frac{1}{5}$ because there are 5 balls and only 1 black.'

Which of her parents is correct?

(b) Carl has another bag containing red and white balls. The probability of picking a red ball from Carl's bag is $\frac{4}{7}$. What is the probability of picking a white ball from Carl's bag?

(c) How many balls of each colour *could* be in Carl's bag?

(d) Write down another possibility for the number of balls of each colour that could be in Carl's bag.

11. The number of people visiting Tower Bridge one day was 11,249. How many of these people would you expect to celebrate their birthdays on a Tuesday in the year 2000?

12. When playing Monopoly, Philip knows that the probability of throwing a 'double' with two dice is $\frac{1}{6}$. What is the probability that he does *not* throw a double with his next throw?

13. Keven bought one ticket in a raffle in which 200 tickets were sold. What is the probability that Kevin did not win the first prize?

14. A coin is biased so that the probability of tossing a head is 56%.
(a) What is the probability of tossing a tail with this coin?
(b) How many tails would you expect when the coin is tossed 500 times?

15. One ball is selected from a bag containing x red balls and y blue balls. What is the probability of selecting a red ball?

16. One ball is selected from a bag containing n yellow balls, m red balls and 7 white balls. What is the probability of selecting a yellow ball?

Listing possible outcomes

When an experiment involves two events, it is usually helpful to make a list of all the possible outcomes. When there is a large number of outcomes, it is important to be systematic in making the list.

- Coins
- Using H for 'head' and T for 'tail', two coins can land as:

H	H
H	T
T	H
T	T

- Two dice
  When a red dice is thrown with a white dice, the outcomes are (red dice first):
  (1, 1), (1, 2), (1, 3), (1, 4), (1, 5), (1, 6), (2, 1), (2, 2), (2, 3)...(6, 6).

The 36 equally likely outcomes can be shown on a grid. Point A shows a 4 on the red dice and a 5 on the white dice. Point B shows a 2 on the red dice and a 4 on the white dice.

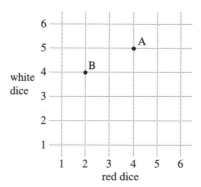

The probability of rolling a two on the red dice and a four on the white dice is $\frac{1}{36}$

Exercise 4

1. A 10p coin and a 20p coin are tossed together. List all the possible outcomes, heads or tails, for the two coins.

2. Three coins are tossed together. List all the possible outcomes for the three coins.
   What is the probability of tossing three heads?
   [See also Question 4 on page 194.]

3. A red dice and a white dice are thrown together.
   (a) Draw a grid to show all the possible outcomes.
   (b) What is the probability of:
      (i)   getting the same number on each dice?
      (ii) a total score of 10?
      (iii) the score on the red dice being double the score on the white dice?

4. Katy has these two spinners. She spins both spinners and adds up the numbers to get a total. For example a '10' and a '2' give a total of 12.
   Make a list of all the possible totals.
   What is the probability of getting a total of 8?

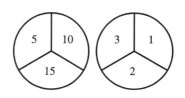

5. A bag contains a 2p coin, a 5p coin and a 10p coin. Two coins are selected at random.
   (a) List all the possible combinations of two coins which can be selected from the bag.
   (b) Find the probability that the total value of the two coins selected is
      (i)   15p
      (ii) 7p
      (iii) 20p

6. A coin and a dice are tossed together.
  (a) List all the possible outcomes.
  (b) Find the probability of getting
     (i) a head on the coin and a 6 on the dice
     (ii) a tail on the coin and an even number on the dice.

7. Four friends, Jen, Ken, Len and Mick, each write their name on a card and the four cards are placed in a hat. Two cards are chosen to decide who does the washing-up that day.
  (a) List all the possible combinations.
  (b) What is the probability that Ken and Len are chosen?

8. The spinner is spun and the dice is rolled at the same time.
  (a) Draw a grid to show all the possible outcomes.
  (b) A 'win' occurs when the number on the spinner is greater than the number on the dice.
     Find the probability of a 'win'.

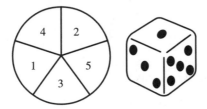

Exclusive events

Events are *mutually exclusive* if they cannot occur at the same time.

Examples

- Selecting a Queen ⎱ from a pack
  Selecting a 3   ⎰ of cards

- Tossing a 'head'
  Tossing a 'tail'

- Selecting a red ball from a bag
  Selecting a white ball from the same bag.

The sum of the probabilities of mutually exclusive events is 1

Exercise 5

1. A bag contains a large number of balls including some green balls. The probability of selecting a green ball is $\frac{1}{4}$. What is the probability of selecting a ball which is not green?

2. A bag contains balls which are either red, blue or yellow.
The probability of selecting a red is 0·3
The probability of selecting a blue is 0·4
What is the probability of selecting a yellow?

3. A bag contains balls which are either red, white or green.
The probability of selecting a red ball is 0·1
The probability of selecting a white ball is 0·6
(a) Find the probability of selecting a green ball?
(b) Find the probability of selecting a ball
which is not red?

4. In a game using an electronic spinner, four possible symbols can be obtained.
The probability of each occurring is:

Star prize	$\frac{1}{16}$
Cat	$\frac{1}{8}$
Mouse	$\frac{1}{4}$
Lose	?

Find the probability of:
(a) losing
(b) getting 'cat' or 'mouse'
(c) not getting 'Star prize'.

5. A bag contains a large number of discs.
Most are numbered 1, 2, 3 or 4.
The rest are blank.
Here are the probabilities of drawing a
disc with a particular number:

$p(1) = 0\cdot2$
$p(2) = 0\cdot15$
$p(3) = 0\cdot25$
$p(4) = 0\cdot1$

What is the probability of drawing a disc,
(a) marked 1 or 2?
(b) marked 2, 3 or 4?
(c) which is blank?

6.3 Gradient, $y = mx + c$

- If we know the coordinates of two points on a line, we can use the formula

$$\text{Gradient} = \frac{\text{Difference between } y \text{ coordinates}}{\text{Difference between } x \text{ coordinates}}$$

The gradient of a line tells us how steep it is.
- Consider the line which passes through (1, 2) and (3, 6).

$$\text{Gradient} = \frac{6-2}{3-1} = \frac{4}{2} = 2$$

Notice that:

- a line sloping upwards to the right has a positive gradient;
- a line sloping downwards to the right has a negative gradient.

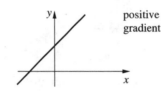

positive gradient

negative gradient

[Some people think of a capital 'N' for negative.]

Exercise 1

1. Find the gradient of the line joining
   (a) (1, 3) and (2, 6)   (b) (1, 3) and (3, 7)
   (c) (2, 5) and (6, 7)   (d) (3, 9) and (9, 11)
   (e) (1, 4) and (3, 2)   (f) (2, 5) and (5, −1)
   (g) (6, 2) and (2, 10)   (h) (3, −2) and (−3, 2)
   (i) (−2, −4) and (−1, 2)   (j) (2, −3) and (−2, 6).

2. Find the gradient of the line joining:
   (a) A and B
   (b) B and C
   (c) C and D
   (d) D and A.

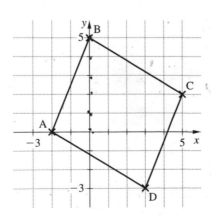

Gradient and intercept

A straight line can be described in terms of

(a) its gradient
(b) where it crosses the *y*-axis (the *y*-intercept).

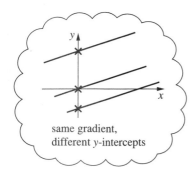

same gradient,
different *y*-intercepts

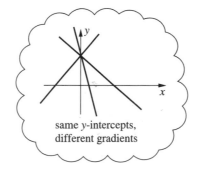

same *y*-intercepts,
different gradients

Exercise 2

Sketch the following straight lines. Use a new pair of axes for each question. Draw about six sketches on one page of your book.

1. Gradient 2, *y*-intercept 3.   **2.** Gradient 1, *y*-intercept −3.

3. Gradient 2, *y*-intercept 0.   **4.** Gradient −1, *y*-intercept 4.

5. Gradient −3, *y*-intercept 0.   **6.** Gradient −2, *y*-intercept −2.

7. Give the gradient and *y*-intercept of each line.

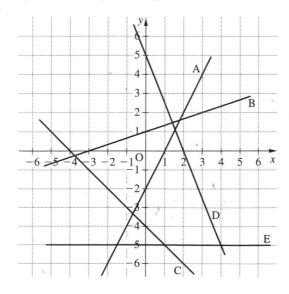

The line $y = mx + c$

$y = mx + c$ is the equation of a straight line with

- gradient m, and
- intercept c. [Hereafter the word 'intercept' is taken to be the y-intercept.]

Sketch the line with equation $y = 3x - 1$.

Gradient $= 3$.
Intercept $= -1$.

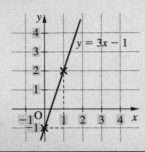

Exercise 3

Write down the gradient and intercept of each of the following lines:

1. $y = 2x - 3$ **2.** $y = 3x + 2$

3. $y = -x - 4$ **4.** $y = \frac{1}{2}x + 3$ (Careful!)

5. $y = -\frac{2}{3}x - 4$ **6.** $y = 2 - 3x$

7. $y = 4 - 7x$ **8.** $y = 2x - 1$

9. $y = 3 - \frac{1}{2}x$ **10.** $y = 7 - 2x$

In Questions **11** to **16** make y the subject and write down the gradient and intercept of the corresponding line:

11. $2x + y - 6 = 0$ **12.** $y - 3x + 7 = 0$

13. $y - 2x = 8$ **14.** $3x + 6y - 10 = 0$

15. $2x - 5y + 12 = 0$ **16.** $3y - 9x + 2 = 0$

Sketch each of the following lines:

17. $y = x + 2$ **18.** $y = 2x - 4$

19. $y = 3 - 2x$ **20.** $y = \frac{3}{4}x - 1$

21. $y = 2 - \frac{1}{3}x$ **22.** $y - 2x + 2 = 0$

23. $2x + 4y + 1 = 0$ **24.** $3y - 9x - 1 = 0$

In Questions **25** to **30** match each sketch with the correct equation from the list below.

25. 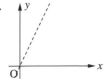   **26.** 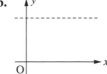   **27.**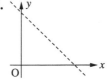

28. 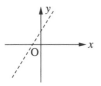   **29.** 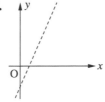   **30.**

(a) $y = -x - 4$ (b) $y = 2x - 1$ (c) $y = 2x + 3$
(d) $y = 3x$ (e) $y = 3 - x$ (f) $y = 5$

Parallel and perpendicular lines

Exercise 4

1. (a) Find the gradient of each side of the square shown.
   (b) What do you notice about the gradient of AB and the gradient of BC?

Repeat with different squares.

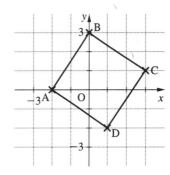

   (c) Copy and complete:
      'For perpendicular lines the product of the gradients is ☐.'

2. Write down the equation of any line which is parallel to
   (a) $y = 2x - 1$ (b) $y = 7x + 3$

3. Write down the gradient of a line which is perpendicular to a line of gradient
   (a) 3   (b) -1 (c) $\frac{1}{4}$ (d) $-\frac{1}{2}$.

4. Write down the equation of any line which is perpendicular to
(a) $y = 2x + 1$ (b) $y = -\frac{1}{4}x$ (c) $y = \frac{1}{3}x + 7$

5. Here are the equations of several straight lines.

A $\boxed{y = 3x - 1}$ B $\boxed{y = x - 3}$ C $\boxed{y = \frac{1}{2}x + 1}$ D $\boxed{y = 3x + 5}$

E $\boxed{y = -2x}$ F $\boxed{y = -x + 7}$ G $\boxed{y = 1 + 4x}$ H $\boxed{y = 4x}$

(a) Find two pairs of lines which are parallel.
(b) Find two pairs of lines which are perpendicular.

6.4 Inequalities

$x < y$ means 'x is less than y' [or 'y is greater than x']

$p \leqslant q$ means 'p is less than or equal to q' [or 'q is greater than or equal to p'].

$a > b$ means 'a is greater than b' [or 'b is less than a']

$n \geqslant t$ means 'n is greater than or equal to t'.

Notice that the inequality signs can be read from left to right or from right to left.

Inequalities occur frequently in everyday life.

- 'The speed limit along Valley Road is 40 m.p.h.'

  We can write $s \leqslant 40$, where s is the speed of cars in m.p.h.

- 'Each plant in the greenhouse produced more than 7 flowers.'

  We can write $f > 7$, where f is the number of flowers.

- 'Applicants for training as prison officers in Switzerland must be at least 1·70 m tall.'

  We can write $h \geqslant 1\cdot70$ m, where h is the height of applicants.

- 'The percentage required for a grade **B** was between 49 and 62 inclusive.'

  We can write $49 \leqslant p \leqslant 62$, where p is the percentage mark.

Illustrate on a number line the range of values of x for which the following inequalities are true:

(a) $x > 1$

The circle at the left hand end of the range is open. This means that 1 is not included.

(b) $x \leqslant -2$

The circle at -2 is filled in to indicate that -2 is included.

(c) $-1 \leqslant x < 3$

[−1 included]   [3 not included]

Exercise 1

[The answers to Questions **1** and **2** can be written down or discussed in class.]

1. Write an inequality for each statement.
   (a) The maximum number of passengers, n, in the school minibus is 16.
   (b) For best results the temperature of the oven, T, has to be between 180 °C and 215 °C.
   (c) The minimum mark, m, for a pass in the Highway Code test is 80%.

2. Here is an advertisement for a job. Write the information given in the form of inequalities. Make up your own symbols for the relevant quantities.

> ### Driver/Bodyguard Wanted
>
> Age 20 to 50. Must have at least 5 years clean driving license.
>
> Applicants must have more than 2 GCSEs and weigh between 10 and 15 stones. Salary in excess of £300 per week.
>
> Phone 0182 996 13274.

3. Write down the inequalities displayed. Use x for the variable.

(a)

(b)

(c)

(d)

(e)

(f)

(g)

(h)

(i)

(j)

(k)

(l)

4. Draw a number line to display the following inequalities.

(a) $x > -1$ (b) $x \leqslant 4$ (c) $a > -2$

(d) $n \leqslant 0$ (e) $-5 < p < 5$ (f) $-1 \leqslant y$

(g) $0 \leqslant x \leqslant 10$ (h) $-2 < t \leqslant 7$ (i) $-3 \leqslant s < -1$

5. Answer true or false:

(a) $71 > 701$ (b) $-3 < 1$ (c) $3\frac{1}{2} < 325$ (d) $-6 < -10$

(e) 1 metre > 1 yard (f) $1\,\text{kg} > 1$ pound (g) 1 inch $< 2\,\text{cm}$ (h) $2^3 < 3^2$

6. Write a possible number for ☐ in each of the following:

(a) $1000 < \boxed{} < 2000$ (b) $2540 < \boxed{} < 2550$ (c) $-3 < \boxed{} < 2$

(d) $2{\cdot}1 \boxed{} < 2{\cdot}2$ (e) $16\,436 < \boxed{} \ 16\,438$ (f) $9842 < \boxed{} < 9843$

7. The variable n satisfies each of these inequalities:

$$2 \leqslant n \leqslant 5 \quad \text{and} \quad 3 < n < 7$$

Mark the solution set for n on a number line.

Solving inequalities

When we solve an equation, like $3x - 1 = x + 9$, we find one value of x which satisfies the equation.

When we solve an inequality, like $2x + 3 < 10$, we find the *range of values* of x which satisfy the inequality.

For example, the solution of the inequality $x - 3 < 11$ is $x < 14$. The variable x can be any value less than 14.

When solving inequalities we can:

- Add the same thing to both sides.
- Subtract the same thing from both sides.
- Multiply or divide both sides by the same *positive* number.

If we multiply or divide by a *negative* number the inequality sign must be *reversed*.

(a) Consider the inequality $4 > -2.$
    Now multiply both sides by (-1) $-4 < 2.$
$$\uparrow$$
sign is reversed.

(b) Consider the inequality $-3 < 6$
    Divide both sides by (-3) $1 > -2$
    Again the inequality sign is reversed.

Solve the inequalities.

(a) $x - 3 < 4$

   Add 3 to both sides.

   $x < 7$

(b) $x + 5 > -2$

   Subtract 5 from both sides.

   $x > -2 - 5$

   $x > -7$

(c) $5x \geqslant 350$

   Divide both sides by 5.

   $x \geqslant 70$

(d) $\dfrac{x}{3} \leqslant -2$

   Multiply both sides by 3.

   $x \leqslant -6$

Exercise 2

Solve the inequalities.

1. $x - 10 \geqslant 2$ 2. $x + 6 < 11$ 3. $y - 6 > -3$

4. $7 + y < 11$ 5. $3 + x \geqslant 9$ 6. $x + 1 < 0$

7. $3n \geqslant 48$ 8. $5y < 1$ 9. $10x < 1000$

10. $x - 3 < -2$ 11. $y + 7 > -7$ 12. $5 + n \geqslant 4$

Find the range of values of x which satisfy each of the following inequalities and show the answer on a number line.

13. $\dfrac{x}{2} < 3$ 14. $\dfrac{x}{5} > \dfrac{1}{2}$ 15. $\dfrac{x}{3} \leqslant -1$

16. $-12 \geqslant 3x$ 17. $\dfrac{1}{4} > \dfrac{x}{2}$ 18. $\dfrac{3x}{2} > 6$

19. $x - 4 > 0$ 20. $7 < x + 10$ 21. $8 + x \leqslant 0$

In Questions **22** to **26** list the solutions which satisfy the given conditions.

22. $3n < 30$; n is a positive integer (whole number).

23. $0 < a < 12$; a is an even number.

24. $\dfrac{3x}{5} < 7$; x is a positive integer.

25. $0 < 2y < 9$; y is an integer.

26. $\dfrac{p}{3} < 8$; p is a prime number.

27. State the smallest integer for which $5y > 21$.

28. Write down any value of x such that $2^3 < x < 3^2$.

208

Exercise 3

In Questions **1** to **8** find, where possible, the range of values of x for which both inequalities are true. If there are no values of x write 'impossible'.

1. $x > 0$ and $x < 3$

2. $x < 2$ and $x > 0$

3. $x > -3$ and $x < -1$

4. $x > 8$ and $x < 11$

5. $x < 6$ and $x > 7$

6. $2x < 3$ and $x > 0$

7. $5x > 1$ and $2x < 1$

8. $1 < 3x$ and $4x < 3$

In Questions **9** to **17** solve each pair of inequalities and then find the range of values of x for which both inequalities are true.

9. $x - 3 < 1$ and $2x + 1 > 0$

10. $\dfrac{x}{2} + 1 < 3$ and $3x > 0$

11. $1 - 5x > 6$ and $2x + 7 > 3$

12. $\dfrac{x}{3} - 3 > 0$ and $12 - x > 1$

13. Given that $1 \leqslant x \leqslant 5$ and $-3 \leqslant y \leqslant -1$, find
   (a) the greatest possible value of $x - y$.
   (b) the least possible value of $x^2 + y^2$.

14. Given that $1 \leqslant a \leqslant 10$ and $-5 \leqslant b \leqslant 6$, find
   (a) the greatest possible value of $\dfrac{b}{a}$.
   (b) the greatest possible value of $b^2 - a$.
   (c) the greatest possible value of $a - b$

15. (a) Given that $5x > 1$ and that $x - 2 < 3$, list all the possible whole number values of x.
   (b) If $3^x > 1000$, what is the smallest whole number value of x?

16.* Find the largest whole number n such that
$$\frac{0 \cdot 07}{n - 7} > \frac{1}{234}.$$

17.* Find the smallest whole number n such that
$$\frac{0 \cdot 009}{500 - n} > \frac{1}{999}.$$

Inequalities in two variables

Exercise 4

1. Copy and complete:
'The shaded region is described by
the three inequalities

$y \leqslant x$, $x \leqslant 4$ and $y \square 1$.

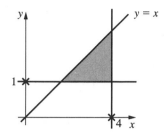

2. Write three inequalities to describe fully the shaded region.

(a) 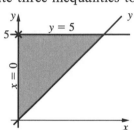   (b) 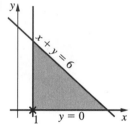   (c)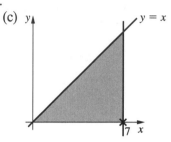

(d) 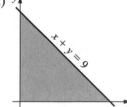   (e) 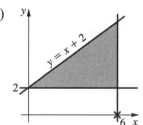   (f)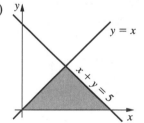

3. Draw sketch graphs and shade the regions indicated.
   (a) $y \geqslant x$, $x \geqslant 1$, $y \leqslant 5$ (b) $y \leqslant x$, $x \leqslant 6$, $y \geqslant 0$

4. The shaded region is bounded by the
line $y = 3$ and the curve $y = x^2$.

Which two inequalities from the list below,
fully describe the shaded region?

$x > 0$ $y > 0$ $y \geqslant x^2$
$y \leqslant x^2$ $y \leqslant 3$ $y < x$

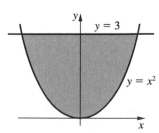

6.5 Trigonometry

In a right angled triangle we use different words to describe the three sides.

The longest side (opposite the right angle) is the *Hypotenuse*, HYP. The side opposite a known second angle, x, is the *Opposite*, OPP. The length touching both, x, and the right angle is the *Adjacent*, ADJ. It is important to be able to identify these sides in order to carry out our calculations.

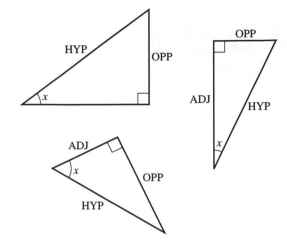

Exercise 1

1. [This question can be done orally.] Use the small letters a, b, c, d etc to label the opposite, hypotenuse and adjacent in relation to the angle marked in each triangle.

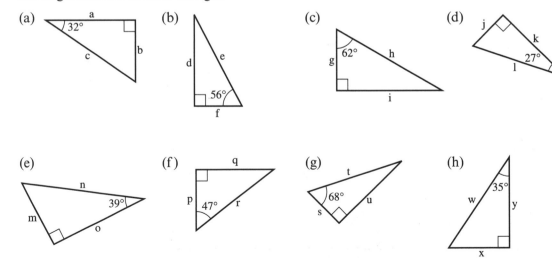

2. All the right angled triangles below have a 30° angle. Make a copy of the table on the next page and write in the measurements as accurately as possible. Calculate the ratios $\dfrac{OPP}{HYP}$, $\dfrac{ADJ}{HYP}$, $\dfrac{OPP}{ADJ}$, and write these in the table. The numbers for the first triangle have been completed for you.

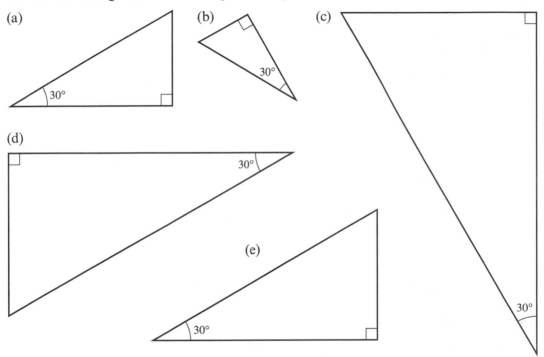

(a)   (b)   (c)   (d)   (e)

Triangle	Lengths			Ratios (to 2 d.p.)		
	Opp	Adj	Hyp	Opp ÷ Hyp	Adj ÷ Hyp	Opp ÷ Adj
(a)	2·5	4·3	5	0·5	0·86	0·58
(b)						
(c)						
(d)						
(e)						

3. Choose a different angle to 30° and draw five more right angled triangles of your own. Keep the angles the same but change the lengths of the sides. Make the table of results as before. Comment on what you notice.

Ratios of sides

You should have found that the ratios $\dfrac{\text{OPP}}{\text{HYP}}$, $\dfrac{\text{ADJ}}{\text{HYP}}$ and $\dfrac{\text{OPP}}{\text{ADJ}}$

remained constant if the angle remained the same. Any slight difference is due to the fact that it is impossible to measure with complete accuracy.

The ratios of these lengths remain constant for any given angle. Before we had calculators these values were printed in tables but now we literally have the answers at our fingertips.

$\dfrac{\text{OPP}}{\text{HYP}}$ = Sine of the angle $\boxed{\text{SIN}}$ on a calculator

$\dfrac{\text{ADJ}}{\text{HYP}}$ = Cosine of the angle $\boxed{\text{COS}}$ on a calculator

$\dfrac{\text{OPP}}{\text{ADJ}}$ = Tangent of the angle $\boxed{\text{TAN}}$ on a calculator

There are now two different types of calculator in common use. Try typing either $\boxed{30}\boxed{\text{SIN}}$ or $\boxed{\text{SIN}}\boxed{30}\boxed{=}$. The answer should be

$0\cdot 5$ $\left(\text{compare with the value you got for } \dfrac{\text{OPP}}{\text{HYP}} \text{ in question 2}\right)$.

Finding a side using sine

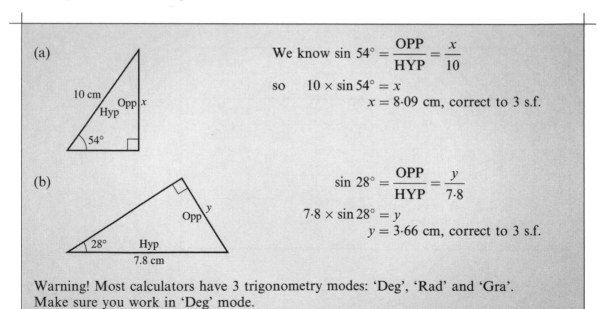

(a)

We know $\sin 54° = \dfrac{\text{OPP}}{\text{HYP}} = \dfrac{x}{10}$

so $10 \times \sin 54° = x$

$x = 8\cdot 09$ cm, correct to 3 s.f.

(b)

$\sin 28° = \dfrac{\text{OPP}}{\text{HYP}} = \dfrac{y}{7\cdot 8}$

$7\cdot 8 \times \sin 28° = y$

$y = 3\cdot 66$ cm, correct to 3 s.f.

Warning! Most calculators have 3 trigonometry modes: 'Deg', 'Rad' and 'Gra'. Make sure you work in 'Deg' mode.

Exercise 2

1. Copy the following triangles and then use sine to find the required length, correct to 3 significant figures.

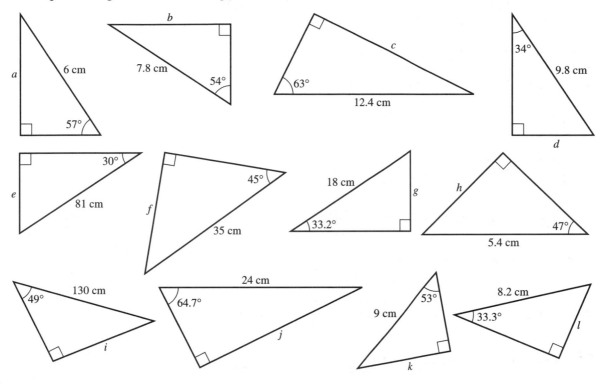

2. An aircraft has travelled 650 m in a straight line since it took off from the ground at an angle of 19°. Assuming the ground below is horizontal, find the height of the plane above the ground.

3. An isosceles triangle has two equal sides of 7·2 cm and equal base angles of 70°. Calculate the vertical height of the triangle.

4. Neil is fishing from the straight bank of a river. He lets out 17 m of line and this is carried down stream so that the line makes an angle of 22° with the bank where Neil is standing. What is the shortest distance from the hook to the bank?

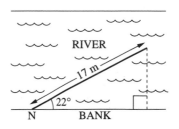

5. A see-saw is made from a 6 foot plank of wood pivoting about the middle on a stand. The piece of wood makes an angle of 32° with the ground when one side of the see-saw is touching the ground. How high is the pivot stand?

6. Carol walks for 1·7 km on a bearing of 042°. How far east has she walked from her starting position?

7. Kalyam wants to draw a circle. She lines her pencil up with the point of the compass. The length of the compass arm is 9 cm and she sets the angle between the arms at 28°. What is the diameter of the circle she can draw?

Finding a side using sine, cosine or tangent

In the last exercise the questions were made easier because you used the sine of an angle every time. In general, when solving a right angle triangle, you may have to use sine, cosine or tangent.

Remember: $\quad \sin x = \dfrac{\text{OPP}}{\text{HYP}}, \quad \cos x = \dfrac{\text{ADJ}}{\text{HYP}}, \quad \tan x = \dfrac{\text{OPP}}{\text{ADJ}}$

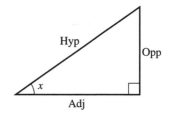

Many people use the word 'SOHCAHTOA' to help them choose the correct function. When solving triangles you should go through three stages:

1. Draw a diagram.

2. Label the sides Opp, Hyp, Adj relative to the given angle.

3. Decide whether you need sin, cos or tan.

Find the sides marked with letters.

(a)

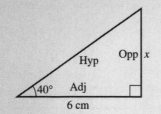

Label Opp, Hyp, Adj.
Since we want 'Opp' and we know 'Adj', choose tan.

$$\tan 40° = \frac{\text{Opp}}{\text{Adj}} = \frac{x}{6}$$

$6 \times \tan 40° = x$
$\qquad x = 5·03$ cm, correct to 3 s.f.

(b)

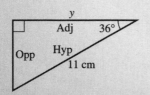

Label Opp, Hyp, Adj.
Since we want 'Adj' and we know 'Hyp', choose cos.

$$\cos 36° = \frac{\text{Adj}}{\text{Hyp}} = \frac{y}{11}$$

$11 \times \cos 36° = y$

Exercise 3

1. Sketch each triangle and find the sides marked with letters, correct to 3 s.f. All lengths are in cm.

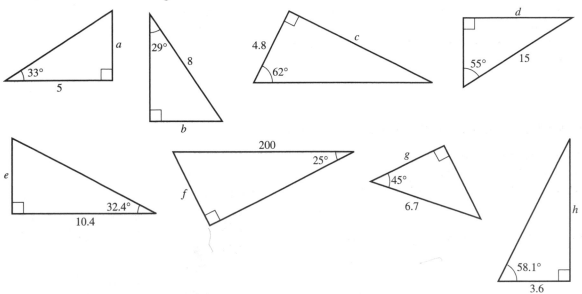

2. Find the sides marked with letters, correct to 3 s.f. All lengths are in cm.

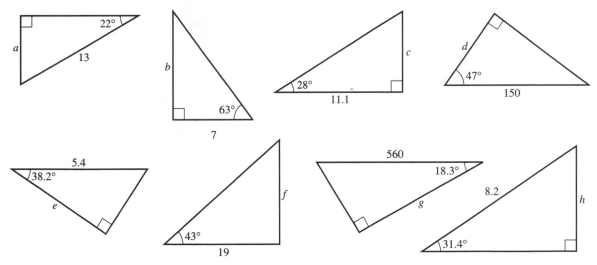

3. In triangle ABC, $A\hat{B}C = 90°$, $B\hat{A}C = 37°$, AC = 5 cm. Find BC.

4. In triangle DEF, $D\hat{F}E = 90°$, $E\hat{D}F = 42°$, DE = 8 cm. Find EF.

5. In triangle GHI, $G\hat{I}H = 90°$, $G\hat{H}I = 67°$, GH = 8 cm. Find HI.

6. In triangle PQR, $P\hat{Q}R = 90°$, $Q\hat{P}R = 35°$, PQ = 10 cm. Find RQ.

7. In triangle STU, $U\hat{S}T = 90°$, $S\hat{U}T = 43°$, UT = 100 cm. Find SU.

8. In triangle WXY, $X\hat{W}Y = 90°$, $W\hat{Y}X = 72°$, WY = 5 cm. Find WX.

9. In triangle ABC, $A\hat{B}C = 90°$, $B\hat{A}C = 53°$, AB = 4 cm. Find BC.

10. In triangle DEF, $D\hat{E}F = 90°$, $E\hat{D}F = 32\cdot2°$, DF = 15 cm. Find EF.

11. A ladder leans against a vertical wall so that it makes an angle of 28° with the wall. The top of the ladder reaches 3 m up the wall. How far from the wall is the base of the ladder?

12. A ladder of length 4 m rests against a vertical wall so that the angle between the ladder and the ground is 66°. How far up the wall does the ladder reach?

13. Paul stands 30 m from the base of a giant Redwood tree. He measures the angle of elevation to the top of the tree as 69°. How tall is the tree?

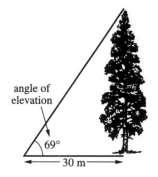

angle of elevation

69°

30 m

14. The sail for a windsurfer is in the shape of a right angled triangle. If the height of the sail is 3·2 m and the longest side makes an angle of 32° with the mast, when in place, how wide is the base of the sail?

15. An isosceles triangle has two equal sides of 15 cm and equal base angles of 68°. How long is the base of the triangle?

16. A girl is flying a kite from a string of length 45 m. If the string is taut and makes an angle of 34° with the horizontal, what is the height of the kite?

17. Robert is standing on the third floor of a block of flats. There is an office block that is 40 m across the street from him. Robert estimates the angle of elevation to the top of the block is 52° and the angle of depression to the base is 27°. Work out the height of the office block, correct to the nearest metre.

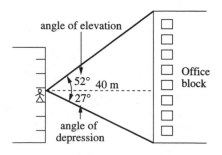

angle of elevation

52° 40 m

27°

angle of depression

Office block

Finding an angle

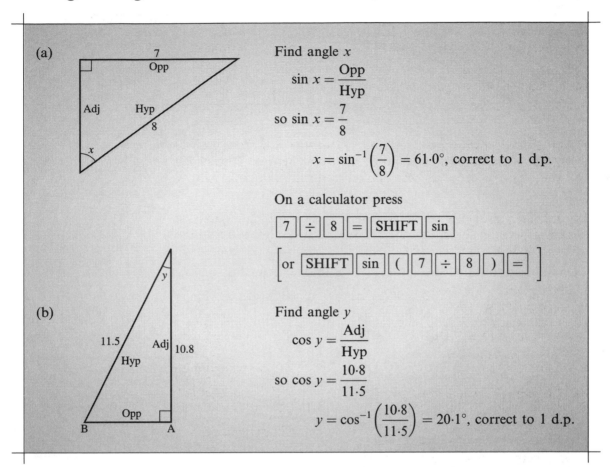

(a)

Find angle x

$$\sin x = \frac{\text{Opp}}{\text{Hyp}}$$

so $\sin x = \dfrac{7}{8}$

$$x = \sin^{-1}\left(\frac{7}{8}\right) = 61 \cdot 0°, \text{ correct to 1 d.p.}$$

On a calculator press

$$\boxed{7}\ \boxed{\div}\ \boxed{8}\ \boxed{=}\ \boxed{\text{SHIFT}}\ \boxed{\sin}$$

$$\left[\text{or}\ \boxed{\text{SHIFT}}\ \boxed{\sin}\ \boxed{(}\ \boxed{7}\ \boxed{\div}\ \boxed{8}\ \boxed{)}\ \boxed{=}\right]$$

(b)

Find angle y

$$\cos y = \frac{\text{Adj}}{\text{Hyp}}$$

so $\cos y = \dfrac{10 \cdot 8}{11 \cdot 5}$

$$y = \cos^{-1}\left(\frac{10 \cdot 8}{11 \cdot 5}\right) = 20 \cdot 1°, \text{ correct to 1 d.p.}$$

Exercise 4

1. Find the angles marked, correct to one decimal place. All lengths are in cm.

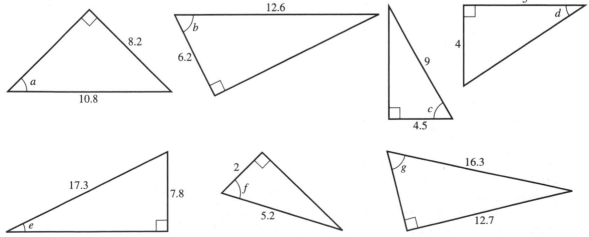

2. Find the angles marked, correct to the nearest degree.

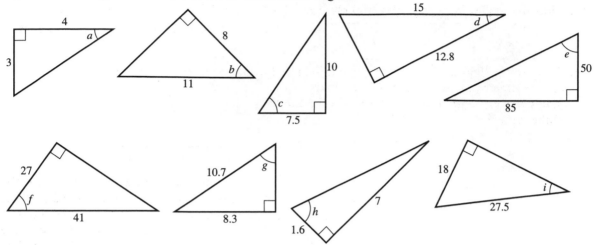

In Questions **3** to **8** find the angles, correct to one decimal place.

3. In triangle ABC, $A\hat{B}C = 90°$, $AC = 8$ cm, $BC = 5$ cm. Find $B\hat{A}C$.

4. In triangle DEF, $D\hat{E}F = 90°$, $DF = 4$ cm, $EF = 3$ cm. Find $E\hat{D}F$.

5. In triangle GHI, $G\hat{H}I = 90°$, $IG = 7$ cm, $HG = 6$ cm. Find $H\hat{G}I$.

6. In triangle JKL, $J\hat{K}L = 90°$, $JK = 7$ cm, $KL = 5$ cm. Find $J\hat{L}K$.

7. In triangle MNO, $M\hat{N}O = 90°$, $MN = 8$ cm, $NO = 10$ cm. Find $M\hat{O}N$.

8. In triangle PQR, $P\hat{Q}R = 90°$, $PR = 10$ cm, $RQ = 3$ cm. Find $Q\hat{P}R$.

9. A ladder of length 4·2 m rests against a vertical wall so that the base of the ladder is 2 m from the wall. Calculate the angle between the ladder and the ground.

10. A point T is 80 m away from a flagpole, which is 27 m high. What is the angle of elevation to the top of the flagpole from T?

11. A chord AB of length 10 cm is drawn in a circle of radius 6 cm, centre O. Calculate the angle AOB.

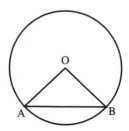

12. An owl sits on a branch 9·5 cm from the ground vertically over the base of a tree. If he sees a mouse on the ground 6·2 m from the tree at what angle to the vertical must he swoop to catch his supper?

13. Find the angles in an isosceles triangle ABC if (i) AB = BC = 7 cm and AC = 3 cm

(ii) AB = BC = 15·3 cm and AC = 12·8 cm.

14. A very thin rigid book of height 28 cm is placed at an angle between two shelves 26 cm apart. What angle, to the nearest degree, will the book make with the bottom shelf?

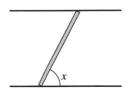

15.

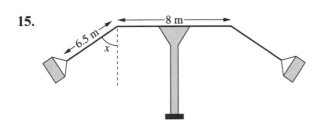

The chains connecting the chairs to the roundabout ride at a funfair are 6·5 m long. The central diameter of the roundabout is 8 m and when the ride is at full speed the chairs trace out a circular path of radius 9·8 m. What angle, to the nearest degree, do the chains make with the vertical?

16. Find the labelled angles in the rectangle.

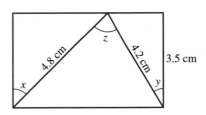

17. A ship sails 16 km due north then 5 km due east. Find the bearing and distance of the ship from its start position.

18. Find the labelled angles in the following shapes.

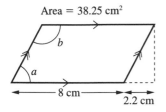

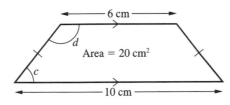

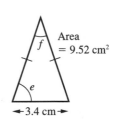

19. Find the labelled angles in the kite.

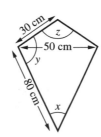

Finding the hypotenuse

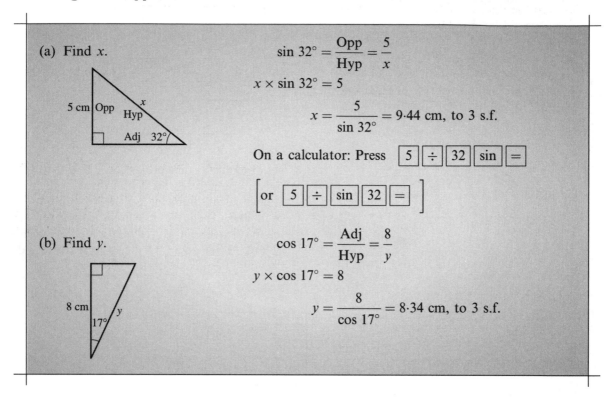

(a) Find x.

$$\sin 32° = \frac{\text{Opp}}{\text{Hyp}} = \frac{5}{x}$$

$$x \times \sin 32° = 5$$

$$x = \frac{5}{\sin 32°} = 9\cdot44 \text{ cm, to 3 s.f.}$$

On a calculator: Press $\boxed{5}$ $\boxed{\div}$ $\boxed{32}$ $\boxed{\sin}$ $\boxed{=}$

$\left[\text{or } \boxed{5} \boxed{\div} \boxed{\sin} \boxed{32} \boxed{=} \right]$

(b) Find y.

$$\cos 17° = \frac{\text{Adj}}{\text{Hyp}} = \frac{8}{y}$$

$$y \times \cos 17° = 8$$

$$y = \frac{8}{\cos 17°} = 8\cdot34 \text{ cm, to 3 s.f.}$$

Exercise 5

Give your answers correct to 3 s.f., unless told otherwise.

1. Find the hypotenuse in the following triangles.

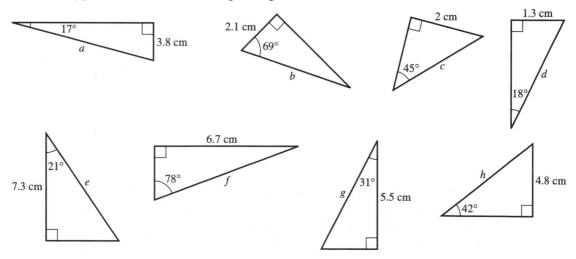

2. Richard cuts across the rectangular grass lawn in the middle of the school grounds. The long side of the rectangle measures 75 m and in order to reach the opposite corner his route makes an angle of 37° with this side. How far does he walk in crossing the grass and how much less is this than if he had walked around the lawn?

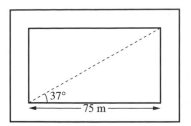

3.

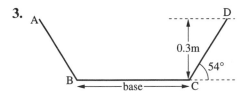

A feeding trough is to be made from a rectangular sheet of metal of width 1·6 m (i.e. AB + BC + CD = 1·6 m). The cross section is to be in the shape of a trapezium with a depth of 0·3 m and sides which make an angle of 54° with the horizontal. Find the width of the base of the trough, to the nearest cm.

4. The distance between two straight river banks is 80 m. Jane tries to swim straight across the river but the current is strong and she is carried down river. Her course makes an angle of 58° with the bank. How far does she actually swim?

5. Find the perimeter of the rhombus.

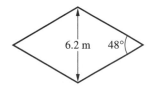

6. A shed roof is to be covered by a rectangular piece of asphalt. The shed is 2·8 m wide and 4·6 m long. The roof makes an angle of 48° with the horizontal. Calculate the area of the rectangle of asphalt.

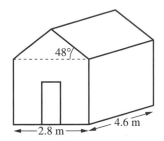

7.* A farm gate is 1·3 m high. The diagonal crossbar has a width of 15 cm and makes an angle of 24° with the horizontal. Find the length of x and y in the diagram. Hence find the width of the gate.

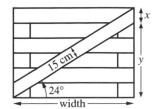

All your trigonometrical problems answered !!!!

If you can remember the following triangles they will help you to solve any trigonometry question in a right-angled triangle.

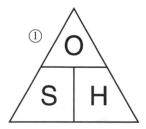 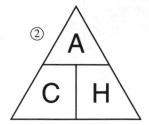 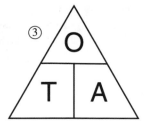

There are various rhymes which help you to remember the order of the letters. One of the 'worst', which usually means it is easier to remember, is:

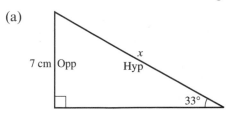

Try to learn this or make up one of your own.
These triangles work in the same way as the distance, speed, time triangle.
You cover up what you are trying to work out and the triangle shows you how to calculate the answer.

Find the value of x in the following triangles.

(a)

7 cm | Opp x Hyp   33°

Here we are given the angle (33°) and the Opposite length and we want to calculate the Hypotenuse.

O and H appear together in triangle ①.

Cover up what we want to find. i.e. Hyp.

This gives us $\text{Hyp} = \dfrac{\text{Opp}}{\sin} = \dfrac{7}{\sin 33°} = 12 \cdot 9$ cm (3 s.f.)

(b)

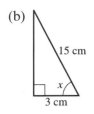

Here we have the Hypotenuse and the Adjacent and we want to work out the angle.

H and A appear together in triangle ②.

Cover up what we want to find. i.e. cos for the angle.

This gives us $\cos x = \dfrac{\text{Adj}}{\text{Hyp}} = \dfrac{3}{15} = 0{\cdot}2$

$$x = \cos^{-1} 0{\cdot}2 = 78{\cdot}5°$$

(c)

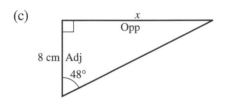

Here we have the Adjacent and the angle (48°) and we want the Opposite.

A and O appear together in triangle ③.

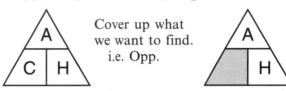

Cover up what we want to find. i.e. Opp.

This gives us $\text{Opp} = \tan \times \text{Adj} = \tan 48° \times 8 = 8{\cdot}88$ cm.

Exercise 6

1. Find the labelled length or angle in the following

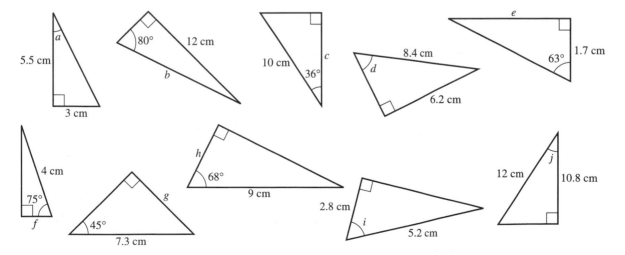

2. Find the lengths (a) AS (b) CS (c) BS

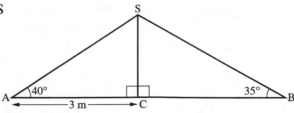

3.

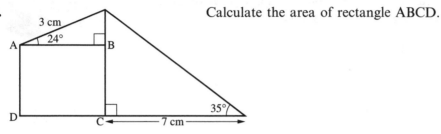

Calculate the area of rectangle ABCD.

4. In rectangle ABCD, AB = 10 cm and AD = 6 cm. Calculate

(a) angle AB̂D

(b) length AE

(c) length DF.

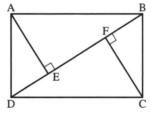

5. Diagram A shows a kitchen floor tiled with regular octogons and squares. Diagram B shows an enlarged view of one octagon.
The squares have sides of length 12 cm.
Find the width of the octagons.

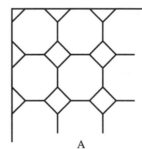

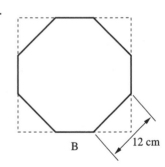

6.

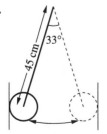

The pendulum of a grandfather clock consists of a circular disc of radius 5 cm attached to a straight arm of length 45 cm. If it swings through an angle of 33°, what is the minimum width of the body of the clock?

7. (a) Alan is making a 'House of Cards'. Each playing card measures 9 cm by 5·8 cm and is of negligible thickness. These cards are balanced against each other with their short sides touching and making an angle of 32° to one another. If Alan's house has five layers as shown, find its total height and the width of its base.

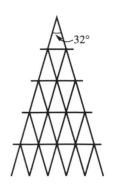

(b) Alan's first attempt soon falls down so he decides to try again, this time joining together the longer sides of the cards to see if this gives more stability. The angle at the top remains 32°. Find the new height and width.

8. Find x. All lengths are in cm.

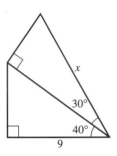
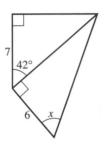
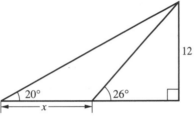
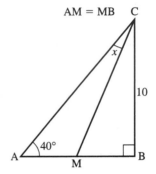

9.

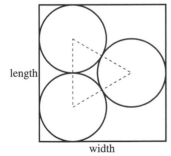

A baker wants to pack three individual apple pies, each of radius 4 cm, into a box as shown. Find the length and width of the box when the pies are packed as shown.

10. The centre of a big wheel at a fun fair is 12 m from the ground. Susan gets into a car at ground level.

(a) Find the height of the car after the wheel has turned through an angle of

(i) 50° (ii) 120° (iii) 215°

(b) Find two possible angles the wheel may have turned through if the height of the car above the ground is

(i) 10 m (ii) 17·5 m (iii) 22 m

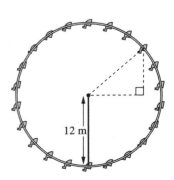

6.6 Mathematical games and cross numbers

Cross numbers

Make three copies of the pattern below and complete the puzzles using the clues given. To avoid confusion it is better not to write the small reference numbers 1, 2... 18 on your patterns. Write any decimal points on the lines between squares.

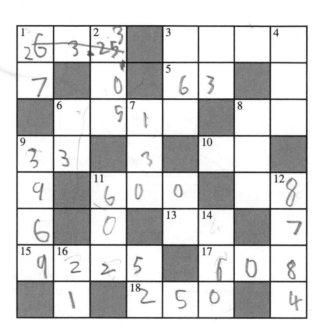

Part A

Across

1. $(0.5) \div \frac{1}{2} \times 253$
3. $0.003\,\text{kg}$ written in mg
5. Next in the sequence   1, 3, 7, 15, 31
6. (1 across) $\times 4 + 500$
8. Number of cm in 6 inches (nearest cm)
9. A third of $(9.9 \div 0.1)$
10. $(1 + 2 + 3 + 4)^2 - 1$
11. Total number of heads and legs of 75 ducks and 75 sheep.
13. $3008 - 2986$ [No calculator!]
15. $15^2 + 10^4 - 10^3$
17. (2 down) $- 2.97$
18. A quarter share of a third share of a half share of £6000.

Down

1. Digit sum of 9873
2. Mid-way between 3 and 3·1
4. $\left(\frac{1}{20}\right)^2 \times 100$ as a decimal
7. 10% of £1304.31 to the nearest pound.
8. Area of a square of side 14 units
9. (5 across)^2
11. (12 down) $\div 12 - (7$ down)
12. Number of hours in a leap year.
14. $720\,\text{km/h}$ in m/s
16. $(1.47 \times 10^4) \div (7 \times 10^2)$

Part B

Across

1. Tenth term of the sequence
   169, 171, 175, 181, ...
3. $10^2 + 2^{10}$
5. (1 down) − (8 across)
6. $1127 \times 7 \times 17 \div 23$ [No calculator!]
8. The value of $2x^2 - x$, when $x = -2$
9. (11 across) − (3 down)
   [You must find 3 down]
10. Middle two digits of $(19 \div \frac{1}{2})^2$
11. $(3 \times 10^{-2}) \div (2 \times 10^{-4})$
13. $1\frac{2}{5} \div 1\frac{1}{6}$
15. Find n if $\sqrt[3]{n - 117} = 19$
17. $\frac{3}{7}$ of 11% of $2 \cdot 6^4$, (2 d.p.)
18. [Number of letters in the word 'cubed']^3

Down

1. Work out $(a + b - c)^2$ when $a = -2$,
   $b = 3$, $c = -4$
2. $31 \cdot 6^2 - \left[\frac{1}{6} + \frac{1}{3} + \frac{3}{50} \right]$
4. (1 down − 5)^2
7. North-west as a bearing
8. $\dfrac{6 \cdot 9 - 0 \cdot 71^2}{2 \cdot 3^2 - \frac{1 \cdot 4}{1 \cdot 7}}$, correct to 2 d.p.
9. $(20^2 - 5^2 - 1^2) \times 3^2$
11. Next in the sequence $5 \cdot \dot{4}$, $16 \cdot \dot{3}$, $49, ...$
12. The hypotenuse in a triangle in which
    the other two sides are 3330 and 7992
14. Angle in degrees between the hands of a
    clock at 2·15
16. Interior angle of a regular quadrilateral.

Part C (Harder)

Across

1. $\frac{13}{104}$ as a percentage
3. 4 more than a cube number
5. (A square number) + 10
6. $(8 \times 10^3) + (50 \div 0 \cdot 1) + 2^5$
8. $10^{-2} \div 10^{-3}$
9. Find the value of x if,
   $3 - 5\%$ of $x = 1 \cdot 35$
10. Surface area, in cm^2, of a cube of
    side 2 cm
11. $\sqrt{\dfrac{1 \cdot 3}{1 \cdot 23^2}} + \sqrt{\dfrac{1 \cdot 515}{0 \cdot 3 - 0 \cdot 261}}$, to 2 d.p.
13. Next in the sequence
    23, 25, 32, 45, 65
15. $346\frac{1}{2} \times$ (1% of 10 across)
17. Area of a triangle with sides 30, 40, 50
18. Longest diagonal in a cuboid
    measuring $4 \times 6 \times 13$ units

Down

1. $\left(4\frac{1}{3}\right)^2$ to the nearest whole number
2. Change 189 km/h into m/s
3. $\left(\frac{1}{3} + \frac{1}{4}\right) \div \frac{1}{5}$, correct to 2 d.p.
4. Number of seconds taken to travel
   500 m at a speed of 10 km/h
6. Solve the equation
   $\dfrac{3}{4} - \dfrac{21}{x + 1} = \dfrac{1}{2}$
7. Square number
8. Next in the sequence
   1·2, 2·4, 7·2, 28·8, ...
9. $3^3 + 4^4 + 5^5$
11. Smallest integer solution of
    $9x - 1 > 6666$
12. Surface area, in cm^2, of a cuboid
    measuring 5 cm × 10 cm × 40 cm
14. Smallest angle in a 3, 4, 5 triangle
    (to 1 d.p.)
16. Angle in degrees between the hands of
    a clock at 3·10.

Creating numbers: a task requiring imagination

Your task is to create every number from 1 to 50.

You can use only the numbers 1, 2, 3 and 4 once each and the operations $+, -, \times, \div$.

You can use the numbers as powers and you must use *all* of the numbers 1, 2, 3, 4.

Here are some examples:
$$1 = (4 - 3) \div (2 - 1)$$
$$20 = 4^2 + 3 + 1$$
$$68 = 34 \times 2 \times 1$$
$$75 = (4 + 1)^2 \times 3$$

'Make your Million' board game

Rules: You are given £10 at the start of the game. The object is to earn as much money as possible by substituting your dice score into the expression on your new square. The person with the biggest balance *when landing on the finish square* wins.

Example. Throwing a 5, then a 1.

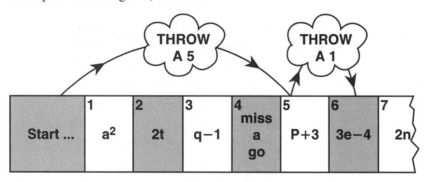

Score on dice	Expression on square	Value of expression using dice score	Balance £
—	—	—	10
5	$P + 3$	$5 + 3 = 8$	$10 + 8 = 18$
1	$3e - 4$	$(3 \times 1) - 4 = 3 - 4 = -1$	$18 - 1 = 17$
•	•	•	•
•	•	•	•
•	•	•	•

Note:
(i) Landing on 'miss a go' means that your balance remains the same.
(ii) Landing on 'back to start' means that your balance becomes *zero*.

BOARD FOR 'MAKE YOUR MILLION'

START ...	1 a^2	2 $2t$	3 $q-1$	4 MISS A GO	5 $p+3$	6 $3e-4$	7 $2m+3$
							8 $3r$

17 $2e+5$	16 n^4	15 $3(b-2)$	14 c^3	13 MISS A GO	12 BACK TO START	11 $q-4$	10 f^2-9	9 $3n-1$
18 $2m+1$								

19 $q-3$	20 f^2-16	21 $3n-5$	22 BACK TO START	23 $p+2$	24 a^2	25 $2t$	26 MISS A GO	27 $6-d$
								28 $3r$

37 $8-d$	36 f^2-4	35 $p+5$	34 $6e-20$	33 $3n-4$	32 x^5	31 $2(b-3)$	30 $2m+4$	29 $2-d$
38 MISS A GO								

39 a^2	40 $3(b-1)$	41 $2t$	42 f^2-9	43 MISS A GO	44 $p+1$	45 $6c$	46 $5e+4$	47 $2m+1$
								48 $4-3e$

57 $p+6$	56 $3r$	55 $q-5$	54 BACK TO START	53 10^x	52 a^2	51 MISS A GO	50 $10-d$	49 $5(b-4)$
58 $12-2d$								

59 MISS A GO	60 10^n	61 $q+1$	62 $p+4$	63 $2m+3$	64 $2t$	65 BACK TO START	... FINISH

Part 7

7.1 Check-up

Arithmetic check-up

Work out the answer to each question.
DO NOT USE A CALCULATOR.

A Decimals
1. $5\cdot4 + 14\cdot9$
2. $18\cdot5 - 11$
3. $3\cdot6 \times 0\cdot3$
4. $37\cdot2 \div 5$
5. $(0\cdot3)^2 + (0\cdot4)^2$
6. $4\cdot11 \div 0\cdot3$

B Long multiplication and long division
1. 42×31
2. 312×54
3. $7498 \div 23$

C Fractions
1. $\frac{3}{4} + \frac{1}{3}$
2. $\frac{2}{5} - \frac{1}{4}$
3. $\frac{2}{3} \times \frac{4}{5}$
4. $\frac{5}{8} \div \frac{1}{2}$

D Percentages
1. 7% of £250
2. Work out 1% of £6660 in your head
3. A camera cost £840. Increase the price by 5%
4. Change $\frac{13}{20}$ into a percentage.

E Standard form
1. Write 56 million in standard form
2. Work out $(3\cdot2 \times 10^3) \times (2 \times 10^5)$
3. Write as an ordinary decimal $2\cdot5 \times 10^{-4}$.

F Negative numbers
1. $-3 + (-2)$
2. $6 - (-6)$
3. $(-3) \times (-2)$
4. $12 \div (-2)$
5. $-5 - (-2)$
6. $(-4)^2 \div (-2)$

G Estimation. Estimate the answer, correct to one significant figure.
1. $9800 \times 207\cdot1$
2. $0\cdot987 \times 21\cdot45$
3. $\sqrt{98\cdot7} \times 49\,704$

H Miscellaneous
1. How many of these statements are true?
   $0\cdot3 = 30\%$; $\frac{5}{8} > \frac{5}{9}$; $0\cdot1 \times 0\cdot2 = 0\cdot2$; $\left(\frac{1}{2}\right)^2 > 0\cdot5$; $(-1)^2 > -1$.
2. Write as a single number: 'eleven million, eleven thousand, eleven hundred and eleven'.

Algebra check-up

1. Solve the equations
   (a) $3x - 1 = 1 + 2x$ (b) $4(2x - 1) = 3(x + 2)$
   (c) $\dfrac{x - 1}{2} = 5$ (d) $\dfrac{x}{5} + 4 = 10$

2. Find the value of each expression when $x = 3$, $y = -2$, $z = -1$.
   (a) $x^2 + y^2$ (b) $xy + 3z$ (c) $2x^2$
   (d) $yz - x^2$ (e) $\dfrac{x + y}{z}$ (f) $3y^2 + z^2$

3. Remove the brackets and simplify.
   (a) $3(2x - 1) - 2(x + 4)$ (b) $4(x - 2y + 3) + 5(2x - y - 2)$
   (c) $(x + 3)(x + 2)$ (d) $(x - 2)(x + 5)$
   (e) $(x - 3)^2$

4. Solve the simultaneous equations.
   (a) $x + 4y = 6$ (b) $3x - y = -14$
       $3x - 2y = 11$ $5x + 2y = -5$

5. Use trial and improvement to find one solution, correct to one decimal place.
   (a) $x(x + 4) = 30$ (b) $x^3 + 3x = 100$

6. Solve the inequalities
   (a) $3 + 3x < 9$ (b) $3x - 7 \geqslant 5 - x$

7. Work out the following and write your answer as an ordinary number.
   (a) 4^{-1} (b) 6^0 (c) $3^{21} \div 3^{19}$

8. Find the next term in each sequence.

(a)	(b)	(c)	(d)
4	1	5	1
10	6	16	3
18	15	39	19
28	28	80	85
?	?	145	261
		?	631
			?

9. Find the nth term in each sequence.
   (a) $5, 10, 15, 20, \ldots$
   (b) $11, 21, 31, 41, 51, \ldots$
   (c) $\frac{1}{2}, \frac{2}{3}, \frac{3}{4}, \frac{4}{5}, \frac{5}{6}, \ldots$
   (d) $1^2, 2^2, 3^2, 4^2, 5^2, \ldots$

10. Make x the subject.
    (a) $a + mx = t$ (b) $\dfrac{v + ax}{e} = y$ (c) $\dfrac{d}{x} = m$

11. Find the gradient of the line joining the points (1, 4) and (3, 10).

12. Find the gradient of each of the following lines:
   (a) $y = 3x - 7$ (b) $y + 2x = 9$ (c) $3x + 2y = 10$

7.2 Multiple choice papers

Test 1

1. Given that $y = 3x^2$, find the value of y when $x = 1$

    A 3
    B 4
    C 6
    D 9

2. The angle representing 5% of a pie chart is

    A 5°
    B 18°
    C 36°
    D 72°

3. Find the length x

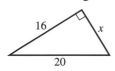

    A 12
    B 16
    C 18
    D 25·6

4. Correct to one significant figure, $\sqrt{0\cdot 1}$ is
[No calculators!]

    A 0·03
    B 0·1
    C 0·3
    D 0·5

5. A class contains b boys and g girls. There are twice as many boys as girls. This can be written as

    A $b = 2g$
    B $g = 2b$
    C $g = b + 2$
    D $b - g = 2$

6. How many of the statements below are true?
$\frac{1}{3} > \frac{1}{4}$, $\frac{1}{2} + \frac{1}{3} = \frac{2}{5}$,
$\frac{1}{3} \div \frac{1}{4} = 1\frac{1}{3}$, $\frac{2}{3}$ of $\frac{1}{5} = \frac{2}{15}$

    A 1
    B 2
    C 3
    D 4

7. Three semicircles are drawn around an equilateral triangle of side 8 cm. Find the shaded area, in cm².

    A 96π
    B 48π
    C 24π
    D 36π

8. After a 10% discount, the price of a chair is £81. Find the original price.

    A £89·10
    B £90
    C £91
    D £81·81

9. The point (3, −1) is reflected in the line $y = x$. The coordinates of the image are

    A (3, 1)
    B (−1, −3)
    C (−3, 1)
    D (−1, 3)

10. Given that $a = mx^2$, find the value of a when $m = 5$ and $x = 3$.

    A 30
    B 45
    C 75
    D 225

11. The area of a circle is 36π cm². Find the circumference of the circle in cm.

    A 6π
    B 12π
    C 36π
    D 324π

12. $3(x+4) - 2(x-3) =$

A $x+1$
B $x+6$
C $x+18$
D $5x+6$

13. Below are four statements about the diagonals of a rectangle. A statement which is not *always* true is
A they bisect each other
B they divide the rectangle into four triangles of equal area
C each bisects the area of the rectangle
D they cross at right angles

14. Given that $y = 2(a+b)h$, then $h =$

A $\dfrac{2y}{a+b}$

B $\dfrac{y}{2}(a+b)$

C $\dfrac{y}{2} - a - b$

D $\dfrac{y}{2(a+b)}$

15. n people buy x drinks at y pence each and divide the cost equally between them. How much does each person pay?

A $\dfrac{y+x}{n}$

B $\dfrac{xn}{y}$

C $\dfrac{x+n}{y}$

D $\dfrac{xy}{n}$

16. Find the area of the parallelogram in square units.

A 3
B $4\frac{1}{2}$
C 6
D 9

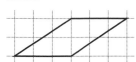

17. Write down what you get if you subtract three from x and then double the result.

A $2x - 3$
B $x^2 - 3$
C $(x-3)^2$
D $2(x-3)$

18. Simplify

$$\frac{a+a+a+a+a}{a}$$

A $4a$
B a^4
C 5
D can't be done

19. The area of one face of a cube is $9\,\text{cm}^2$. The total length, in cm, of all the edges of the cube is

A 36
B 48
C 54
D none of the above

20. Find the size of each interior angle of a regular polygon which has 9 sides

A 130°
B 140°
C 150°
D 160°

21. The point (2, 8) does *not* lie on the graph whose equation is

A $y = 2x^2$
B $y = 3x + 2$
C $y = 12 - 2x$
D $y = \frac{1}{4}x$

22. How many points inside and outside the square are the same distance from B and C and are also 5 cm from A?

A 0
B 1
C 2
D more than 2

23. A solid cylinder has volume $280\,\text{cm}^3$ and radius 3 cm. Find an approximate value for the height of the cylinder. (Take $\pi = 3$)

A 5 cm
B 8 cm
C 10 cm
D 15 cm

24. The maximum number of obtuse angles in a quadrilateral is

  A 0
  B 1
  C 2
  D 3

25. Find x

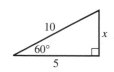

  A $5 \cos 60°$
  B $10 \sin 60°$
  C $5 \tan 30°$
  D $\dfrac{10}{\sin 60°}$

Test 2

1. The equation of the line could be:

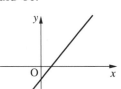

  A $y = 2x + 1$
  B $y = 3x - 1$
  C $y = 4x$
  D $y = -3x - 1$

2. Find x when
$3(5x - 2) - 5(4x - 3) = 13$

  A -6.8
  B $\frac{34}{35}$
  C -0.8
  D 1.6

3. Find which of the five numbers below is the mean of the other four.
23, 17, 22, 24, 34

  A 17
  B 22
  C 23
  D 24

4. £320 decreased by 0·5% is:

  A £1·60
  B £321·60
  C £318·40
  D £160

5. Find x, given that
$2x + y = 5$ and
$3x - 2y = 11$

  A $x = 5$
  B $x = 2$
  C $x = -1$
  D $x = 3$

6. Find the diameter of a circle of area 30 cm^2, correct to 1 d.p.
Use $\pi = 3.14$

  A 9·6 cm
  B 6·2 cm
  C 3·5 cm
  D 3·1 cm

7. A length of one inch is approximately

  A 1 cm
  B 2·5 cm
  C 4 cm
  D 30 cm

8. Find
$(3.2 \times 10^7) \div (8 \times 10^{-5})$
and give your answer in standard form

  A 4×10^{11}
  B 40
  C 0.4×10^{13}
  D 2.56×10^3

9. $(a^6)^2 \div a^4$ is the same as:

  A a^3
  B $(a^2)^4$
  C $a^4 \times a^2$
  D a^9

10. Solve the inequality
$2x - 1 > 0$

  A $x > -\frac{1}{2}$
  B $x < 2$
  C $x < \frac{1}{2}$
  D $x > \frac{1}{2}$

11. If $s = ut + \frac{1}{2} at^2$, find the value of s when $u = 60$, $t = 10$ and $a = -9.8$.

  A 5402
  B 110
  C 3001
  D 1090

12. Find the length d, correct to 1 d.p.

3.1 cm

  A 7·3 cm
  B 1·3 cm
  C 2·9 cm
  D 7·9 cm

13. Find the probability of getting 'Heads' and a '6' when a coin is tossed and a dice is rolled.

  A $\frac{2}{3}$
  B $\frac{1}{3}$
  C $\frac{1}{12}$
  D $\frac{1}{8}$

14. Which angles are the same?

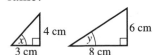

  A x and y
  B y and z
  C x and z
  D x, y and z

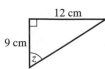

15. Find the value of x.

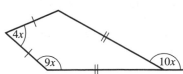

    A 15·7° to 1 d.p.
    B 11·25°
    C 15°
    D You can't tell

16. If $x = \dfrac{-b + \sqrt{b^2 - 4ac}}{2a}$, find the value of x when $a = 2$, $b = 5$ and $c = -3$

    A $-3\frac{1}{4}$
    B 6
    C -1
    D $\frac{1}{2}$

17. A lottery prize of 4000 million pounds is shared equally between 13 thousand people. How much does each person receive, correct to 1 s.f.

    A £3 million
    B £300 000
    C £30 000
    D £0·3

18. If it takes 3 men 4 days to dig an 80 m trench, how many days should 5 men take to dig a 100 m trench?

    A 2
    B 3
    C 4
    D 5

19. If $H = \dfrac{1}{2}\left(\dfrac{1}{x} + \dfrac{1}{y}\right)$, find H when $x = 4$ and $y = 6$.

    A $\frac{1}{20}$
    B $\frac{5}{24}$
    C $\frac{1}{10}$
    D $\frac{3}{7}$

20. ABCDE is a regular pentagon. Find the angle x.

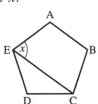

    A 108°
    B 36°
    C 72°
    D 90°

21. A circular pond has radius 1·6 m. How much does the water level rise, correct to 2 d.p., when 20 litres of water is poured into the pool?

    A 0·25 mm
    B 0·25 cm
    C 2·50 cm
    D 1·99 cm

22. A piece of wire 48 cm long is bent to form a rectangle in which the length is twice the width. Find the area of the rectangle.

    A 48 cm²
    B 128 cm²
    C 256 cm²
    D 512 cm²

23. Work out, correct to 3 significant figures

$$\left(\frac{3}{4 - \sqrt{3}}\right) \times \left(\frac{\sqrt{5}}{2 - \sqrt{2}}\right)$$

    A 4·23
    B 4·71
    C 2·05
    D 5·05

24. Find the odd one out.

    A $\frac{1}{2} \div \frac{1}{3}$
    B $1 \div \frac{2}{3}$
    C $0\cdot\dot{3} \div 0\cdot5$
    D $0\cdot15 \div 0\cdot1$

25. How long is the perimeter of the rectangle shown?

5 cm — rectangle with $4x - 1$ cm (top), $2x - 3$ cm (bottom)

    A 12 cm
    B 14 cm
    C 24 cm
    D can't be found

Test 3

1. On a map of scale 1 : 500 000, what actual distance is represented by 2·5 cm on the map?

    A 1·25 km
    B 2 km
    C 12·5 km
    D 20 km

2. Find the coordinates of A.

$y = x^2 - 3x + 2$

    A (2, 0)
    B (0, 2)
    C (0, 1)
    D (0, −3)

3. Convert a speed of 20 m/s into km/h.

    A 72 km/h
    B 7·2 km/h
    C 5·5 km/h
    D 0·02 km/h

4. AB = BC = AC = CD.
Find x

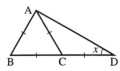

A   30°
B   40°
C   45°
D   60°

5. 35% of a sum of money is paid in tax. If the tax paid is £672, find the sum of money.

A   £19·20
B   £235·20
C   £907·20
D   £1920

6. When £306 is divided between three people in the ratio 2 : 3 : 4, the largest share is

A   £136
B   £102
C   £34
D   £68

7. Find the area of the triangle in cm².

A $12x^2$
B $15x^2$
C $16x^2$
D   none of the above

8. How many of the statements below are true?
$5\% = \frac{1}{20}$, $5^{-1} = 0\cdot5$
$\frac{1}{3} = 0\cdot3$, $\frac{1}{2} \div \frac{1}{2} = \frac{1}{4}$.

A   1
B   2
C   3
D   4

9. Four people each toss a coin. What is the probability that the fourth person will toss a 'head'?

A $\frac{1}{2}$
B $\frac{1}{4}$
C $\frac{1}{8}$
D $\frac{1}{16}$

10. Given $-2x > 12$, then

A $x > -6$
B $x < -6$
C $x > 14$
D $x > 6$

11. Find x correct to 2 d.p.

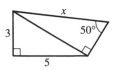

A   7·61
B   4·47
C   9·07
D   7·15

12. Sarah's father is 4 years older than her mother and the mean of her parents' ages is 39. The mean age of Sarah and her father is 23. How old is Sarah?

A   5 years
B   7 years
C   11 years
D   13 years

13. The distance AB is

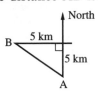

A $\sqrt{25}$ km
B $\sqrt{10}$ km
C $\sqrt{50}$ km
D   25 km

14. In the diagram above, the bearing of B from A is

A   045°
B   135°
C   225°
D   315°

15. Simplify
$$\frac{x + 2x + 3x + 4x + 5x}{5}$$

A   3
B $3x$
C $3x^5$
D $11x$

16. Find the area, in square units, of a triangle with vertices at (1, 1), (4, 2) and (1, 5)

A   5
B   6
C   8
D   can't be done.

17. The total surface area of a cube is 54 cm². Find the volume of the cube.

A   8 cm³
B   27 cm³
C   54 cm³
D   23·16 cm³

18. Given AB = BC and DE = DB, find x.

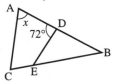

A   36°
B   68°
C   72°
D   84°

19. If $a = \frac{1}{2}$ and $b = 0\cdot1$ find, *without* a calculator, which of the following has the largest value.

A ab
B $a + b$
C $a \div b$
D $b \div a$

20. The scatter graph shows

A positive correlation
B negative correlation
C no correlation
D both positive and negative correlation

21. How many whole numbers have a square root between 50 and 51?

A 0
B 1
C 100
D none of the above

22. How many whole numbers satisfy both of the inequalities below?
$3x > 2$ and $2x - 5 < 20$.

A 0
B 11
C 12
D 25

23. Find the probability of rolling a total of 10 with two fair dice.

A $\frac{1}{10}$
B $\frac{1}{12}$
C $\frac{10}{36}$
D $\frac{1}{36}$

24. The value of x which satisfies both of the equations below is
$3x + y = 11$
$2x - y = 9$

A 1
B 2
C 3
D 4

25. Find the largest angle in the triangle.

A 13°
B 52°
C 68°
D 80°

7.3 Revision exercises

Revision exercise 1

1. Use the graph to write down the solutions to the following pairs of simultaneous equations
   (a) $x + y = 8$
        $x - 3y = 8$

   (b) $2x - y = 1$
        $x + y = 8$

   (c) $x - 3y = 8$
        $2x - y = 1$

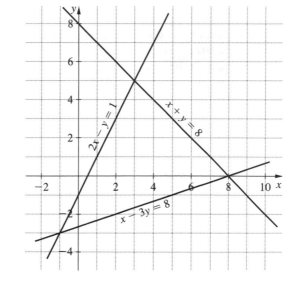

2. Draw axes with x and y from -2 to 8.
   Solve the simultaneous equations by drawing suitable graphs.
   (a) $y - x = 2$
        $2y + x = 10$
   (b) $2x + y = 8$
        $x - 2y = 4$

3. Find the side or angle marked with a letter. All lengths are in cm.

(a)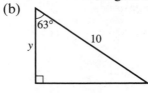

(b)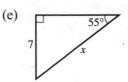

(c)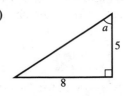

(d)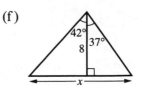

(e)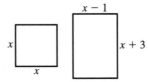

(f)

4. Multiply out the brackets
(a) $(x+3)(x+7)$ (b) $(x-3)(x+5)$ (c) $(x-3)^2$

5. Solve the equation $(x+2)(x+1) = (x-3)(x+4)$

6. The square and the rectangle have the same area.
(a) Form an equation and solve it to find x.
(b) Write down the dimensions of the rectangle.

7. (a) Write the following numbers in standard form:
(i) 56 000   (ii) 0·000 002   (iii) 250 million.
(b) Give the answers to the following in standard form:
(i) $(4\cdot3 \times 10^4) \times (6\cdot5 \times 10^{12})$
(ii) $(3\cdot6 \times 10^7) \div (2 \times 10^{11})$
(iii) $(4\cdot8 \times 10^{-3}) \times (2 \times 10^{-8})$

8. A sales manager reports a decrease of 11% in sales this year compared to last year. The decrease was £40 150.
What were the sales last year?

9. Do not use a calculator for this question.
(a) The square root of 73 lies between which two whole numbers?
(b) The cube root of 20 lies between which two whole numbers?
(c) Estimate the value of $\dfrac{\sqrt{897\cdot2} \times 10\cdot93}{\sqrt{34\cdot95}}$, correct to one significant figure.

10. Estimate the value of the following, correct to *one* significant figure. You must show your working.

(a) $\dfrac{78 \cdot 63 \times 1 \cdot 924}{40 \cdot 27}$ (b) $962 \cdot 9 \times 21 \cdot 97$

11. Use a calculator to work out, correct to 3 s.f.

(a) $\dfrac{3 \cdot 2}{1 \cdot 9} + \dfrac{8 \cdot 5}{6 \cdot 2}$ (b) $8 \cdot 2^2 - \dfrac{11 \cdot 9}{7 \cdot 2}$

12. A cuboid with a square base of side x and height 4 cm has the same volume as a cube of side 6 cm. Calculate the value of x, correct to 3 s.f.

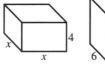

13. (a) Given that $5x > 1$ and that $x - 2 < 3$, list all the possible whole number values of x.

(b) If $3^x > 1000$, what is the smallest whole number value of x?

Revision exercise 2

1. Solve the following pairs of simultaneous equations

(a) $x + 3y = 18$
    $2x + y = 11$

(b) $2x - y = 6$
    $3x + 2y = 2$

2. John and Sam are each thinking of a number.
The sum of their two numbers is 20.
Twice John's number plus three times Sam's number makes 53.
Write down two simultaneous equations using x and y. Solve the equations to find the numbers they were thinking of.

3. The numbers are written in a repeating pattern. The first base number is 1, the second base number is 6, the third base number is 11 and so on.

(a) What is the 100th base number?

(b) What is the nth base number?

4. Use trial and improvement to find a solution to the equations below, giving your answers correct to 1 decimal place.

(a) $x(x - 3) = 100$

(b) $x(x + 8) = 95$

5. The length of the rectangle shown is
3 cm more than the width x cm.
   (a) Write down the length of the rectangle
       in terms of x.
   (b) The area of the rectangle is 80 cm².
       Form an equation involving x.
   (c) Use trial and improvement to solve the
       equation, giving your answer correct to
       1 decimal place.

6. A photograph measuring
5 cm by 3·5 cm is enlarged
so that it fits exactly into a
frame measuring 8 cm by x cm.
Calculate the value of x.

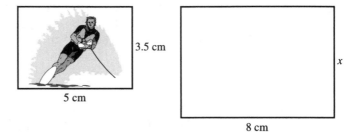

7. A photograph measuring 6 cm by 4 cm is reduced to fit frame **A**
and another copy of the photograph is enlarged to fit frame **B**.

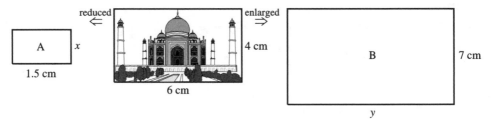

Calculate the value of x and the value of y.

8. Cylinder A has radius 3·5 cm and
height 8 cm.
Cylinder B has radius 5 cm.
If each cylinder has the same
volume calculate the height h
of cylinder B.

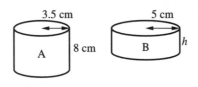

9. Water flows from a full cubical
tank of side 50 cm into a
cylindrical tank of diameter 70 cm.
What is the depth, d, of water in
the cylindrical tank when all the
water has been transferred?

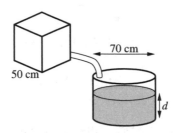

10. In a diving competition divers A, B, C,... H each perform one dive. The dives are given a mark by three different judges. Here are the results:

Diver	A	B	C	D	E	F	G	H
Judge 1	9	4	2	2	6·5	5	8	6
Judge 2	7	6	8	3·5	7	2·5	3	4
Judge 3	7	4·5	2·5	3	6	4	7	5·5

(a) Draw two scatter graphs for the marks.

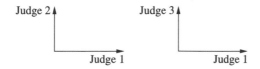

(b) Comment on the results. Can you draw a line of best fit in each case?
What correlation (if any) is there between the marks of judges 1 and 2? What about judges 1 and 3?

(c) Another diver was given 3 marks by judge 1. Estimate, if possible, the mark which might have been awarded by:
(i) judge 2;   (ii) judge 3.

11. Ten gold coins of radius 0·6 cm and thickness 0·3 cm are melted down to form a solid gold cube of side x cm. Calculate the value of x.

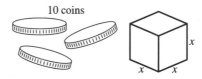

12. Find the range of values of x which satisfy the inequalities.

(a) $3x - 1 < 14$

(b) $\dfrac{x}{3} + 4 > 8$

(c) $9x + 10 \geqslant 12$

(d) $3(x - 2) \leqslant 4$

13. Find the whole number values of x which satisfy each pair of inequalities.

(a) $3x > 10, \quad x - 2 < 5$

(b) $2x + 1 < 12, \quad \dfrac{x}{2} > 1$

14. Find the smallest whole number value of x which satisfies the inequality $3^x > 300$.

242

Revision exercise 3

1. Find x in each triangle.

(a)

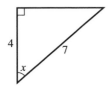

(b)

2. A reservoir, when full, contained 2×10^9 litres of water.
 (a) During a dry summer, the volume of water in the reservoir
 was reduced by 5×10^7 litres each day until it was empty.
 How many days supply did the reservoir hold when full?
 (b) Find the volume of water in the reservoir when it was half
 full, giving your answer in standard form.

3. It is given that
 (area of square A) + (area of square B)
 = (area of square C)
 (a) Form an equation involving x.
 (b) Use trial and improvement to find x,
 correct to 1 decimal place.

 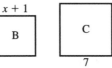

4. After a 4% pay rise, Mrs Hamilton is paid £23 400 per year.
 What was she paid before the increase?

5. Given that $m = -2$ and $n = 5$, find the value of
 (a) $3m + 4n$ (b) $3m^2$ (c) $5n - 3m$

6. Simplify the following.
 (a) $\dfrac{x}{4} \div \dfrac{x^2}{3}$ (b) $(x - 1)^2 + (x + 3)^2$ (c) $\dfrac{x}{5} + \dfrac{x}{3}$

7. PQRS is a rectangle. Lengths
 PQ and SA are shown and the
 perimeter of the rectangle is $6x + 20$.
 (a) Giving each answer in its simplest
 form, find, in terms of x, an
 expression for   (i) AR   (ii) QR
 (b) If $QR = 6\frac{1}{2}$ cm, find the area of triangle AQR.

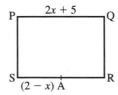

8. Work out, correct to 3 significant figures.
 (a) $\dfrac{(3 \times 10^{12}) \times (3 \cdot 8 \times 10^4)}{(7 \times 10^{-2})}$ (b) $\dfrac{9 \cdot 74}{1 \cdot 3} - \sqrt{\dfrac{5 \cdot 1}{7 \cdot 2 - 3 \cdot 47}}$

 (c) $\dfrac{1}{7 \cdot 3} + \dfrac{3}{5 \cdot 2} - \dfrac{5}{9 \cdot 7}$ (d) $\dfrac{3 \cdot 9}{1 \cdot 7 - 0 \cdot 821} - \left(\dfrac{1 \cdot 4}{7 \cdot 3}\right)^2$

9. Find the values of x and y below.
   (a) $\frac{3}{4}$ of $1448 + 65\%$ of $y^2 = 2980$
   (b) $92\cdot5 - 22\%$ of $x = 63$

10. Draw x and y axes with values from -8 to $+8$.
   Plot and label the following triangles:
   $\triangle1$: $(-1, -3)$ $(-1, -5)$ $(-5, -5)$
   $\triangle2$: $(1, 3)$ $(1, 7)$ $(3, 3)$
   $\triangle3$: $(3, -3)$ $(7, -3)$ $(7, -1)$
   $\triangle4$: $(-5, -5)$ $(-5, -1)$ $(-3, -1)$
   $\triangle5$: $(1, -6)$ $(3, -6)$ $(3, -5)$
   $\triangle6$: $(-3, 7)$ $(-5, 7)$ $(-3, 3)$

   Describe fully the following transformations
   (a) $\triangle1 \rightarrow \triangle2$ (b) $\triangle1 \rightarrow \triangle4$ (c) $\triangle1 \rightarrow \triangle5$
   (d) $\triangle1 \rightarrow \triangle6$ (e) $\triangle5 \rightarrow \triangle3$ (f) $\triangle2 \rightarrow \triangle3$

11. On the putting greens at St Andrews golf course, there are 30 blades of grass per square centimetre.
   How many blades of grass are there on a circular green of radius 20 metres? Give your answer in standard form, correct to 2 significant figures.

12. A ship sails 6 km on a bearing 160° and then a further 10 km on a bearing 240°. Make a scale drawing of the journey using a scale of 1 cm to 1 km.
   (a) How far is the ship from its starting point?
   (b) On what bearing must the ship sail so that it returns to its starting point?

Revision exercise 4

1. 540 people were asked how they travelled to work. The pie chart shows the results of the survey.
   (a) How many people travelled by car?
   (b) How many people travelled by bus?
   (c) What percentage of the people travelled by train?

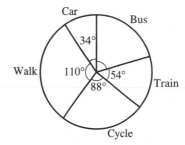

2. The dimensions of the rectangle are given correct to one decimal place. Write down the smallest possible length of the rectangle.

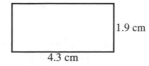

1.9 cm

4.3 cm

3. 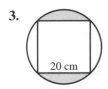 A square of side 20 cm is drawn so that its corners lie on the circumference of a circle.
Find the shaded area.

4. A cylinder is $\frac{1}{2}$ full of water After 40 ml of water is added the cylinder is $\frac{2}{3}$ full.

Calculate the volume of the cylinder when full.

5. L'Oreal 'Plenitude' face cream was advertised on television. According to the advert:
'Tests show that skin treated with L'Oreal Plenitude is 71% more radiant'.
After 2 months treatment with the above face cream, Georgina's skin is measured at 215·3 on the S.R.U. scale (Skin Radiance Units).
If the claims in the advert are true what was Georgina's S.R.U. scale reading before being treated? Give your answer correct to one decimal place.

6. One link of a chain is 2 cm long. When two links are joined together the maximum length is 3·4 cm. Work out the maximum total length when
(a) 3 links are joined together
(b) 300 links are joined together
(c) n links are joined together.

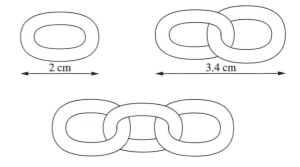

7. The mean of five positive whole numbers is 6. The mode is 10 and the median is 7. Write down the five numbers.

8. The number of eggs in the nests in a large tree is shown in the table.

number of eggs	frequency
3	4
4	7
5	x

   (a) If the mean number of eggs per nest is 4·25, find x.
   (b) If the median number of eggs per nest is 4, find the largest possible value of x.
   (c) If the modal number of eggs per nest is 4, find the largest possible value of x.

9. The lace edge of a table cloth consists of a number of hexagons joined together as shown.

   t = 1
   h = 4

   t = 2
   h = 7

   t = 3
   h = 10

   (a) How many hexagons will be needed when $t = 7$?
   (b) How many hexagons will be needed when $t = 1000$?
   (c) How many hexagons will be needed for the nth pattern?

10. Matching place mats are made up of hexagons as shown.

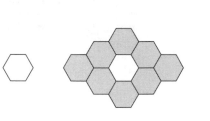

   t = 1   t = 2   t = 3

Copy and complete the table.

t	hexagons on outer edge	total number of hexagons
1	0	1
2	8	9
3	16	25
4	–	–
5	–	–
n	–	–

7.4 KS3 Practice papers

The questions in these practice papers are written to reflect the style and content of questions in recent KS3 papers at levels 5–7 and 6–8.

Paper 1. You may use a calculator but remember to show your working.

1. Here are some of the ingredients for a cake using imperial measures.

$\frac{1}{2}$ pound of apples,
1 pint of milk,
2 eggs,
cook the cake in a
12 inch tray

Copy this table where the amounts are converted approximately into metric units.

About ____ grams of apples,

About ____ litres of milk,
__ eggs,

cook in a ____ cm tray.

2. Emma's photo measures 4 cm × 6 cm.
(a) She wants to enlarge the photo so that it just fits a frame 12 cm × 18 cm.
By what scale factor should she multiply the original photo?
(b) Emma also wants a small photo to stick into an identity card.
The small photo is 24 mm by 36 mm.
By what scale factor should she multiply the original photo?

6 cm

4 cm

3. David has four packets of sweets and 5 sweets left over.
Each packet contains *n* sweets

(a) Which of these expressions gives the correct total number of sweets?
A 9*n*   **B** (4 + 5)*n*   **C** 4*n* + 5

(b) There are 73 sweets altogether.
Form an equation involving *n* and solve it to find the number of sweets in one packet.

4. The instructions to draw the square are

FORWARD 3, RT 90, FORWARD 3, RT 90,
FORWARD 3, RT 90, FORWARD 3.

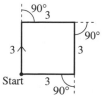

Write instructions to draw each of these shapes. For each
shape the first instruction is 'FORWARD 4'.

(a)

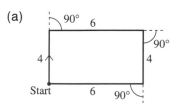

(b)

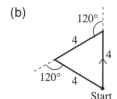

5. A sports shop had a closing down sale.
The sale started on Wednesday.
For each day of the sale, prices were
reduced by 20% of the prices on the day
before.

A tennis racket had a price of £30 on
Tuesday.
What was the price of the racket on
Thursday?

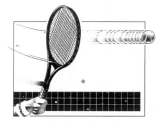

6. You have to find the answer to this calculation:

$$\frac{53 \times 16 - 18^2}{22 \times 8}$$

(a) Show which keys you press on a calculator.
(b) The numbers 53 and 18 are lengths which have been
rounded to the nearest whole centimetre.
(i) Write down the longest length 53 cm could have been.
(ii) Write down the shortest length 18 cm could have been.

7. Max and Sophie have bikes with different size wheels.
(a) The wheels on Max's bike have a diameter of 55 cm. Max
rolls the bike forward so that the wheels turn round
exactly once.
How far has Max moved?
(b) The wheels on Sophie's bike have a diameter of 62 cm.
Sophie rolls forward a distance of 1200 cm.
Calculate how many times the wheels go around *completely*.

8. Solve these equations

(a) $3 - 2a = 18 - 5a$

(b) $3n + 11 = 2(n - 2)$

(c) $\dfrac{3c}{2c - 1} = 4$

9. The diagram shows a flag in the shape of a triangle.

(a) Find the area of the triangle.

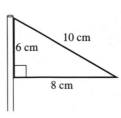

(b) The flag has a red circle of diameter 3 cm. Work out the area of this circle.

(c) A rule for advertising states that the area of the circle must be less than 30% of the area of the flag. Is the area of this circle within the rule?

10.

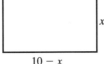

Lisa draws a rectangle with sides x cm and $(10 - x)$ cm

(a) Work out the perimeter of the rectangle.

(b) The *area* of the rectangle is 20 cm^2. She wants to find x so that $x(10 - x) = 20$.

Between which *one decimal place* numbers does x lie? Write your answer as 'x is between _____ and _____'.

11. A ladder AB leans against a vertical wall and a rope of length 1·8 m ties the ladder to the base of the wall. The rope is perpendicular to the ladder. If the ladder rests at an angle of 72° to the ground, calculate the length of the ladder.

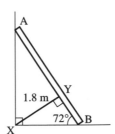

12. A vet does a survey in which he records the number of kittens born in each litter. Here are the results for 20 litters.

Number of kittens	Number of litters
2	1
3	2
4	6
5	5
6	5
7	1

(a) Work out the mean number of kittens born in each litter.

(b) From the table, the mode is 4 and the median is 5.
Every year 400 female cats have kittens.
Work out how many kittens you would expect to be born.
Explain your method.

(c) About how many litters would you expect to have 7 kittens?

13. Chocolates are sold in the boxes shown.
(a) The area of the lid is 165 cm².
Work out the volume of the box.

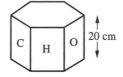

(b)

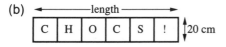

The label that goes round the tin has an area of 960 cm².
Work out the distance around the tin.

(c) A Super deluxe Xmas Special Offer tin of chocolates comes in the shape of a cylinder.
Work out the volume of one of these tins.

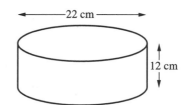

14. A room has a bed in this position.
[All the diagrams are views looking down on the room.]

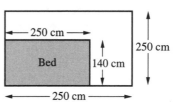

Calculate if the room is wide enough to turn the bed as shown below into a new position.

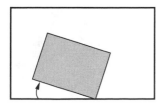

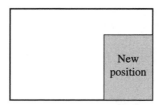

Paper 2. No calculators allowed.

1. Here are four expressions involving an unknown number n

     A   B   C   D

$2n+1$	$n-5$	$2n+3$	$3n+1$

  (a) Find the value of n if the expressions A and B are equal.
  (b) Find the value of n if the expressions C and D are equal.
  (c) Which two expressions could never be equal for *any* value of n?

2. This solid cube is made from
alternate black and white centimetre cubes.
  (a) Find the volume of the black cubes.
  (b) How many centimetre cubes are on
     the outside of the cube?

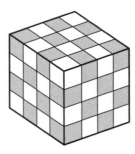

3. This is a series of shapes with black and white tiles.

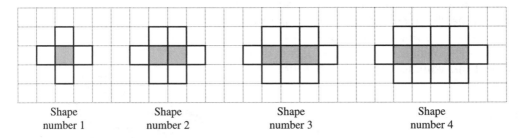

     Shape   Shape   Shape   Shape
   number 1   number 2   number 3   number 4

  (a) How many black tiles and how many white tiles are there
     in shape number 10?
  (b) How many black tiles and how many white tiles are there
     in shape number 150?
  (c) How many white tiles are there in shape number n?

4. Andy, Brian, Chris and Don are in a diving competition. The
order in which they dive is decided by drawing cards with
their names on from a bag. The names are taken out one at
a time without looking.
  (a) Write down all the possible orders of diving with Chris
     going first.
  (b) In the main competition there are 12 divers.
     The probability that Chris dives first is $\frac{1}{12}$.
     Work out the probability that Chris does *not* dive first.

5. This is shape A. 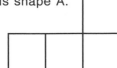 By adding one more square the new shape has the dashed line as a line of symmetry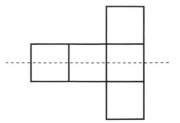

Copy each of the diagrams below and add the number of squares stated so that the dashed line is a line of symmetry.

(a)

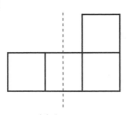

add 1 square

(b)

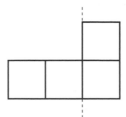

add 2 squares

(c)

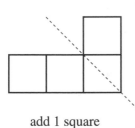

add 1 square

(d)

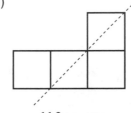

add 2 squares

6. (a) A lorry is loaded with 240 parcels each weighing 37 kg.
Work out the total weight of the parcels.
(b) The maximum load allowed on the lorry is 9 tonnes.
How many more parcels could go on the lorry?
(c) All the parcels have a height of 22 cm.
The height inside the lorry is 190 m.
How many layers of parcels can be put into the lorry?

7. The square shown has four lines of symmetry. One line of symmetry is shown by the broken line.
(a) Copy and complete this sentence with the correct equation.
'The broken line has equation [, $y = -x$; $x + y = 6$; $y = x + 6$].
(b) Write down the equation for each of the other lines of symmetry.

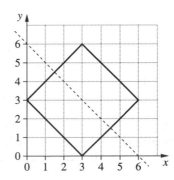

252

8. Use the graph shown to solve the following pairs of simultaneous equations:

(a) $x - y = 2$

$3x + 5y = 30$

(b) $x - y = 2$

$2x + y = 7$

(c) $3x + 5y = 30$

$2x + y = 7$

[Give x and y correct to 1 d.p.]

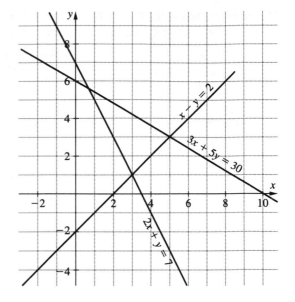

9. The prices for coating a metal plate with preservative are:

Up to 2000 cm²   £3
From 2000 cm² to 4000 cm²   £550
From 4000 cm² to 8000 cm²   £850.

The measurements of a plate are shown.

(a) *Estimate* its area. Show your working.

(b) Using your estimate, what price would you pay for the coating?

49 cm

103 cm

(c) Without a calculator, work out the exact area of the plate.

10. Mr Davis is buying things for his new shop. He buys computers, televisions, videos and phones.
He buys n computers.
Your answers to the following questions will involve n.

(a) He buys twice as many televisions as computers. How many televisions does he buy?

(b) He buys ten more videos than televisions. How many videos does he buy?

(c) He buys twice as many phones as televisions. How many phones does he buy?

(d) How many things does he buy altogether?

11. When a spinner with unequal sectors is spun, the probability of getting each colour and number is given in the tables.

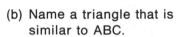

colour	probability
red	0·45
green	0·25
white	0·2
blue	0·1

number	probability
1	0·55
2	0·2
3	0·25

(a) What is the probability of spinning either 1 or 2?
(b) What is the probability of spinning either 3 or white?
(c) Why is the probability of spinning either 3 or red *not* 0·25 + 0·45?

12. AB = BD = 3 cm
BC = 5 cm
CE = 2·4 cm

(a) Name a triangle that is congruent to ABC.

(b) Name a triangle that is similar to ABC.

(c) Find the length DE.

13. Here is a number chain 5 → 8 → 11 → 14 → 17 →
The rule is 'add on 3 each time'.

Here is the start of another number chain 1 → 6 →
(a) Show *three* different ways to continue this number chain
(b) For each chain write down the *rule* you are using.

14.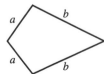
The perimeter of this shape is $2a + 2b$.
We write $p = 2a + 2b$.

Write an expression for the perimeters of each of these shapes.

 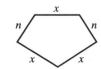 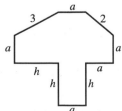

Paper 3. Calculators may be used.

1. (a) A square tile has sides of length l cm.
    Write an expression for the perimeter of the tile.
    Write the answer as a number multiplied by l.

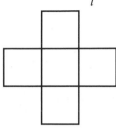

   (b) A cross is made from five tiles.
       Write an expression for the
       perimeter of the cross.

   (c) The perimeter of the cross is 60 cm.
       Use your answer to part (b) to form an equation involving l.
       Solve your equation to find the value of l.

2. The cost of advertising in a local paper for one week is

   > 28p per word plus 75p

   (a) What is the cost of an advertisement of 15 words for one week?
   (b) What is the greatest number of words in an advertisement costing up to £8 for one week?
   (c) If an advertisement is run for two weeks, the cost for the second week is reduced by 30%. Calculate the total cost for an advertisement of 22 words for two weeks.

3. After being ill for 2 months, the weight of a dog went down by 10%. Find the original weight of the dog if it weighed 24·3 kg after the illness.

4. The diagonal of a square has length 5 cm. What is the area of the square (in cm²)?

5. The mean weight of 8 apples is 120 g. If two extra apples weighing 135 g and 125 g are added, what is the new mean weight?

6.

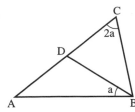

You are given that AB = AC
and BD = BC

Calculate the value of *a*.

7. (a) $81 = 9^n = 3^a$. Find the values of *n* and *a*.

(b) If $3^{10} = 59049$, work out 3^9.

(c) Work out $(200)^2 \times 100\,000$ and write the answer in standard form.

8. Describe fully the following transformations.
   (a) $\triangle A \rightarrow \triangle B$
   (b) $\triangle A \rightarrow \triangle C$
   (c) $\triangle C \rightarrow \triangle D$

Find any *pair* of successive transformations which will map $\triangle A$ onto $\triangle C$.

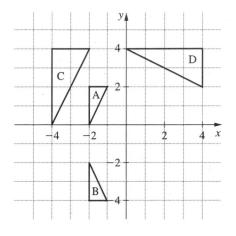

9. The *n*th term of a sequence is $\dfrac{3}{n^2 + 1}$.

The first term is $\dfrac{3}{2}$

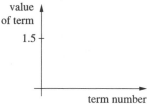

(a) Write down the next three terms.
(b) The sequence goes on and on for ever. Draw a sketch graph to show how the sequence continues.

10. Multiply out and simplify these expressions
   (a) $2(x + 1) + 3(x - 2)$ (b) $(x + 3)(x + 5)$
   (c) $(x - 2)(x + 1)$ (d) $(x + 3)^2$

INDEX